Easy AutoCAD™

Other McGraw-Hill Books in Mini and Mainframe Computing

ISBN	AUTHOR	TITLE
0-07-056578-3	Sherman	*The CD-ROM Handbook*
0-07-039006-1	Lusardi (hardcover)	*Database Experts' Guide to SQL*
0-07-039002-9	(softcover)	
0-07-016609-6	DeVita (hardcover)	*Database Experts' Guide to FOCUS*
0-07-016604-8	(softcover)	
0-07-036488-5	Larson (hardcover)	*Database Experts' Guide to Database 2*
0-07-023267-9	(softcover)	
0-07-000474-9	Adrian	*The Workstation Data Link*
0-07-057336-0	Simpson, Casey	*Developing Effective User Documentation*
0-07-007248-5	Brathwaite	*Analysis, Design, and Implementation of Data Dictionaries*
0-07-035119-8	Knightson	*Standards for Open Systems Interconnection*
0-07-044938-4	McClain (hardcover)	*VM and Departmental Computing*
0-07-044939-2	(softcover)	
0-07-046302-6	Nemzow	*Keeping the Link*
0-07-038006-6	Lipton	*User Guide to FOCUS™*
0-07-057296-8	Simon	*How to Be a Successful Computer Consultant*
0-07-016188-7	Dayton (Ranade, Ed.)	*Integrating Digital Services*
0-07-002673-4	Azevedo (Ranade Series)	*ISPF: The Strategic Dialog Manager*
0-07-050054-1	Piggott (Ranade Series)	*CICS: A Practical Guide to System Fine Tuning*
0-07-043152-3	Morgan, McGilton	*Introducing UNIX™ System V*
0-07-050686-8	Prasad (Ranade Series)	*IBM Mainframes*
0-07-065087-X	Towner (Ranade Series)	*IDMS/R Cookbook*
0-07-062879-3	Tare (hardcover)	*UNIX™ Utilities*
0-07-062884-X	(softcover)	
0-07-045001-3	McGilton, Morgan	*Introducing the UNIX™ System*
0-07-029750-9	Hood (hardcover)	*Using AutoCAD™ with AutoLISP™*
0-07-029749-5	(softcover)	

For more information about other McGraw-Hill materials, call 1-800-2-MCGRAW in the United States. In other countries, call your nearest McGraw-Hill office.

Easy AutoCAD™

A Tutorial Approach

John D. Hood, CET
Cambrian College

Second Edition

McGraw-Hill Publishing Company

New York   St. Louis   San Francisco   Auckland   Bogotá
Caracas   Hamburg   Lisbon   London   Madrid   Mexico
Milan   Montreal   New Delhi   Oklahoma City
Paris   San Juan   São Paulo   Singapore
Sydney   Tokyo   Toronto

Library of Congress Cataloging-in-Publication Data

Hood, John D.
   Easy AutoCAD : a tutorial approach / John D. Hood.—2nd ed.
     p. cm.
   ISBN 0-07-029750-9:—ISBN 0-07-029749-5 (pbk.) :
   1. AutoCAD (Computer program) 2. Architectural drawing—Data
processing—Programmed instruction. 3. Computer-aided design—
Programmed instruction. I. Title.
NA2728.H66 1989
720'.28'40285—dc20   89-37167

       67890   DOC/DOC   98765432

ISBN 0-07-029750-9

ISBN 0-07-029749-5 {PBK.}

*The editors for this book were Theron Shreve and Nancy Young,
the designer was Naomi Auerbach, and the production supervisor
was Dianne L. Walber. It was set in Century Schoolbook
by Professional Composition, Inc.*

Printed and bound by R. R. Donnelley & Sons Company.

AutoCAD and AutoLISP are trademarks of Autodesk, Inc.

*For more information about other McGraw-Hill materials,
call 1-800-2-MCGRAW in the United States. In other
countries, call your nearest McGraw-Hill office.*

For Shirley,
who made it possible

Contents

Preface to Second Edition

It seems that every six months there is a new version or release of AutoCAD on the market. That is what has made AutoCAD such a great CAD program—it is continually being improved.

This edition of *Easy AutoCAD* incorporates the latest changes to AutoCAD up to and including Release 10. While making the modifications, a decision regarding the format to follow had to be made. Should the text use pull-down menus and dialogue boxes introduced with Release 9, should it continue to use the screen menu for invoking commands, or should both be discussed?

The primary purpose of this text is to teach the new user how to apply AutoCAD to *real* drafting projects. Since the fundamental rule of teaching is to be methodical and consistent, the author made a decision to maintain the format used in the previous edition. It is important that the AutoCAD drafter understand the sequence of commands. Once the commands are understood, it is easy to use pull-down menus, dialogue boxes, icons, and a digitizing tablet menu. As you progress through *Easy AutoCAD*, you will find yourself automatically applying your pull-down menus and/or tablet menu where it is more convenient.

One of the first things the student should do is read Appendixes A, D, E, F, and G in the back of this text. They contain numerous hints on how to use your fixed drive, solve problems encountered with AutoCAD, and use the mouse or digitizing tablet for the screen menu, pull-down menus, and dialogue boxes.

The author has attempted to make this edition applicable to *all* versions and releases of AutoCAD. The commands illustrated are for Release 10, with notations where other releases or versions are significantly different.

The student is introduced to Release 10's user-coordinate system (UCS) and viewports in Chap. 17. Experienced CAD drafters may see areas in earlier projects where the use of UCS's and viewports might be applicable; however, the novice is challenged enough learning the basic drawing processes. After completing Chap. 17, the reader will be able to make knowledgeable decisions about when and how UCS's and viewports can be used in any drawing project.

When using Release 10, the UCS icon (x-y symbol in lower-left corner of screen) may be distracting when completing drawings in Chaps. 1 through 16. The icon may be turned off by entering the commands outlined in App. A.1, item 36.

What is particularly different about *Easy AutoCAD* from similar texts is that the student is immediately involved in the drawing process. The author has found that serious students are quickly bored with drawing lines, circles, boxes, and strange shapes. Industry requires CAD drafters who can handle the *total* project—which involves the determination of text heights, dimension scales, hatch scales, and linetype scales. Once those skills have been mastered, the student is much better prepared to enter industry as a CAD drafter.

J. D. Hood

Introduction

Practice is the only way to learn a skill.

My purpose in writing this book is to provide a set of tutorial notes that will supplement the *AutoCAD Reference Manual*, which is supplied with the AutoCAD program. The manual does an excellent job of explaining the AutoCAD commands; however, it does little to demonstrate the application of those commands in an integrated drafting project.

In this text emphasis is placed on the application of AutoCAD to efficiently complete drawings in a number of disciplines, using practical drawing projects.

Having taught CAD to a number of students, it has been my observation that the biggest problem students and experienced drafters have when starting to use CAD is a lack of confidence to sit down behind the computer keyboard and begin a drawing. It is really quite a simple thing to do—start at the beginning and work toward the end. It has been my goal to provide a set of projects demonstrating that fact.

I.1 The AutoCAD Program

AutoCAD is a computer-aided drafting, CAD, program, from Autodesk Inc. It is written in the C programming language, which is machine independent, and is composed of an intricate set of drawing and editing capabilities.

The program is primarily written to run on the IBM-PC microcomputer (and compatibles) under MS-DOS or PC-DOS. Versions are available for other systems as well. AutoCAD drawings can also be interchanged with most large CAD systems.

AutoCAD is sold with three options called ADE-1, ADE-2, and ADE-3 (for Advanced Drawing Extension) which act as overlays and extend the abilities of the software. Most of the projects in this text are based on the user having AutoCAD and ADE-3.

At the time this text was written, AutoCAD had over 250,000 licensed users and had become the de facto standard microcomputer CAD program in industry and in educational institutes.

Because of the open architecture of AutoCAD, numerous third-party firms have developed extensions to AutoCAD and tools to work with it. Some of the programs written to work with AutoCAD, such as Auto-COGO for use in surveying and civil engineering, operate from within the AutoCAD environment, performing special functions while allowing the user to perform the standard AutoCAD functions.

Prior to Release 10 AutoCAD was primarily a two-dimensional CAD program; with the introduction of the user-defined coordinate system in Release 10, AutoCAD is a full three-dimensional CAD system.

The AutoCAD program is relatively easy to learn to use because it is entirely menu driven. This means that the user does not have to remember complex commands. All commands may be displayed and selected from the screen menu. Job-specific menus (see Chap. 11) that contain macros (see Chap. 12) and call block files (see Chap. 10) may be purchased or written by experienced users to tailor AutoCAD to any drafting discipline.

I.2   How to Use Easy AutoCAD

This text is composed of a series of tutorial projects, each about 3 hours in length, which are designed to bring a novice user, with no CAD or other computer experience, to the level of a fully trained CAD operator in a short period of time.

Experienced CAD operators will find the text invaluable since it demonstrates the efficient utilization of a number of AutoCAD commands to complete complex drafting procedures.

The tutorials are written to complement the *AutoCAD Reference Manual* supplied with the AutoCAD software. Commands are not introduced in a specific order but rather as required to complete specific drawing projects. The reader should refer to the *AutoCAD Reference Manual* when using *Easy AutoCAD* whenever more information about a command is desired.

It is recommended that a new user start at the beginning of this text and complete all projects. Although there is sufficient repetition of instructions in the projects, the author has designed the projects assuming that the reader has completed prior projects and understands the application of commands used earlier.

There is one exception to the preceding paragraph. In *Easy AutoCAD* the process of configuring AutoCAD and plotting is not discussed until Chap. 7. This has generally proven to work best in the classroom for the author. If you wish to begin using AutoCAD by first configuring your copy of the AutoCAD program, you should read Sec. 7.1. If you wish to plot drawings prior to reaching Chap. 7, read Sec. 7.2.

When an AutoCAD command is invoked, the program requests spe-

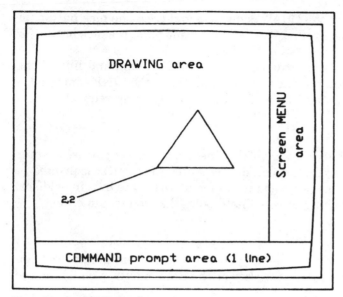

DRAWING area

Screen MENU area

2,2

COMMAND prompt area (1 line)

Figure I-1 AutoCAD drawing screen.

cific information in the command line at the bottom of the screen (see Fig. I-1). The format of those requests has changed moderately with each version of AutoCAD. The format illustrated in this text is for Ver. 10, with notes outlining where earlier versions differ significantly. If the format on your version is different from that illustrated in the text, refer to your *AutoCAD Reference Manual* for the procedure to enter the data.

When drawing with AutoCAD, the SCREEN MENU is listed in a vertical strip on the right side of the monitor, as illustrated in Fig. I-1. All of the available commands can be displayed on the screen, but since there are a number of commands, they are grouped in a hierarchical tree structure. The primary menu is called *AutoCAD*.

Prior to reaching a desired command, you may have to go through branch menus. To call a command, it is highlighted in the menu and then the pick button on the mouse (or digitizer puck—both will be called a mouse) is pressed, or, if you do not have a mouse, the Enter key is pressed. In this text <pick> is used to indicate the pick button on the mouse (either the left or the 0 button) and <return> is used to indicate the Return button on the mouse (either the middle or 1 button) or Enter key on the keyboard. If you do not have a mouse or digitizer, <pick> may be replaced with the Enter key or space bar, and <return> with the Enter key (Refer to Sec. 1.4.1.1). The commands you enter to call the LINE command are written as:

    DRAW <pick> LINE <pick>

In summary: Select the DRAW command and press the pick button (or Enter key), then select the LINE command and press the pick button (or Enter key).

AutoCAD will display the commands in the Command line at the bottom of the monitor as they are entered. When the LINE command is entered, the Command line will display the following request:

```
Line from point:
```

You are to enter the start point of the line. In some cases you are to enter data by typing it on the keyboard. The AutoCAD request is printed in computer type in this text and the data you are to type in is in boldface. To draw a line starting at coordinate point 2,2, you would enter:

```
Line from point: 2,2 <return>
```

In summary: AutoCAD prompts you with "Line from point:" and you type in 2,2 and press the Enter key or the Return button on the mouse (the middle or 1 button).

AutoCAD will respond in the Command line with:

```
To point:
```

You are to enter the next point for the line. This may be entered from the keyboard as previously illustrated, or the point may be entered by moving the cursor (cross hairs) on the screen to the point and pressing the mouse pick button (or the Enter key if you do not have a mouse). This is called *digitizing* the point. If the line from 2,2 is to be attached to the left corner of a triangle on the screen (see Fig. I-1) by moving the cursor and digitizing the point, the information in the text would appear as follows:

```
To point: Move the cursor to the left side of the triangle and digitize the point. <pick>
```

In summary: AutoCAD prompts you with "To point:," you perform the function specified, and press the pick button.

AutoCAD will draw the line and respond with:

```
To point:
```

If you do not wish to extend the line further, you may press the mouse Return button or the Enter key without entering a value. If you do, the previous command entry would appear in these notes with a second <return> indicated:

```
To point: Move the cursor to the left side of the triangle and digitize the point. <pick> To
Point: <return>
```

Occasionally, for clarity of reading the text, some AutoCAD responses are not displayed (for instance, the last "To point:" response may be deleted, and the final entries would appear as <**pick**><**return**>. If you wish to verify what you have on the screen, refer to the *AutoCAD Reference Manual*, which will describe the command in full.

When typing in alphabetical data from the keyboard, you may use either uppercase or lowercase letters.

I.3   CAD Hardware

The version of AutoCAD used in this text is written for the IBM-PC microcomputer or compatibles. The microcomputer should have 640K of RAM; however, earlier versions will run on a system with less RAM. To run the ADE-3 package's AutoLISP, 640K of RAM is required. You will need a floppy drive and a single hard disk drive to run AutoCAD. AutoCAD is written to operate with MS-DOS (or PC-DOS) Ver. 2.0 or later versions.

A graphics monitor is required to display the drawing. The display screen may be a black and white, monochrome, or color monitor. You will need a color/graphics adapter to display the graphics.

The standard resolution for the IBM monitor is 640 by 200 pixels, which means 600 positions across and 200 positions down the screen. A diagonal line drawn on the screen will have the "jaggies" in that it will appear as a stepped line because of the lower resolution of the screen (while all diagonal lines are composed of a number of short horizontal lines, the lower the resolution of the screen, the more jaggies). This will make it more difficult to read the drawing on the monitor but will not affect the paper plot of the drawing where the line will appear as a uniform line.

I.3.1   Pointing devices

The cursor may be moved about the screen to draw lines, select points, etc., using the cursor keypad. If you are doing a lot of drawing, you will want to have some type of pointing device. The most common pointing devices are the mouse and the digitizing tablet.

A mouse is a locating device that uses relative motion to move the cursor on the screen as the mouse is moved about the top of a desk. A mouse may have rollers on its base that rotate as the mouse is moved along a smooth surface causing the cursor to move on the screen, or it may be an optical mouse which is moved on a small (8 by 9 in) reflecting plate set on a tabletop. The mouse usually has buttons on its surface that are used to pick (digitize) points on the monitor. A mouse usually costs around $100 and is one of the cheaper pointing devices available. The mouse is limited in that it is a relative-motion device and cannot be used to trace over paper drawings and transfer the points into the AutoCAD drawing.

The best pointing device is a digitizing tablet which comes in a number of sizes from 11 by 11 in up, with price ranges from $800 and up. The digitizing tablet uses either a pen-like stylus or a puck with one to sixteen buttons and is moved on the surface of the tablet to select points on the monitor. The tablet has two distinct advantages over the mouse. It can be aligned with the coordinate system on an existing paper drawing so that the drawing elements can be transferred into the computer database, providing an exact copy of the drawing which can then be modified as any other AutoCAD drawing. Tablets further allow you to set aside space on the tablet for menus containing standard AutoCAD commands or macros. The commands or macros are then selected by picking them with the tablet pointing device, greatly speeding up the design process.

I.3.2 Plotters

If you complete a drawing using AutoCAD, you will want to produce a hard copy of the drawing. Some versions of AutoCAD support the use of a dot matrix printer to plot drawings. The standard printer will not provide the type of output you would desire for construction or production drawings but will provide quick cheap preliminary drawings.

AutoCAD supports a number of plotters. Usually the main consideration when selecting a plotter is the maximum plot size the device can draw. Most serious drafting requires an E-size (34 by 44 in) drawing, although D-size (22 by 34 in) and smaller drawings are also used. Another consideration is the number of pens the plotter can use during a plot. If drawings are to be done in a number of colors or are to have a number of different line types, the plotter should be able to access more than one pen during the plot. Different line types and colors can be used with a one-pen plotter but the process is extremely time consuming.

Recent developments in vector-to-raster conversion and color technology have also made available to the CAD user printer/plotters that challenge pen plotters in quality and versatility.

First Steps

1.1   Operating the Microcomputer

The power is turned on as follows:

1. Turn on all peripherals, i.e., plotter, digitizing tablet, etc.
2. Turn on the computer (see your manual for the location of the power switch.)

In order to run any programs the microcomputer must first have a copy of the operating system, referred to as MS-DOS or PC-DOS, etc., loaded into it. The procedure for doing that is described in Sec. 1.2. After the computer has loaded the operating system, you may then load and run your AutoCAD program.

When using AutoCAD, the cursor is at the cross point of a vertical and horizontal line (cross hairs) on the monitor. The cursor location is the cross point of the lines. For some selections the cursor is a small box.

The standard IBM-PC keyboard is illustrated in Fig. 1.1. If your keyboard is different, refer to your computer manual and locate the equivalent of the keys that are discussed in the following paragraphs.

The following keys are used to move the cursor on the monitor. Locate them on the keyboard:

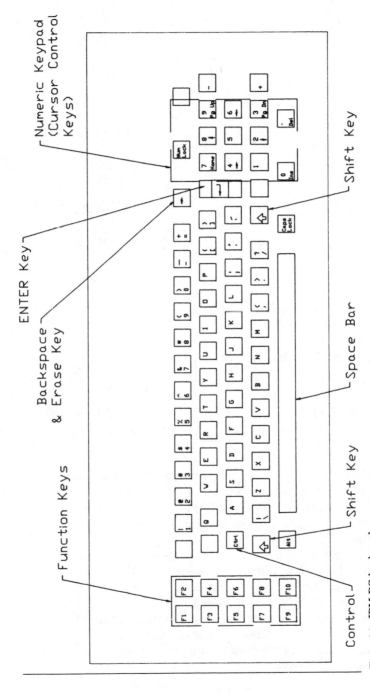

Figure 1.1 IBM-PC keyboard.

1. Numeric keypad cursor control keys (the arrow keys located on the 8, 4, 6, and 2 keys on the numeric keypad on the right side of the keyboard)

2. PgUp key (located on the 9 key on the numeric keypad)

3. PgDn key (located on the 3 key on the numeric keypad)

4. Home key (located on the 7 key on the numeric keypad)

5. Ins key (located on the 0 key on the numeric keypad)

The Num Lock key should *never* be used with AutoCAD. If you want to enter a number, use the number keys along the top of the keyboard.

The Backspace (and erase) key is on the right side of the top row of the keyboard and is marked with an arrow. This key is used to backspace and erase typed data.

The Enter key is the large key on the right side of the keyboard and on the left side of the numeric keypad. It is also usually marked with an arrow but may be marked as Return or Enter.

A few commands require the pressing of two keys together. One of the keys is the Ctrl (control) key, which is on the left side of the keyboard beside the A key. Others are the Alt (alternate) key, which is located two keys lower on the keyboard, and the Del (delete) key, which is located on the far right side of the bottom row of keys.

Alphabetic keys are similar to typewriter keys. Pressing the key prints the lowercase letter, i.e., a. To print the uppercase letter, hold down the shift key, which is marked with an open arrow (see Fig. 1.1), and press the alphabetic key, i.e., A.

To access the symbols on the top of the keys along the top row, press the shift key and the key desired together. For instance to print @, hold down the shift key and press the 2 key on the top row of the keypad.

With AutoCAD the Space Bar is used to print a blank space when printing text *and issued as a replacement for the Enter key* at all other times. It is the long key at the bottom of the keypad.

Review this section prior to starting Projects 1 and 2 until you remember the location of each of the keys.

1.2 DOS Operations

Disk operating software, referred to as MS-DOS or PC-DOS, etc., is supplied with your computer when you purchase it. The following discussion is to familiarize you with the system software and DOS operations that are required to run AutoCAD. Refer to your DOS manual for a more thorough discussion.

1.2.1 System programs

Programs (software) are required in order to run a microcomputer. There are two major types of software—system software and applications software. AutoCAD is an applications program used for computer-aided drafting.

System software is used to control the operation of the microcomputer and manage communication between the microcomputer and other hardware, such as disk drives. In order to run application programs like AutoCAD, the microcomputer must first be under the control of system software. AutoCAD is designed to be used with MS-DOS or PC-DOS. DOS is an acronym for "disk operating system."

1.2.2 Loading DOS

Loading the DOS program and starting it running is often referred to as "booting up" the system. This is performed as follows:

1. Turn on the microcomputer.

2. DOS will automatically be loaded from the fixed disk, which is drive C.

3. If the system asks for the date, enter it in the format MO-DA-YR and press the Enter key, i.e.,

   ```
   Current date is Tue 1-01-1980
   Enter new date (mm-dd-yy): 12-30-89 <return>
   ```
   (where <**return**> means press the Enter key)

4. If the system asks for the time, it may be entered in the format HR:MIN based on a 24-hour clock, i.e.,

   ```
   Current time is 0:01:30.00
   Enter new time: 3:30 <return>
   ```

5. A DOS startup message followed by the system command prompt C:>_ or C:\>_ should now be displayed. The system prompt indicates that DOS is loaded, the current drive is drive C (the fixed drive), and the user may enter a DOS command.

6. If it is necessary to reboot the system at any time, press the Ctrl-Alt-Del keys together and reenter the date and time.

1.2.3 Handling floppy disks

If your system has two floppy drives, either the left or upper drive is drive A and either the right or lower drive is drive B. To insert a floppy disk into a drive open the drive latch and slowly insert the disk into the drive, with the label on the disk pointing up and under your thumb when grasping the disk. Disks should not be inserted or removed from the disk drive when the red disk operation light is on. If the disk light is on, wait until it goes off (indicating that the drive is not reading or writing) and then insert the disk. Close the drive latch.

1.2.4 Preparing a data disk

New blank disks (disks that do not contain any programs) must be prepared for use. This is called "formatting." The disk is formatted only prior to its first use. If it is reformatted after data is stored on it, the data will be lost.

When using AutoCAD in a classroom setting, the drawings will usually be stored on a data disk in a floppy drive. In this text drive B (either the right or lower drive) is used. Other users with fixed drives will also wish to store original or backup drawings on a data disk. A data disk is formatted for use as follows:

1. Boot up DOS. The system prompt C:>_ must be displayed.

2. Invoke the DOS format command by entering:

```
C:>format b: <return>
```

3. The following message will be displayed:

```
Insert new diskette in drive B:
and strike any key when ready_
```

Place a new blank disk into drive B and press any key.

4. The computer will format the disk in drive B and display the following message:

```
Format another (Y/N)?_
```

If you wish to format another, press Y and repeat step 3. If you are through, press N.

The disk in drive B is now a formatted data disk ready to receive data.

1.2.5 Changing the current drive

When DOS is booted, the default drive is drive C. When any DOS commands are entered which require the computer to access a disk drive, the current drive is used. The current drive may be changed by typing the drive letter and then a colon. To change the current drive to B enter:

```
C:\>b: <return>
B:\>_
```

Note that the system command prompt now appears as B:>_.

1.2.6   Displaying the directory of a disk

The files stored on a disk are listed in the disk directory. The directory of the disk in the current drive is displayed by typing:

```
C:\>dir <return>
```

If the directory is too large to display all the files on the screen, it may be listed in pages by typing:

```
C:\>dir/p <return>
```

Files similar to those listed below may be displayed:

```
COMMAND   COM    15597   10-20-84   12:00p
ACAD      EXE   167424   10-10-24    9:30a
ID        DRV        4   10-10-24    3:30p
ACAD2     OVL    14848   10-10-24   12:00p
HOUSE     DWG     3200   10-26-85   11:30p
HOUSE     BAK     2800   10-25-85    2:30p
ELECT     MNU      580   12-18-85    3:10p
```

The left column is the file name. A file name begins with an alphabetical letter and is followed by a maximum of seven alphabetical letters, numbers, or symbols: $-_/!@#%&( ){ }$".

The file name may also have a three-letter extension, as illustrated in the second column. The following is a list of extensions and the specific types of file they indicate:

com   A command file that contains instructions DOS needs to carry out commands.

exe   An executable file that contains a program DOS runs when you type the file name.

drv   A driver file that contains information related to specific hardware that AutoCAD uses to access that hardware.

ovl   An overlay file that contains additional AutoCAD operational files.

dwg   An AutoCAD user's drawing file.

bak   Contains a backup copy of a user's drawing file. When a drawing is saved, AutoCAD automatically converts any previous dwg file for that drawing to a bak file.

mnu   An AutoCAD menu file. This is discussed in Chapter 11.

1.2.7 Deleting files

A file may be deleted from DOS by entering the command DEL or ERASE followed by the file name and the file name extension: i.e.:

```
C:\>del b:house.bak <return>
```

This will delete the file House.bak from the disk in drive B.

If you are running out òf disk space, you may delete specific backup files individually as outlined above. Remember that the reason for backup files is to provide you with a previous copy of the drawing. If for some reason you cannot access your drawing file, you may wish to at least access the previous copy rather than restart the entire drawing. If that happens, you will suddenly see the value of the bak file (see Sec. 1.2.9, "Renaming Files"). If you wish to delete all bak files on the disk in drive B use the following command:

```
C:\>del b:*.bak <return>
```

The asterisk, *, is a wildcard. Any file in drive B with the extension bak will be deleted by this command.

If you wish to delete a file on the fixed disk, the path to the file must precede its name. Assuming the path to the backup files to be deleted is acad\easy (see App. D), you would enter:

```
C:\>del \acad\easy\*.bak <return>
```

When AutoCAD is running, it creates temporary files on the data disk that are erased automatically when the program is ended properly. If the program crashes, those files are not erased and may fill the data disk. The working files contain a $ symbol in the file name extension. If the program crashes, you should erase those files prior to rebooting Auto-CAD. This is done by deleting any files with a $ symbol in their extension:

```
C:\>del b:*.$* <return>
C:\>_
```

Note: If the $ sign is left out of the preceding, *all* files on the disk in drive B will be deleted. Be very careful when entering this command.

1.2.8 Copying files

If you have drawing files that you do not wish to lose, they should be copied onto another disk and the disk should be stored in a safe place. To copy a file from one disk to another, use the COPY command followed by the file name and the drive letter, i.e., to copy the file House.dwg from a disk in drive A to a disk in drive B, do the following:

1. Prior to copying data onto a new disk, the new disk must be formatted. If the disk you are going to copy the files onto has not been formatted, follow the procedure in Sec. 1.2.4 to format the disk before continuing.

2. Place the disk to be copied into drive A and the formatted disk to be copied onto into drive B. Close the drive latches and enter:

   C:\>copy a:house.dwg b: <return>

Wildcards may also be used. For example, to copy all .dwg files from a disk in drive A to a disk in drive B type:

   C:\>copy a:*.dwg b: <return>

3. The programs being copied from the disk in drive A to the disk in drive B will be displayed on the monitor.

1.2.9   Renaming files

If the user wishes to access a .bak (backup) file from AutoCAD, the file must be renamed to a .dwg (drawing) file. To rename house.bak to house1.dwg in drive B use:

   C:\>rename b:house.bak b:house1.dwg <return>

The file may now be accessed from AutoCAD as House1.

1.3   The Hard Disk Drive

Prior to running AutoCAD you will have to install the software onto your fixed drive. Refer to the chapter on Software Installation in your *AUTOCAD Installation & Performance Guide* for the procedure to transfer the program from the floppy diskettes supplied by AutoCAD to your fixed disk (also see App. D in this book).

1.3.1   Running AutoCAD

The following is based on the assumption that you have set up AutoCAD on the hard disk, as outlined in App. D, "Preparing the Hard Disk." The

AutoCAD files are in a subdirectory named Acad, the AutoCAD Sample Drawing files are in a branch of Acad named Sample, and you will be saving the drawings created using *Easy AutoCAD* in a branch of Acad named Easy or on a floppy disk in drive B (if you have only one floppy drive it may be called drive B or A).

1.3.1.1   Drawing files saved in a file on the hard disk.   If AutoCAD is used in a classroom setting, each student will probably want to save his or her drawings on a personal floppy disk. If so, skip to Sec. 1.3.1.2, "Drawings Files to Be Saved on a Floppy Disk."

1. Prior to booting AutoCAD use the DOS PATH command to tell DOS where the AutoCAD files are to be found:

```
C:\>path c:\acad <return>
```

2. Transfer control to the drawing-file branch of the Acad subdirectory; for instance, to load an AutoCAD sample drawing from the Sample branch of the Acad subdirectory enter:

```
C:\>cd\acad\sample <return>
```

Load AutoCAD using:

```
C:\>acad <return>
```

AutoCAD will be loaded. The sample drawing Stair may be accessed by selecting item 2, "Edit an EXISTING Drawing," from the main menu (refer to Sec. 1.4, item 4). When the name of the drawing is requested enter:

```
Enter NAME of drawing: stair <return>
```

After the drawing is loaded, you may return to the main menu by entering the QUIT command:

```
Command: QUIT <return>
Really want to discard all changes to drawing? y <return>
```

3. To do the projects in Easy AutoCAD, complete step 1 above and then transfer control to the Easy drawing-file branch of the Acad subdirectory:

```
C:\>cd\acad\easy <return>
```

Then load AutoCAD using:

```
C:\>acad <return>
```

AutoCAD will be loaded and the main menu displayed, as illustrated in Sec. 1.4, item 4. The remaining steps are as specified in each of the *Easy AutoCAD* projects with one exception—when entering the drawing name, *do not precede the name with B:*; for instance, in Sec. 1.4.1 when entering the name of the drawing use:

```
Enter NAME of drawing: proj-1 <return>
```

Each of the projects in *Easy AutoCAD* is started following the procedure in steps 1, 2, and 3, above. In this text, file names are preceded with a drive designation B:. You will use the same file name for drawing files but will *not* use the drive designation B: in front of the name.

1.3.1.2   Drawings files to be saved on a floppy disk.

In a classroom setting each student will probably want to save his or her drawings on a personal floppy disk. If so, the following procedure should be used to run AutoCAD and load or save drawing files:

1. Change the current directory to the ACAD subdirectory:

   ```
   C:\>cd\acad <return>
   ```

2. Load AutoCAD:

   ```
   C:\>acad <return>
   ```

3. AutoCAD will be loaded. All of the other commands are as specified in this text. Drawing names are all preceded with B: (as specified) and will be stored on the disk in drive B.

You have only to remember that prior to loading AutoCAD you are to log on to the Acad subdirectory as specified in step 1 above.

You must understand that if the drawing name is not preceded with B:, the drawing will be stored in the Acad subdirectory of the fixed disk. If this happens (and it will), the file may be transferred to a floppy data disk and later deleted from the hard disk as follows:

a. Log on to the Acad subdirectory using:

`C:\>cd\acad <return>`

b. To list the drawing files in the Acad subdirectory enter:

`C:\acad\>dir *.dwg <return>`

c. Assuming that the file named Proj-1.dwg is listed in the directory and is to be transferred to the disk in drive B enter:

`C:\acad\>copy proj-1.dwg b: <return>`

d. To delete the file from the hard disk, enter:

`C:\acad\>del proj-1.dwg <return>`

To return to the root directory, enter:

`C:\acad>cd\`

1.4 Loading AutoCAD

The following procedure is used to load AutoCAD from a hard drive or floppy drive system:

1. Boot up DOS.
2. With Ver. 2.5 and higher, load AutoCAD as outlined in Sec. 1.3.1.1 or 1.3.1.2 and continue to step 4. With Ver. 2.18 on floppy disks remove the DOS disk from drive A and insert the AutoCAD executable (Acad.exe) disk in drive A. Close the latch and type:

`A:>acad <return>`

3. When loading AutoCAD from floppy disks with Ver. 2.18, the response is:

```
Can't find overlay file ACAD.OVL.
Enter new drive letter or '.' to quit.
```

Remove the executable disk from drive A and insert the AutoCAD overlay (Acad.ovl) disk into drive A. Close the drive latch and type:

> A: <return>

4. When AutoCAD is loaded, the following main menu will appear:

```
0. Exit AutoCAD
1. Begin a NEW drawing
2. Edit an EXISTING drawing
3. Plot a drawing
4. Printer plot a drawing (Not on all versions)
5. Configure AutoCAD
6. File utilities
7. Compile shape/font description file
8. Convert old drawing file
Enter Selection:_
```

If the drawings created are to be stored on a data disk, prior to selecting any items, place a data disk into drive B and close the drive latch. (With Ver. 2.18 and a floppy drive system, do not remove the Acad.ovl disk from drive A.)

1.4.1   Begin a new drawing

From the main menu select item 1:

```
Enter Selection: 1 <return>
```

The computer will respond with:

```
Enter NAME of drawing:_
```

The name of the drawing must begin with an alphabetical letter and may be followed by up to seven alphabetical letters, numbers, or the character $, -, _. *The name must not contain any embedded blanks.* If the drawing data is to be stored on the disk in drive B, precede the name with B:. To start a new drawing named Proj-1 and to store the file on the disk in drive B:

```
Enter NAME of drawing: b:proj-1 <return>
```

Note: With Ver. 2.18 and a *floppy disk system* the drawing data must be stored on the disk in drive B. The AutoCAD overlay disk in drive A does not have sufficient space to store your working and drawing files, and the program will probably crash if the program attempts to write the files to drive A. You should always precede the drawing name with B:.

Remember if you are using a fixed disk and your drawings are to be stored on the data disk in drive B, precede the drawing name with B:. If the drawings are to be stored on the hard disk, do *not* precede the drawing name with the drive designation B: (refer to Sec. 1.3.1).

Note that AutoCAD adds the extension .dwg to the drawing name. It must not be input by the user.

1.4.1.1 Entering Commands. AutoCAD commands may be entered by typing them using the keyboard, by selecting them from the screen menu on the monitor, by selecting them from the tablet overlay on the digitizing tablet, or by selecting the pull-down menus with Release 9 and 10. The procedures illustrated in this text are based on the assumption that you are selecting the commands from the screen menu.

To select AutoCAD commands from the screen menu, move the mouse or digitizing puck to the right or, if you do not have a mouse, press the Ins key (may be marked as Insert) on the keypad. The cursor should move to the screen menu on the right side of the monitor (see Fig. I.1), highlighting one of the commands. If instead you get a 0 printed on the Command line at the bottom of the monitor (see Fig. I.1), press the Num Lock key on the numeric keypad to turn the Num Lock off. Then press the backspace key, which is usually located on the right side of the top row of keys and marked with an arrow. This should erase the 0 in the Command line.

The cursor may be moved up and down the menu by moving the mouse (or digitizer puck) up or down or, if you do not have a mouse, by pressing the up and down arrow keys on the numeric keypad. Try it. If you press the left arrow key, the cursor may move onto the screen as a set of cross hairs. To return the cursor to the menu, press the Ins key.

To select the DRAW command, move the cursor up or down until the DRAW command is highlighted, then press the pick button on the mouse (usually the left or the 0 button) or, if you are using the keyboard, press the Enter key or Space Bar.

If you selected the DRAW command, the menu should have changed to a submenu which now contains the LINE command. Move the cursor up or down the menu to the LINE command and press the pick button on the mouse or the Enter key to select the command.

The Command line at the bottom of the monitor should now say (AutoCAD command line requests are printed in computer-like type in this text):

```
Line from point:
```

This means that AutoCAD has invoked the Line command and is waiting for you to enter some data—the start point of the line. Move the mouse to the left or, if you do not have a mouse, press the Home key to move the cursor into the drawing area. Use the mouse or the cursor control arrow keys (see Fig. 1.1) to move the cursor around the screen. If you press the Home key, the mouse will freeze up. To regain use of the mouse, press the Del key.

Press the PgUp key once and move the cursor about the screen using the arrow keys on the keyboard. Notice the movement steps. Press the PgUp key again and then move the cursor. If the step movements did not get larger, they are at their maximum. Press the PgDn key and then move the cursor. The step movement will be smaller. There are three settings—coarse, medium, and fine. If you have a mouse, you must press the Del key to regain control of the mouse. If you are using a mouse, there will be times when you may find it easier to make fine movements on the screen using the keyboard arrow keys.

Move the cursor to a point and "digitize" the point by pressing the <pick> button on the mouse or the Enter key if you do not have a mouse. The Command line now should say:

```
To point:
```

Move the cursor to another point and digitize it. Notice the Command line. Move to another point and digitize it. Now type in a **c** in response to the command and then press the Enter button on the mouse (usually the middle or the 1 button) or the keyboard Enter key (remember, AutoCAD requests are printed in computer-like type, data you type in is bold computer-like type, and the Enter key is indicated as <return>:

```
To point: c <return>
```

Notice how the lines closed onto the first point and the Command line does not contain a prompt.

Note: On a mouse or digitizer puck, points are digitized on the screen, and screen menu commands are selected using the pick (left or 0) button. A command sequence is ended and a keyboard entry is made by pressing the Enter key on the keyboard or the Return (middle or 1) button on the mouse. In this text both are indicated as <return>. You will get used to the procedure quickly.

You have completed your first AutoCAD drawing. To exit the drawing editor and save your drawing execute the following series of commands:

```
AUTOCAD <pick> UTILITY <pick> End <pick>
```

The program should now return to the AutoCAD main menu.

1.4.2 Edit an existing drawing

From the main menu select item 2, "Edit an EXISTING Drawing":

```
Enter Selection: 2 <return>
```

The computer will respond with:

```
Enter NAME of drawing:__
```

The name must exactly match the name used when saving the drawing. To edit the drawing named Proj-1 that is stored on the disk in drive B enter:

```
Enter NAME of drawing: b:proj-1 <return>
```

Note that the name is preceded with the drive letter B: if the drawing is stored on the disk in that drive. If it is stored on the fixed drive, do *not* precede the drawing name with the drive designation B:.

Your previous drawing will now appear on the screen. Add a few more lines and then exit as outlined previously.

1.4.3 File utilities

This procedure may be used to list the files on a disk, which is useful if you forget the name of a drawing file. From AutoCAD's main menu select item 6, File Utility:

```
Enter Selection: 6 <return>
```

The computer will respond with the following menu:

```
File Utility Menu
   0. Exit File Utility Menu
   1. List Drawing flies
   2. List user specified files
   3. Delete files
   4. Rename files
   5. Copy file
Enter Selection:__
```

To list the drawing files, select 1:

```
Enter Selection: 1 <return>
```

The computer will respond with

```
Enter drive <A>:__
```

To list the drawings on drive B:

```
Enter drive <A>: b: <return>
```

If you are using a fixed drive and have stored the drawings on the hard drive, the default item (displayed in angle brackets < >) will be the drive path. To select that path press Enter. To specify another file subdirectory you will have to enter the appropriate path (see App. A).

Your drawing Proj-1.dwg should be listed. Notice that it is listed in uppercase even though we stored it using lowercase. This does not mean anything. Notice also it has the extension .dwg. This tells AutoCAD that it is a drawing file.

To return to the File Utility menu, press Enter. Then, to exit the File Utility menu select item 0, which will return you to AutoCAD's main menu.

Other items in this File menu will be discussed throughout the text.

Chapter 2

Drawing Construction

OBJECTIVE *Begin a new drawing—set limits, units, and precision; use draw commands—LINE, CIRCLE, POINT, and FILLET; edit a drawing—ERASE, oops, BREAK, and CANCEL; use display controls—ZOOM (all, extents, previous, and window); exit procedures—END, QUIT, and SAVE.*

DRAWING *Boot up AutoCAD and, from the main menu, select item 1, "Begin a NEW drawing:", with the name B:Proj-2. Draw the trapezoid illustrated in Fig. 2.1. The commands are discussed in the text.*

2.1   Load AutoCAD

Turn the computer on. If your system is operated from a floppy disk, wait until the disk drive diode light is off and then place your MS-DOS disk into drive A. Close the latch and press the Ctrl-Alt-Del keys together.

If your system is operated from a fixed drive, DOS will be loaded automatically when the microcomputer is turned on.

Enter the date (MO/DA/YR) and press the Enter key twice. The DOS command prompt should be displayed as:

```
A:>_ or C:>_
```

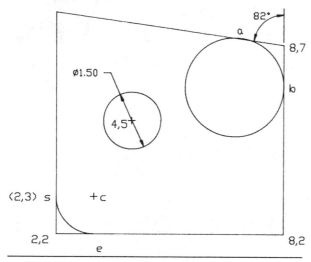

Figure 2.1   Project 2.

Note: In all of the AutoCAD commands illustrated in this text the following format is used:

- Data you are to type is in computer-like boldface.
- The Enter key is indicated by <return>.
- AutoCAD responses or requests are printed in computer-like type.
- AutoCAD commands [which may be selected from the screen menu (see Fig. I.1) or typed in] are printed in computer-like type—usually in uppercase letters.
- Instructions you are to follow are in text type.

2.1.1   Loading AutoCAD from a floppy disk
(Ver. 2.18 only)

If AutoCAD is to be loaded from a floppy disk, remove the DOS disk from drive A, insert the Acad executable (Acad.exe) disk in drive A, and close the latch. Type **acad** and press the Enter key:

    A>**acad** <return>

AutoCAD will respond with:

    Can't find overlay file ACAD.OVL.
    Enter new drive letter or '.' to quit:

Replace the Acad.exe disk that is in drive A with your Acad overlay (Acad.ovl) disk. Insert the data disk, which you formatted in Sec. 1.2.4, into drive B and close both drive latches. Type:

a: <return>

2.1.2   Loading AutoCAD from a fixed disk

...ie hard disk, first specify the ... and .ovl files. Then transfer ...Acad subdirectory. Assuming ...as outlined in App. D and Sec.

...a disk in drive B instead of on

Sec. 1.4.3 will now be displayed. ...by typing a 1:

AutoCAD will now request the drawing name. We will precede the drawing name with b:, indicating that the data file for the drawing is to be stored on the data disk in drive B. If you are using a fixed disk and wish to save the drawing in the Easy branch of the Acad subdirectory, do *not* precede the drawing name with the drive designation B:.

Enter NAME of drawing: b:proj-2 <return> or: proj-2 <return>

The AutoCAD drawing editor should now appear on the screen (see Fig. I.1).

2.2 AutoCAD Commands

AutoCAD commands may be entered by typing in the command (this will not work for commands that call submenus) or by selecting the command from the screen menu. To move the cursor to the menu, press the Ins key (see Fig. 1.1); be sure that the Num Lock key is *not* on. The cursor will move to the menu and will highlight one of the items. Move the cursor up or down to the item desired with the up and down arrow keys that are on the numeric keypad. When the item desired is highlighted, press the Enter key or the Space Bar to select that item. The command line at the bottom of the screen (see Fig. I.1) displays the command and may also display a request for further information that AutoCAD requires to complete the command. Enter the information requested.

If your system uses a mouse or a digitizer, the cursor may be moved to the menu by moving the mouse or digitizer puck. To select an item, move the puck to the right until the item desired in the menu is highlighted, then press the Select button on the puck or digitizer (see your *AutoCAD Installation and Performance Guide* regarding the mouse and digitizer buttons).

2.3 AutoCAD Drawing Cursor

To move the cursor to the drawing editor, press the Home key (ensure that the Num Lock key is not on).

The cursor is moved about the screen by the up, down, right, and left cursor control arrow keys (see Fig. I.1). AutoCAD provides three movement steps, coarse, medium, and fine. Fine movements are obtained by pressing the PgDn key, and coarse movements are obtained by pressing the PgUp key. Movement precision can be changed by the SNAP command which will be discussed in Chap. 6.

If you are using a mouse or digitizing tablet to control the cursor, moving the mouse or digitizing puck around will cause the cursor to move on the monitor. If at any time you use the cursor control keys to move the cursor, you may find that your mouse or digitizing puck seems to be "hung up." If this happens, press the Del (delete) key on the keyboard and then retry moving the cursor with the mouse or digitizer puck.

2.4 Screen Limits

Enter the following commands by selecting them from the screen menu as specified in Sec. 2.2.

Ver. 2.1

UTILITY <**pick**> LIMITS <**pick**>

Ver. 2.5 to Release 10

SETTINGS <**pick**> LIMITS <**pick**>

All versions

ON/OFF <Lower left corner> <0,0>: <**return**> This will select the default coordinates of 0,0 displayed in the wedge brackets < >.

ON/OFF <Upper right corner> <12,9>: <**return**> This will use the default coordinates of 12 units horizontal and 9 units vertical.

2.5   Set Units and Precision

Enter the following commands:

LAST <**pick**> **next** <**pick**> **UNITS** <**pick**>

The units available are:

Type	Example
1. Scientific	1.67E+10
2. Decimal	16.70
3. Engineering	1'–4.5
4. Architectural	1'–4½
5. Fractional	16½

Enter choice (1 to 5) <4>: **2** <**return**>

Note that here the default is 4 (architectural units) and a 2 is entered to select decimal units.

AutoCAD now requests the number of digits to be used to the right of the decimal point. For this drawing two digits will be selected:

Number of digits to right of decimal point, 0 to 8 <4>: **2** <**return**>

Next, AutoCAD requests the system of angle measurement to be used. The display will depend on your version of AutoCAD (some options are not in Ver. 2.1).

```
System of angle measurement
1.  Decimal degrees
2.  Degrees/minutes/seconds
3.  Grads
4.  Radians
5.  Surveyor's units
Enter choice (1 to 5) <2>: 1 <return>
Number of fractional places for display of angles (0 to 8) <4>: 0 <return>
```

You may change the coordinate system to be used for designating angles. Generally you will use the cartesian coordinate system as illustrated in Fig. 2.2 and Sec. 2.6. In each case the default value—in angle brackets < >—is selected by pressing Enter for each of the requests:

```
Direction for angle 0:
  East 3 o'clock = 0
  North 12 o'clock = 90
  West 9 o'clock = 180
  South 6 o'clock = 270
Enter direction for angle 0 <0>: <return>
Do you want angles measured clockwise?<N>: <return>
Command: Press the F1 key (see Fig. 1.1) to return to the drawing editor.
```

2.6   Lines and Cartesian Coordinate System

Two-dimensional points on the AutoCAD drawing screen are located based on the cartesian coordinate system illustrated in Fig. 2.2.

In the cartesian coordinate system, horizontal lines drawn from left to right are said to be along the x axis in a positive direction. Vertical lines drawn in an upward direction are said to be along the y axis in a positive direction. Positive angles are measured from the positive x axis in a counterclockwise direction. In Fig. 2.2, the coordinates of point b are 2,3 (2 along the positive x axis and 3 units along the positive y axis). The coordinates of point a are $-2, -1.5$. Line $a-b$ is at an angle of 48 degrees. Refer to Chap. 17 for three-dimensional drawings with Release 10.

Lines: To draw a line, select the following commands from the screen menu following the procedure specified in Sec. 2.2:

DRAW <**pick**> LINE <**pick**>

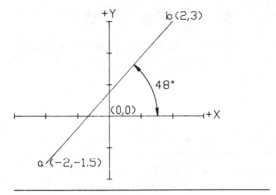

Figure 2.2   Cartesian coordinate system.

The trapezoid illustrated in Fig. 2.1 will be drawn using the four available methods of drawing lines. Any one method is acceptable for all lines.

1. *Lines by real coordinates.*   A point may be located on the drawing by entering the screen coordinates of the point:

Line from point: **2,2** <**return**>

2. *Lines by relative* xy *distances.*   A point may be specified by entering its distances relative to the last point entered. To draw a line from coordinate 2,2 to coordinate 8,2 as illustrated in Fig. 2.3, the relative distances from point 2,2 are 6.00 units in the x direction and 0 units in the y direction. The command to draw the line using relative coordinates is:

To point: **@6,0** <**return**>

The @ symbol tells AutoCAD that the point is relative to the last point entered. In this case the point is 6 units to the right and 0 units above the previous point. Points to the right of the previous point are positive and

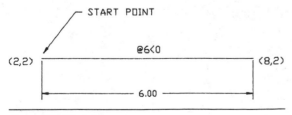

Figure 2.3   Line 1.

points above the previous point are positive. Negative points may be entered for relative points.

3. *Lines by relative distance and angle.*   Points may also be located by giving their relative distance and angle with respect to the last point. To drawn Line 2 in Fig. 2.4, enter:

```
To point: @5<90 <return>
```

The @ symbol tells AutoCAD the point is relative to the last point entered. The < indicates that the next value is the angle of the line. Angles are based on rectangular cartesian coordinates where angles are positive if rotation from the x axis is counterclockwise and negative if rotation from the x axis is clockwise. Angles are always measured from the horizontal in degrees (unless you redefine the location of 0 degrees when defining the angle units; see Sect. 2.5).

4. *Lines by digitized points.*   Points may be entered by locating them on the drawing screen using the cursor control keys (see Fig. 1.1) or a mouse or digitizing tablet. First, press Ctrl-D (hold down the Ctrl key and press the D key) to turn on the display of the current screen coordinates which is located at the top of the screen.

Using the arrow keys on the keyboard (or a mouse or digitizing puck), move the cursor around on the screen. If the coordinates displayed at the

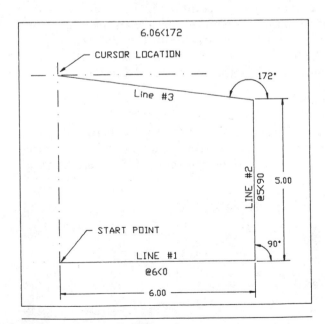

Figure 2.4 Line 4, digitizing points.

top of the screen do not change as the cursor is moved, press Ctrl-D again.

Coordinates may be displayed as x,y coordinates (i.e., 5.25,3.10) or as distance<angle (i.e., 4.10<56) by toggling the Ctrl-D key. Toggle Ctrl-D until the distance<angle is displayed and move the cursor on the screen until the distance to the next point is shown as 6.06<172. The vertical cursor should be lined up with the start point (2,2) as illustrated in Fig. 2.4. Press Enter to digitize the point.

2.6.1 Close command

A set of lines may be closed on the first point in the set entered by entering c:

    To point: c <return>

Note: If the set of lines was discontinued and restarted from a new point, the line will close on the new start point. If the trapezoid did not close on coordinate 2,2 (the start point), select the UNDO command from the screen menu to undo the last line, and enter the coordinates of the start point 2,2 to close the trapezoid. You will then have to press Ctrl-C to exit the line command. The UNDO command may be used to undo a "group" of commands. For a more thorough discussion, refer to Sec. A.1.1 in App. A and your *AutoCAD Reference Manual*. If the command undoes more than you wanted, the REDO command may be entered *immediately* to undo the UNDO.

2.7 Command Exiting

A command may be exited by pressing the Ctrl and C keys together (shown as Ctrl-C). If the command line at the bottom of the monitor shows a command request, press Ctrl-C. If the last command entered was C (in Sec. 2.6 above), the command line will be clear and Ctrl-C will not have to be entered.

2.8 CIRCLE Command

Three methods for drawing circles will be tried. Enter the following commands:

    LAST <pick> CIRCLE <pick> CEN,DIA <pick> Center point: 4,5 <return>
    DIAMETER/<Radius>:D Diameter: 1.5 <return>

The commands will draw a circle with its center at point 4,5 and a 1.5 unit diameter.

Other circle commands are:

3-Point <**pick**> 1'st Point: Digitize point *a* on the top line of the trapezoid; see Fig. 2.5.
<**pick**> 2'nd point: Digitize point *b* on the right side of the trapezoid. <**pick**> 3'rd
point:DRAG <**return**> Move the mouse and drag the circle to the upper-right corner of the
trapezoid. If the keyboard is used, press the PgUp key twice and *slowly* drag the circle
tangent to the right upper corner of the trapezoid. Pressing the PgUp key sets coarse
movements of the cursor. Pressing the PgDn key sets fine movements of the cursor. When
dragging the circle, do not rush the computer since the circle has to be redrawn each time the
cursor is moved. <**pick**>

Now try a 2-point circle:

2-Point <**pick**> 1'st Point: Digitize a point on the drawing. <**pick**> 2'nd Point:DRAG
Move circle to the desired location. <**pick**>

2.9   POINT Command

This command is used to place a single point on the drawing.

DRAW <**pick**> POINT <**pick**> POINT: Digitize a point on the drawing.

In many cases the Draw menu is larger than one screen. For example,
to select the POINT command from the menu, you will first have to select
the NEXT command, which will display the remainder of the Draw
menu that contains the POINT command. This happens for a number of
commands and will not always be specified in this text.

2.10   ARC Command

DRAW <**pick**> ARC <**pick**>

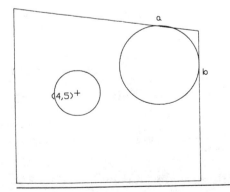

Figure 2.5 Circles.

A number of ARC commands are available. The following symbols are used in the commands:

A   Included angle
C   Center
D   Starting direction
E   End point
L   Length of chord
R   Radius
S   Start point

Select the SCE (start, center, end) command.

Arcs are always drawn in a counterclockwise direction. To draw the arc SCE illustrated in Fig. 2.6 with a radius of 1 use:

```
Arc center/<Start point> : 2,3 <return> Center : @1<0 <return> Angle/Length
of chord <End point> : Drag : @1<270 <return>
```

Note that the start point was entered as real coordinates and the other points were entered as relative distance<angles. The points could have been entered using any of the methods discussed for line drawing.

Three-point arcs are drawn by entering three points on the arc. Practice with a number of the arc commands, noting the following:

- Enter @ to start the arc on the last point drawn.

- Arcs are always drawn counterclockwise.

- ADE-2 uses the drag mode for last point; however, you do not have to drag the last point into location using the cursor. You can enter the coordinates of the last point via the keyboard.

2.11   ERASE and Oops Commands

The ERASE command is only used to erase whole entities, and it will not break an entity. This means that if a line is drawn, the ERASE command

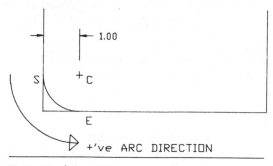

Figure 2.6 Arcs.

is used to erase the *entire line*. If a portion of the line is to be deleted, another command (BREAK) should be used.

EDIT <**pick**> ERASE <**pick**> Select objects: l (last) <**return**><**return**>

Last, or L, erases the last entity drawn.

When asked to "Select Objects," the screen cross hair is replaced with a small box. You may select the object by placing the box on it and pressing the mouse select button. The following options are also available: L (last), W (window), P (previous), U (undo), R (remove), A (add). These options are used throughout the text.

The item(s) selected to be erased is shown on the monitor with a dashed line. The second Enter (<return>) at the end of the command is required to indicate that you are through selecting items to be erased. After you have entered L, AutoCAD is still under the ERASE command and you may select other items by digitizing them or using the W (window) command.

Notice that the last entity drawn was erased. If you wish to restore the entity, use the oops command:

oops <return>

The previous entity that was erased should now return to the screen. The oops command only works **immediately** after the entity has been erased. If any other commands were entered between the ERASE and the oops command, it may not retrieve the entity erased.

Other entities may be erased by selecting the object, i.e., digitizing a point on the object. When Enter is pressed, the entity is not erased immediately. The command line is still under the ERASE command and other entities may be digitized. After all the entities are digitized, the Enter (<return>) key is pressed a second time and the entities selected are erased.

ERASE <**pick**> Select objects: Place the cursor box on the circumference of the circle as shown in Fig. 2.7. <**pick**> Place the cursor on the bottom line of the trapezoid as shown in Fig. 2.7. <**pick**><**return**>

The items did not erase until the Enter key (<**return**>) was pressed.

Restore the items using the oops command:

oops <return>

Another method of erasing entities is to place a window around the entities to be erased. All *complete* entities in the window will be erased as follows:

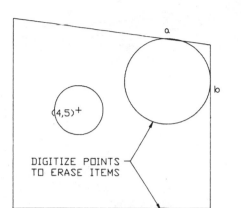

Figure 2.7 Erasing entities by digitizing.

ERASE <**pick**> Select objects: WINDOW <**pick**> First corner: Move the cursor so that the horizontal cursor line is slightly below the bottom of the large circle and the vertical cursor line is slightly to the left of it as illustrated in Fig. 2.8. <**pick**> Second corner: Move the cursor to the right and upward so that the window created completely encloses the circle as illustrated in Fig. 2.8. <**pick**> <**return**>

The circle should now be erased. If it has not been erased, you did not enclose all of the circle in the window. Try again.

Notice that part of the top line of the trapezoid and part of the right side of the trapezoid was enclosed in the window; however, those lines were not erased. That is because the ERASE command can be used only to erase whole entities and the entire line was *not* enclosed in the window. Only whole entities in the window will be erased.

Restore the circle using the oops command.

2.12 ZOOM Command

The ZOOM command is used to enlarge or shrink the view of a portion of the drawing. The commands used to call the ZOOM command are:

AutoCAD <**pick**> DISPLAY <**pick**> ZOOM <**pick**> All/Center/Dynamic/Extents/
Left/Previous/Window/<Scale(x)>:

The ZOOM command is used to enlarge or shrink a portion of the drawing. If a number is entered, it indicates the multiplier of the full view. For instance, entering 2 would display the object twice as large as the full view, whereas entering 0.5 would draw the object one-half as large as the full view. The other commands available are called by typing

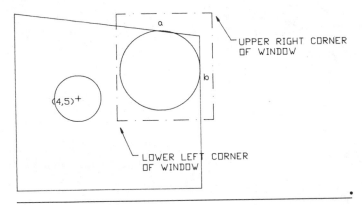

Figure 2.8 Erasing entities by windows.

one of the following letters (or selecting the command from the screen menu):

A   All; zooms to drawing limits
C   Center; asks for center point and height
E   Extents; shows entire drawing to current extents
L   Left; asks for lower left corner and height
P   Previous; restores previous view
W   Window; asks for a window around portion to be enlarged
D   Dynamic; allows the user to zoom and pan at the same time. Refer to Sec. 5.7 for a discussion of this option.

If the command line at the bottom of the screen does not display the ZOOM command, invoke the set of commands illustrated above and then enter:

Window **<pick>** First corner: Digitize a point to become the lower left corner of a window enclosing an area to be enlarged on the screen. **<pick>** Second corner: Digitize the upper right corner of the window. **<pick>**

To return to the previous view, press the Enter key or the Space Bar to recall the ZOOM command and type **p** or select Previous from the screen menu:

p (previous) **<return>**

Notice how the Space Bar or Enter key was used to recall the previous command. This speeds up the drafting process.

Use the ZOOM <return> (Window) command to place a window around and zoom in on the upper right corner of the trapezoid including points *a* and *b* in Fig. 2.1. How accurately were you able to place the circle along the top line? A more precise method for placing lines tangent to circles will be discussed in later projects.

2.13 BREAK Command

This command is used to delete a portion of an entity. The command will be used to form a fillet by deleting the corner of the trapezoid from *a* to *b* and the lower part of the circle from *a* to *b*:

EDIT <pick> BREAK <pick> Select object: Digitize a point on the top line of the trapezoid well to the left of the circle so AutoCAD has no doubt about the item being selected. See Fig. 2.9. <pick> Enter second point or F: f <return> Enter first point: Digitize the intersection point of the circle and the top side of the trapezoid, the first point in Fig. 2.9. <pick> Enter second point: Digitize the top right corner of the trapezoid, the second point in Fig. 2.9. <pick>

The f was entered in the previous set of commands to force AutoCAD to ask for the first point of the break. Occasionally the point used to select the object is the first point of the break. In those cases you would enter the second point rather than force AutoCAD to ask for the first point by entering f. After the first point of the break is entered, AutoCAD then requests the second point. When breaking any entity, always select the object in an uncluttered location so that AutoCAD has no doubt about which item is being selected. The break can be undone as follows:

EDIT <pick> Undo <pick> Auto/Back/Control/End/Group/Mark/<number>: 1 <return>

Then undo the undo as follows:

REDO <pick>

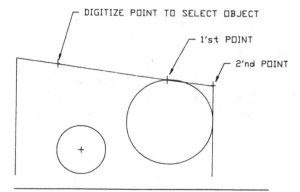

Figure 2.9 Break points on lines.

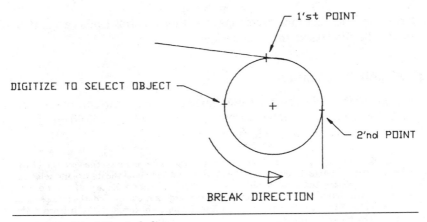

Figure 2.10   Breaking circle lines.

Using the same procedure outlined above, delete the trapezoid from point *b* (Fig. 2.8) to the top corner.

When breaking a circle or arc, AutoCAD always breaks the entity in a *counterclockwise* direction between the first and second point. To break the circle from *a* to *b* (Fig. 2.8):

EDIT <**pick**> BREAK <**pick**> Select object : Digitize a point on the circumference of the circle. <**pick**> Enter second point or F: **f** <**return**> Enter first point : Digitize point *a* in Fig. 2.10. <**pick**> Enter second point : Digitize point *b*. <**pick**>

2.14   Files

The FILES command is used to list the drawing files:

AutoCAD <**pick**> UTILITY <**pick**> FILES <**pick**>

The File Utility menu illustrated in Sec. 1.4.3 will be displayed. Review the procedure outlined in Sec. 1.4.3. When you exit the File Utilities menu, you will be returned to the AutoCAD Drawing Editor.

2.15   Exit a Drawing

SAVE   Saves the current state of the drawing but does not exit the drawing editor. If the default name is used, the last file is saved with a .bak extension.

END   Returns to the main menu and updates the drawing file. The file name is the drawing name entered when the drawing is started, with a file extension .dwg added. A previous file for this drawing is given the .bak extension so that the previous file (one level back) is not erased.

QUIT   Returns to the main menu but does not update the drawing file.

End the drawing using:

```
AutoCAD <pick> UTILITY <pick> END <pick>
```

From the AutoCAD main menu select 0 to exit AutoCAD.

Relocating Entities

OBJECTIVE *Practice commands from the previous project; use MOVE and DRAG commands to relocate an entity; use the COPY command to copy entities; draw center ticks and center lines for circles.*

DRAWING *Boot up AutoCAD and begin a new drawing with the name* **B:Proj-3.** *Draw the V block illustrated in Fig. 3.1 using the procedures outlined in this lesson.*

3.1 Drawing Screen Limits

The V block will require a space of about 6 by 5 units. The default AutoCAD limits are lower left corner 0,0 and upper right corner 12,9. AutoCAD drawings are always drawn 1:1 scale on the monitor. If scaling is to be done, it is done when the drawing is plotted. The screen size will be reduced to 6,5. In order to start the lower left corner of the V block at 0,0, the lower left corner of the screen will be set as -1, -1, and the right corner will be 5,4. The commands are:

```
SETTINGS (or UTILITY) <pick> LIMITS <pick>
Lower left corner <0,0>: -1,-1 <return>
Upper right corner <12,9>: 5,4 <return>
```

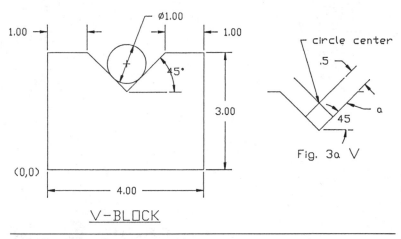

Figure 3.1 Project 3.

A tick should appear on the screen locating the new limits. To reset the monitor to the new limits, zoom in on the limits (the command line response is slightly different for Ver. 2.1):

```
AutoCAD <pick> DISPLAY <pick> ZOOM <pick> All/Center/Dynamic/Extents/
Left/Previous/Window/<Scale> All <pick>
```

The previous commands could have been typed in from the keyboard. You would have typed:

zoom <return> a <return>

Note: Each time the screen limits are changed, the commands ZOOM <return> A (all) must be entered to reset the monitor to the new limits.

3.2 Set Units and Precision

Set the units to decimal with two digits to the right of the decimal point. Refer to Sec. 2.5 for the procedure.

Press Ctrl-D to turn cursor position coordinate display on.

3.3 V-block Drawing

Draw the V block (do not include the circles or arc yet). Select the LINE command from the Draw menu and start the lower left corner of the V block at coordinate 0,0. Draw the V block in a counterclockwise direction. The commands are summarized below.

Note: Try to draw the lines of the block without looking at the commands below. If you draw a line and wish to change it, use the UNDO command immediately after the line is drawn. If UNDO is invoked during a line sequence, only the last line is undone. If UNDO is invoked after exiting LINE, all lines drawn in that sequence are undone. To undo UNDO, invoke REDO.

DRAW <**pick**> LINE <**pick**> Line from point: **0,0** <**return**> To point: **@3<0** <**return**> undo <**pick**> To point: **@4<0** <**return**> To point: **@3<90** <**return**> To point: **@1<180**<**return**> To point: **@−1,−1** <**return**> To point: **@−1,1** <**return**> To point: **@1<180** <**return**> To point: **c** <**return**>

In the preceding set of commands, the −1,−1 coordinates specify that the bottom of the V is 1 unit to the left (-ve) and 1 unit below (-ve) the top right end of the V. The relative coordinates to draw the line from the bottom of the V to the top left end are −1,1. Note how the UNDO command was used to correct an input error in the sequence.

3.4   Save Drawing

Prior to continuing, the work done so far should be saved (in Ver. 2.1, the SAVE command is in the utility menu):

AutoCAD <**pick**> SAVE <**pick**> File name: **b:proj-3** <**return**>

If AutoCAD crashes for some reason or if the power plug is accidentally kicked out of the socket, etc., you will lose only the work done after the last SAVE command. Get into the habit of saving your drawing regularly during the operation of AutoCAD.

3.5   Using MOVE and DRAG

Now the 1-unit diameter circle will be drawn in the V at the top of the V block. Three different procedures will be used. In the first, the circle will be drawn above the V and dragged into location as illustrated in Fig. 3.2. The commands are:

DRAW <**pick**> CIRCLE <**pick**> CEN, RAD <**pick**> Center point: Move the cursor so that it is in the initial position shown in Fig. 3.2. <**pick**> Diameter / <Radius> **0.5** <**return**>

Prior to moving the circle into place, use the ZOOM and window commands to enlarge the view of the V:

DISPLAY <**pick**> ZOOM <**pick**> Window <**pick**> First corner: A window is to be placed around the V and the circle, see Fig. 3.2. Digitize a point on the screen that will represent the lower left corner of that window. <**pick**> Second corner: Digitize the upper right corner of the window. <**pick**>

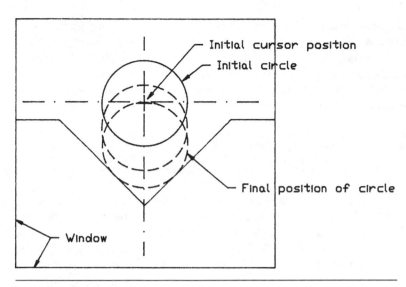

Figure 3.2 Moving entities.

The MOVE command will now be used to relocate the circle so that it fits into the V and is tangent to the sides of the V. As the circle is being moved, its initial view will remain on the screen. When the final position is selected, press Enter to fix the circle in the location selected; this will delete the initial view. The DRAG command will be used to drag the circle into place. When the DRAG command is used, the user moves the cursor across the screen and drags the item that is being relocated with the cursor. As the cursor is moved across the screen, the object is redrawn a number of times, so be careful and **move the object slowly** so that you do not get ahead of the computer.

The MOVE command is under the Edit submenu and is used as shown below for the different versions of AutoCAD.

Ver. 2.1

EDIT <**pick**> MOVE <**pick**> Select objects or Window or Last:**l** (for Last since the circle was the last item drawn) <**return**> <**return**> Base point or displacement: Digitize a point on the bottom of the circle directly above the V. <**return**> Second point of displacement: **drag** <**return**> Using the mouse, slowly drag the circle down until its sides are tangent with the sides of the V. <**return**>

Ver. 2.5 to Release 10

EDIT <**pick**> NEXT <**pick**> MOVE <**pick**> Select objects: Last <**pick**> <**return**> Base point or displacement: Digitize a point on the bottom of the circle directly above the V. <**pick**> Second point of displacement: Using the mouse, slowly drag the circle down until its sides are tangent with the sides of the V. <**pick**>

Note that the drag mode, by default, is set on automatic for a number of commands. In the MOVE command, the second point can be automatically dragged into place by moving the cursor or a numeric coordinate value may be entered. If you do not wish the drag mode to be automatic, use the DRAGMODE command to set the drag mode to on rather than auto. Notice that the initial circle is not erased until its copy has been moved into location and the Enter key has been pressed to digitize the new location.

3.6 Using COPY Command

The next procedure used will be based on a procedure you might use if the drawing was to be done using standard drafting equipment.

The circle drawn in the V has a radius of 0.5 units. Since the circle is tangent to the sides of the V, two lines drawn parallel to the side of the V and 0.5 units from each side and on the inside of the V will cross at the center of the circle as illustrated in Fig. 3.3. To erase the previously drawn circle and draw the lines:

EDIT <pick> ERASE <pick> Select object: LAST <pick> <return>

Note: Note that Enter is pressed at the end of the last command sequence. When the item is selected, its line type is changed to a dotted line. The ERASE command is still in control and other items to be erased may be selected. To exit the command and erase all entities selected, the Enter key is pressed.

A line will now be drawn parallel to the right side of the V and 0.5 units to the left of it. The line will be a copy of the right side of the V, which is at a 45-degree angle (see Fig. 3.3). The direction of movement is perpendicular to the side, giving an angle of 135 (45 + 90) degrees.

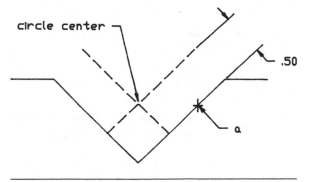

Figure 3.3 Copying entities.

EDIT <**pick**> COPY <**pick**> Select objects: Digitize a point on the right side of the V, point *a* in Fig. 3.3 <**pick**> <**return**> Base point or displacement: @ (To reselect point *a*) <**return**> Second point of displacement: **@0.5<135** <**return**> <**return**>

Note the two Enters at the end of the command string. The first is required to execute the second point of displacement entry, and the second is used to recall the COPY command. This is a handy way to recall a previous command and should be used whenever possible.

The format of the COPY command follows:

- Select the object to be copied.

- Indicate the displacement by selecting a first point in response to the displacement request and then a second point with respect to the first point, which can be located by digitizing a point on the screen or via the keyboard. The displacement may be located anywhere on the monitor.

Copy the left side of the V. Try to do so without looking at the following commands:

Select objects: Digitize a point on the line to be moved. <**pick**> <**return**> Base point or displacement: @ <**return**> Second point of displacement: **@0.5<45** <**return**>

Draw a circle with the center point where the two copied lines cross:

DRAW <**pick**> CIRCLE <**pick**> CEN,RAD <**pick**> Center point: Digitize the cross point of the parallel lines. <**pick**> Radius (or D): **0.5** <**return**>

Erase each of the parallel lines:

EDIT <**pick**> ERASE <**pick**> Select objects: Digitize one of the parallel lines. <**pick**> Digitize other parallel line. <**pick**> <**return**>

Note the Enter needed to complete the ERASE command.
Display the entire drawing:

AutoCAD <**pick**> DISPLAY <**pick**> ZOOM <**pick**> All/Center/Dynamic/Extents/ Left/Previous/Window/<scale>: All <**pick**>

3.7   Using TTR Command

A circle may be very easily placed tangent to two lines using the TTR (tangent, tangent, and radius) command as follows (this command is not available on Ver. 2.1):

AUTOCAD <**pick**> EDIT <**pick**> ERASE <**pick**> Select objects: Digitize a point on the circumference of the circle. <**pick**> <**return**>

DRAW <**pick**> CIRCLE <**pick**> TTR <**pick**> Enter Tangent spec: Place the cursor target over the left side line of the V. <**pick**> Enter second Tangent spec: Place the cursor target over the right side line of the V. <**pick**> Radius: **0.5** <**return**>

3.8 Draw Center Marks and Lines in Circle

The style and size of circle center marks is governed by the DIMCEN variable, which is a subcommand of DIM VARS (dimension variables). If the number stored in DIMCEN is zero, no center marks are drawn. If the number is greater than zero, the value specifies the size of the center mark. If DIMCEN is positive, center marks (ticks) are drawn; if it is negative, center lines are drawn. The default value of DIMCEN is 0.09. In later projects scaling will be discussed. For now DIMCEN will simply be changed to -0.09 so that center lines rather than center marks will be drawn by AutoCAD:

AUTOCAD <**pick**> DIM <**pick**> DIM VARS <**pick**> DIMCEN <**pick**> Current value <**0.09**> New value: **-0.09** <**return**> DIMMENU <**pick**> CENTER <**pick**> Select circle or arc: Digitize a point on the circumference of the circle. <**pick**> **Ctrl-C** (or EXIT to exit DIM command.)

3.9 Exit

To exit from the drawing editor and save the drawing:

AUTOCAD <**pick**> UTILITY <**pick**> END <**pick**>

or type **end** <return>.

If you wish to exit from AutoCAD without saving the drawing, select QUIT rather than END; however, we wish to save this drawing.

Return to DOS by selecting 0 (Exit AutoCAD) from the main menu.

Project 4—Dimensioning

OBJECTIVE *Dimension a drawing; calculate and set dimension scale; use linear, angular, and radius dimensioning; set dimension text controls; use ARC command; calculate text scale.*

DRAWING *Boot up AutoCAD and start a new drawing named* **b:proj-4.** *Complete the drawing illustrated in Fig. 4.1, inserting all dimensions and text using the procedures outlined in this lesson.*

4.1 Set Drawing Limits and Units

Set the limits of the monitor so that the 14 × 10 unit object will fit the screen allowing room for the dimensions. The lower left corner of the *object* will be assumed as point 0,0, so the lower left corner of the *monitor* will have negative coordinates. The limits can be reset later so you do not have to worry too much about the exact proper values for this initial setting. Refer to Chap. 3 for the procedure.

When the limits are set, use ZOOM A (all) to set the screen to the new limits:

    DISPLAY <**pick**> ZOOM <**pick**> All/Center/Dynamic/Extents/Left/Previous/
    Window/<Scale>: **All** <**return**>

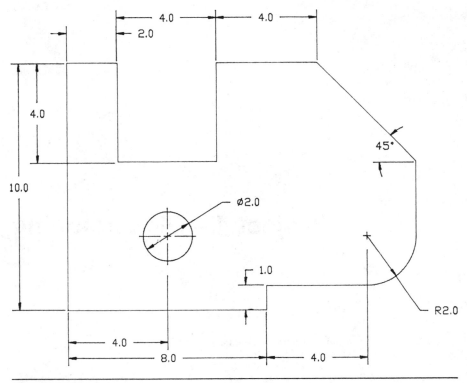

Figure 4.1 Project 4.

Set the units to decimal with one digit to the right of the decimal point. Refer to Chap. 3 if you have trouble. To return to the drawing editor, press the F1 key.

Press Ctrl-D to activate the cursor coordinate display.

4.2 Draw Lines and Arc

Begin drawing lines using the lower left corner of the plate as 0,0 and draw in a counterclockwise direction:

DRAW <**pick**> LINE <**pick**> Line from point: **0,0** <**return**> To point: **@8<0** <**return**> To point: **@1<90** <**return**> To point: **@4<0** <**return**>

The LINE command must be exited to enter the ARC command. To exit (cancel) a command:

To point: Press Ctrl-C or press the Enter key or select Cancel from the screen menu.

4.2.1 Last point

An arc is to be drawn starting from the end of the last line drawn. That point is the last point drawn.

When AutoCAD requests a point and the point is to be the same as the last point drawn, you can indicate that the last point is to be used by entering @. This command will be used when drawing the arc since the start point of the arc is the end point of the last line drawn.

4.2.2 Draw arc

Refer to Sec. 2.10 for a definition of the symbols displayed when the ARC command is called. To draw an arc starting at the end of the last line and with a radius of 2 units, select SCE (start, center, end) from the list of options. The arc will then be drawn in a counterclockwise direction starting at the last point, as illustrated in Fig. 4.2. The center is 2 units directly above the start point, so the relative command @2<90 is entered next. The end point is entered as 2 units to the right of the center @2<0:

```
DRAW <pick> ARC <pick> SCE <pick> Start point or C: @ <return> Center:
@2<90 <return> End point: @2<0 <return>
```

Arcs must always be drawn in a counterclockwise direction.

Draw the remainder of the lines to complete the plate. If you draw a line incorrectly, use UNDO to erase it and then redraw the line. To start the line sequence at the end of the arc, use the relative @ command. When drawing the diagonal line, relative coordinates are used to locate the next point.

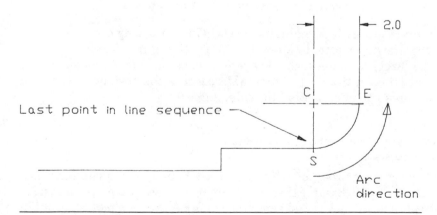

Figure 4.2 Arc drawing sequence.

LAST <pick> LINE <pick> From point: @ <return> To point: @3<90 <return> To point: @−4,4 <return> etc.

Draw a circle with a diameter of 2.0 units at location 4,3.

4.3   Set Text Scale

When using AutoCAD, height or size refers to the number of drawing units. The number of units used for the size of text and dimension variables must reflect either the drawing limits set or the size desired for text and dimensions variables on the plotted drawing.

We will consider two methods to calculate the text height—the first based on a drawing not plotted to scale and the second based on a scaled plot.

4.3.1   Text scale method 1—drawing not plotted to scale

To calculate the text height, assume the following specifications for this drawing:

- Limits are set as −3,−3 and 17,13, giving a drawing size of 20 by 16 units.

- Plot size is to be an A-size sheet (8.5 by 11 in).

- Text height desired on plotted sheet is ³⁄₁₆ in (0.1875).

AutoCAD lettering height, h, is calculated by setting up a ratio of:

$$\frac{\text{Screen text height}}{\text{Screen dimension}} = \frac{\text{plot text height}}{\text{plot dimension}} \qquad (4.1)$$

Based on the drawing height, $h/16 = 0.1875/8.5$, giving $h = 0.35$. Based on the drawing width, $h/20 = 0.1875/11$, giving $h = 0.34$.

The larger value governs. *For lettering, set h = 0.35.* When text is inserted into a drawing, AutoCAD requests the text height. If the drawing is not to be plotted to scale, enter 0.35.

4.3.2   Text height method 2—drawing plotted to scale

If the drawing is to be plotted to scale, the text height is calculated based on the plot scale. Assume that this drawing is drawn in inch units and is to be plotted on an A-size sheet (8.5 by 11 in). A drawing plot scale of 1 in = 2 in, or 1/2 scale, should be satisfactory. If we wish the text height on the plotted drawing to be 3/16 in (0.1875 in), the height (h) of the text on the monitor will be calculated as follows:

$$1/2 * h = 0.1875 \qquad \text{giving } h = 0.375 \text{ drawing units (inches)}$$

Text will not be added to this drawing; however, the text height of 0.375 units will be used to calculate the height of dimension text and other dimension variables.

4.4 Dimension Scale

Dimension variables (arrow size, dimension text height, extension line offsets, circle and arc center lines and marks, etc.) may be set individually or by setting the scale factor for all dimensions using DIMSCALE. The default value for DIMSCALE is 1. AutoCAD's default size for dimension text is 0.18 drawing units multiplied by DIMSCALE, which has a default setting of 1.0.

In Sec. 4.3.2 it was determined that the text should be 0.375 units high on the monitor to obtain 3/16-in text on the plotted drawing. DIMSCALE is calculated using the following formula:

$$\begin{aligned} \text{DIMSCALE} * 0.18 &= \text{Text Height} \\ \text{DIMSCALE} * 0.18 &= 0.375 \qquad \text{giving DIMSCALE} = 2.08 \end{aligned} \qquad (4.2)$$

Set DIMSCALE using:

```
AutoCAD <pick> DIM <pick> DIM VARS <pick> next pick> DIMSCALE <pick> Cur-
rent value <1.0> New value: 2.08 <return>
```

To provide sufficient room for dimensioning, reset LIMITS to −3,−3 and 17,13:

```
Ctrl-C (to exit DIM command) AutoCAD <pick> SETTINGS <pick> LIMITS <pick>
Lower left corner <default>: −3,−3 <return> Upper right corner <default>:
17,13 <return> AutoCAD <pick> DISPLAY <pick> ZOOM <pick> All/Center/
Dynamic/Extents/Left/Previous/Window/<Scale>: All <return>
```

4.5 Add Center Lines and Marks
to Circles and Arcs

In Chap. 3 we learned that the default value in DIMCEN is 0.09, that a positive number in DIMCEN causes AutoCAD to draw center marks (+), and that a negative number causes AutoCAD to print center lines. The value in DIMCEN is always multiplied by DIMSCALE (see Sec. 4.5). This means that center marks (+), 0.09 by 2.08 units long (using 2.08, the DIMSCALE set in Sec. 4.4), will be drawn for the arc by entering the commands:

AutoCAD <**pick**> DIM <**pick**> CENTER <**pick**> Select circle or arc: Digitize a point on the circumference of the arc. <**pick**>

To add center lines to the circle we must first change DIMCEN to a negative value. The command line at the bottom of the monitor should indicate that you are still under the DIM command. If not, go to LAST MENU and select DIM. To add center lines to the circle:

DIM VARS <**pick**> DIMCEN <**pick**> Current value <0.1> New value: **−0.09** <**return**> DIMMENU <**pick**> CENTER <**pick**> Select circle or arc: Digitize a point on the circumference of the circle. <**pick**> EXIT <**pick**>

Prior to continuing, save the drawing using the name b:Proj-4. Refer to Sec. 3.4 if you require assistance.

4.6 Linear Dimensions

Linear dimensions may be horizontal, vertical, aligned (parallel to a diagonal line), or rotated (drawn at a specified angle, not necessarily parallel to the item being dimensioned).

When linear dimensions are inserted into a drawing, AutoCAD requests the "First extension line origin." This is one point on the object from which the dimension is to start (see Fig. 4.2). When the point is entered, AutoCAD asks for the "Second extension line origin," which is the second point on the object for the dimension desired. AutoCAD then asks for the "Dimension line location." The point entered is where the dimension line will be drawn. These are illustrated in Fig. 4.3.

Prior to entering the dimension commands, if the command line does

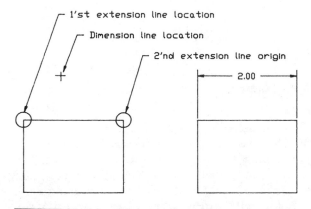

Figure 4.3 Dimensioning selection points.

not show AutoCAD as being under the DIM command, select: DIM
<pick>.

If the menu on the right side of the screen does not contain the
LINEAR command, enter the command DIMMENU.

Dimensions along the top of the plate are entered as follows:

LINEAR <pick> HORIZ <pick> First extension line origin: Locate the cursor on
point a in Fig. 4.4 <pick> Second extension line origin: Digitize point b or enter:
@2<0 <return> Dimension line location: Digitize point c to locate the dimension
line. <pick>

Next, you are asked for the dimension text. The dimension displayed
in the angle brackets, <>, is the default value that AutoCAD measured
between the first and second points entered. If the points were precisely
entered, the default will be 2.0, and you do not have to enter a number
but can press the Enter key to use the default value. *You must press the
Enter key, not the Space Bar, however, to accept the default value. The
Space Bar is used to enter a null value.* If the default value is not correct,
you may type a number via the keyboard and then press Enter.

A null dimension value is entered by pressing the Space Bar and then
the Enter key. AutoCAD will then print the dimension lines but will
leave the dimension value blank. This is one time when the Space Bar
does not replace the Enter key.

Dimension text <2.0>: Type **2.0** if the default value is not 2.0. <**return**>

4.6.1 Undo

If a dimension is inserted, the entire dimension (value and dimension
lines) may be undone immediately after it has been drawn by invoking
the UNDO command. If you undo the wrong entity, enter the REDO
command immediately.

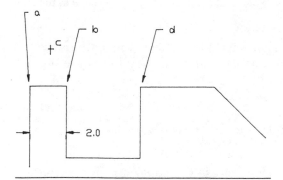

Figure 4.4 Dimensioning selection points.

4.6.2 Continuous dimensions

When dimensions are continuous as on the top of the plate being drawn, after the first dimension in the string is completed, you may indicate that the next dimension is a continuation of the previous one by selecting CONTINUE. The dimensions will then be continued along the same line as the last set of dimensions and consequently you will only be asked to enter the second point for the dimension, which is marked as point d in Fig. 4.4.

To continue the dimension string previously entered:

CONTINUE <**pick**> Second extension line origin: Digitize point d illustrated in Fig. 4.4. <**pick**> Dimension text <4.0>: Type **4.0** if the default value is not 4.0. <**return**>

Notice how AutoCAD first moved the continuous dimension string up one row so that it would not interfere with the 2.0 dimension, which would not fit within the dimension lines and was consequently printed outside of the dimension lines.

Use the CONTINUE command to complete the dimensions across the top of the plate as illustrated in Fig. 4.1.

4.6.3 Baseline dimensions

The BASELINE command is used to continue a linear dimension from a baseline, such as the 4.0- and 8.0-unit dimensions along the base of the plate (Fig. 4.1) which both use the left side of the plate as a baseline.

The command line should indicate that AutoCAD is still under the DIM command. If not, select DIM <return> LINEAR <return>.

To add the horizontal dimensions along the base of the plate:

HORIZONTAL <**pick**> First extension line: Digitize point a in Fig. 4.5. <**pick**> Second extension line: Digitize point b in Fig. 4.5. <**pick**> Dimension line location: Digitize point c. <**pick**> Dimension text <4.0>: Type **4.0** if the default value is not 4.0. <**return**> BASELINE <**pick**> Second extension line: Digitize point d. <**pick**> Dimension text: **8.0** <**return**> CONTINUOUS <**pick**> Second extension line: Digitize point e. <**pick**>

Insert the vertical dimensions on the left side of the plate. Since the BASELINE command should be used and the baseline is the top left corner of the plate, begin with:

VERTICAL <**pick**> First extension line: Digitize the top left corner. <**pick**> Second extension line: Digitize a point at the bottom left corner of the cut; see Fig. 4.1. <**pick**> Dimension line location: Digitize the desired location of the dimension line. <**pick**> Dimension text <10.0>: <**return**> BASELINE <**pick**> (etc.)

If you have trouble, use UNDO to erase the faulty dimension and use another Vertical dimension command to insert the 10.0 dimension.

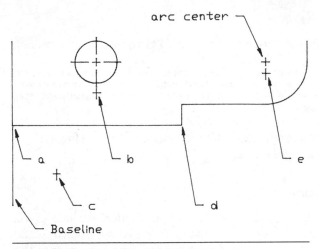

Figure 4.5 Dimensioning selection points.

4.7 Radius Dimensions

When a radius or diameter dimension is added to a circle, AutoCAD automatically inserts the center marks or center lines for the arc or circle as it adds the dimensioning. Since you have already added center marks and center lines, this function will be turned off so that the center marks and center lines are not drawn over those already on the drawing. (It would have been more efficient to place the center marks and center lines in with the dimension. It was done the other way in this text to demonstrate the command.) To cancel the center marks and center line command, enter a value of 0 in DIMCEN:

```
DIM <pick> DIM VARS <pick> DIMCEN <pick> Current value <-0.09> New value: 0
<return> DIMMENU <pick>
```

The RADIUS command is used to dimension the radius of a circle or an arc. The command line should indicate that the DIM command is still invoked. If it is not, recall the DIM command. Enter the following commands to dimension the radius:

```
RADIUS <pick> Select arc or circle: Digitize a point on the circumference of the arc.
<pick> Dimension text <2.0>: If the default value is not 2.0 type 2.0. <return> Text
does not fit. Enter leader length for text: Move the cursor to the desired location for
the end of the leader. <pick> Dimension text <2.0>: If the default value is not 2.0, type
R2.0. <return>
```

If the radius dimension will not fit inside of the arc or circle, AutoCAD asks for the location of the leader, as illustrated in this assignment.

4.8 Diameter Dimension

The command line should indicate that the DIM command is invoked.

> DIAMETER <**pick**> Select circle: Digitize a point on the circumference of the circle.
> <**pick**> Dimension text <2.0>: If default value is not 2.0, type **2.0**. <**return**> Dimension does not fit. Enter leader length for text: Digitize leader length by moving the cursor to draw the leader. <**pick**>

If the text fits within the circle, the leader length is not called for, and the dimension is all within the circle.

4.9 Angular Dimension

An angular dimension is required for the slope of the right side of the plate. The arc must be dimensioned so that it is always less than 180 degrees. For this arc a line must first be drawn to act as the base of the angular dimension.

> <**Ctrl-C**> AutoCAD <**pick**> DRAW <**pick**> LINE <**pick**> Line from point: Digitize point *a* illustrated in Fig. 4.6. <**pick**> To point: Digitize point *b*. <**pick**> <**Ctrl-C**>

> AutoCAD <**pick**> DIM <**pick**> ANGULAR <**pick**> Select first line: Digitize point *c*. <**pick**> Second line: Digitize point *d*. <**pick**> Enter dimension line arc location: Digitize point *e*. <**pick**> Dimension text <45>: If the default value is not 45, type **45**. <**return**> Enter text location: Digitize point *f*. <**pick**> EXIT <**pick**>

Use the END command to update the drawing file and exit the drawing editor. Select item 0 from the main menu to exit AutoCAD.

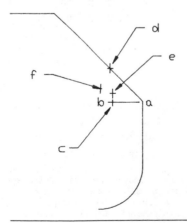

Figure 4.6 Angular dimensioning.

Object Snaps

OBJECTIVE *Use object snaps to select the nearest point, tangents, and intersections; draw a line tangent to two circles; use dynamic zooms; set dimension scale; dimension a drawing; use a leader line; use TEXT and DTEXT command and control codes; change dimension text style; draw fillets; and practice using BREAK command.*

DRAWING *Boot up AutoCAD and begin a new drawing with the name **B:Proj-5**. Draw the control block illustrated in Fig. 5.1. This project is longer than the previous ones and you may wish to complete it in two stages. If you do, use the END command to exit from the drawing editor and save your drawing. Continue the drawing later by booting AutoCAD and selecting item 2, "Edit an EXISTING drawing," from the main menu. The name of the drawing will be requested. The name entered must exactly match the name used when starting the drawing.*

5.1   Set Drawing Limits and Units

Set the screen limits to −1,−1 and 10,8 (refer to Sec. 3.1 if you have forgotten the commands). Enter the ZOOM and A (all) commands to reset the monitor to the new screen limits.

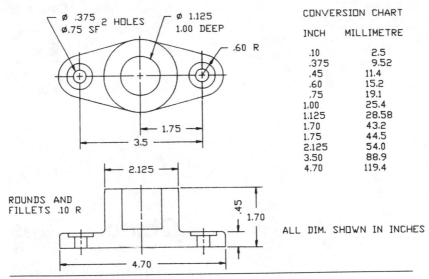

Figure 5.1   Project 5.

Set the units to decimal with three digits to the right of the decimal (refer to Sec. 2.5). Press the F1 key to return to the drawing editor.

5.2   Draw Circles

The center point of the top view will be located at coordinates 3,5. The 1.125-unit-diameter circle will be drawn first. Next the CIRCLE command is recalled to draw the 2.125-unit-diameter circle by pressing Enter or the Space Bar a second time. When the CIRCLE command is recalled in this manner, it requests the radius rather than the diameter. If you wish to enter the diameter, input D in response to "Diameter/<Radius>:." The diameter will then be requested.

```
DRAW <pick> CIRCLE <pick> CEN,DIA <pick> 3P/2P/TTR/<Center point>: 3,5
<return> Diameter/<Radius>:D Diameter: 1.125 <return> <return> Center
point: 3,5 <return> Diameter/<Radius>: d <return> Diameter: 2.125 <return>
```

Draw the 0.375- and 0.75-diameter circles on the left side of the block. A 0.60-unit-radius circle will also be drawn for the arc at the end of the block. Part of that circle will later be broken out when the tangent lines are drawn. Begin the commands by pressing the Space Bar or Enter key to recall the circle command:

```
<return> Center point: 1.25,5 <return> Diameter/<Radius>: d <return> Diam-
eter 0.375 <return> <return> Center point: @ (Same as last point) <return>
```

Diameter/<Radius>: **d** <**return**> Diameter: **0.75** <**return**> <**return**> Center
point: @ <**return**> Diameter/<Radius>: **0.6** <**return**>

Use a similar set of commands to draw the circular elements on the
right side of the top view.

5.3 Tangent Lines

Before continuing, save the drawing done up to this point using the file
name B:Proj-5 (this saves it on the disk in drive B):

AutoCAD <**pick**> SAVE <**pick**> File name: **b:proj-5** <**return**>

Object snap is an ADE-2 mode that lets you refer to points already on
the drawing. In this section you will use object snap to draw lines that
are tangent to the circles previously drawn.

Object snap(s) may be turned on temporarily to assist in locating a
point on the drawing by entering the object snap command when Auto-
CAD requests the point or by setting a running object snap, using the
OSNAP: command, which will be applied to all points selected until the
object snap is turned off. The "running" object snap can be turned off
temporarily by entering the NONE command. When object snap is on, a
target (box) will be added to the intersection point of the cross hairs. To
snap onto a line or other element, the target is placed on the line or
elements. AutoCAD then searches within the target for the object snap
location. The target appears only when a point, such as the start point of
a line, etc., is to be located on the monitor.

Selecting "* * * *" *from the screen menu* displays the object snap menu.
When the desired temporary object snap is selected from the menu, the
previous menu is returned to the screen.

Versions of AutoCAD prior to 2.5 do not have the selection * * * * in the
menu. With those versions you will have to type the name of the desired
object snap—this can also be done with later versions. When typing
object snap names, only the first *three* letters of the name have to be
entered. This is illustrated by the format used in the object snap menu
where, for example, TANGENT is written as TANgent. Throughout the
text where the selection * * * * is indicated, if it is not available in your
version, ignore that selection and type in the object snap mode specified.
As is usual for typed commands, the Enter key is pressed to enter the
command.

In this drawing you are to draw tangent lines joining the center circle
and the side circles. AutoCAD has an object snap command named
TANgent which will be used to place the lines tangent to the circles.
Prior to drawing the tangent lines, enlarge the top view:

AutoCAD <**pick**> DISPLAY <**pick**> ZOOM <**pick**> All/Center/Dynamic/Extents/
Left/Previous/Window/<Scale>: Window <**pick**> First point: Digitize a point
slightly to the left and below the top view. <**pick**> Second point: Move the cursor up and
to the right so that the window created encloses the entire top view. <**pick**>

With the help of the TANgent object snap, the line joining the two circles
is inserted tangent to the circles with minimum effort:

DRAW <**pick**> LINE <**pick**> Line from point: * * * * <**pick**> TANgent <**pick**> to
Place the object snap target on the top of the 2.10 unit diameter center circle (point *a* in Fig.
5.2). <**pick**> To point: * * * * <**pick**> TANgent <**pick**> to Place the object snap target
on the top of the right side circle, as illustrated in Fig. 5.2. <**pick**> To point: <**return**>

Add the remaining tangent lines to the drawing.

5.4   Break Circles at Tangents

Save the drawing before continuing.

The 0.6-unit-radius circles will now be broken at the tangent points to
delete the section of the circle inside the object. The point where each
circle is to be broken is at the tangency point of the circles and the lines
previously drawn. This point cannot be accurately selected visually;
however, AutoCAD can accurately select the intersection point with the
INTersect object snap command.

Remember that AutoCAD *draws and breaks circles in a counterclockwise direction*. If you make a mistake and break the wrong section of the
circle, it can be restored with the UNDO and 1 command. Earlier
versions of AutoCAD do not have an UNDO command. With those
versions, if you accidentally break the wrong segment of the circle, erase
the entire circle, then redraw the circle and try BREAK again.

When the BREAK command is called, you will be asked to "Select the
object." This is done by digitizing a point on the circumference of the

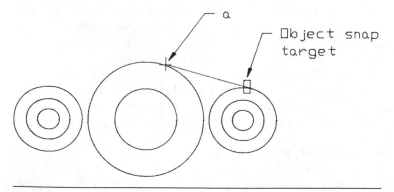

Figure 5.2 Tangent object snap location.

circle to be broken—point a in Fig. 5.3. The point may be selected anywhere on the circumference and should be in a clutter-free location where AutoCAD will not be confused about which item is being selected.

Once the circle has been selected, AutoCAD will ask you to "Enter the second point or F:." If the point used to select the circle to be broken is the location of the start of the break point, you would now digitize the end (second) point of the break. However, the first point has not been selected yet, so F (first) is entered to force AutoCAD to ask for the first point of the break. The INTersec (intersection) OSNAP will be used to locate the intersection point of the line and the circle when locating the first and second points of the break. The left-side circle is broken as follows:

EDIT <**pick**> BREAK <**pick**> Select object: Digitize point a in Fig. 5.3. <**pick**> Enter second point or F: **F** (first) <**return**> Enter first point * * * * <**pick**> INTersec <**pick**> of Place the object snap target on the intersection of the circle and tangent line on the bottom of the circle as shown in Fig. 5.3. Both the tangent line and circle must be inside of target. The bottom tangent is selected first since BREAK erases the circle in a counterclockwise direction. <**pick**> Enter second point: * * * * <**pick**> INTersec <**pick**> of Place the target on the second intersection at top of circle. <**pick**>

Press Enter or the Space Bar to recall the BREAK command, and break the right-side circle following similar procedures.

SAVE the drawing before continuing.

5.5 Calculate Text Height and Set Dimension Variables

The plot will be done on an A-size sheet (8½ by 11 in) using a plot scale of ¾ in = 1 in. If the desired text height on the plotted drawing is ⅛ in (0.125), the text height (h) on the monitor should be:

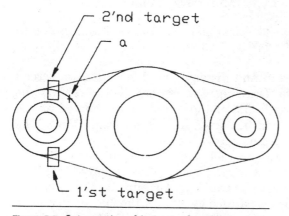

Figure 5.3 Intersection object snap locations.

$$\frac{3}{4} * h = 0.125 \text{ in} \qquad \text{which gives } h = 0.17$$

DIMSCALE is then calculated using Eq. 4.2:

$$\text{DIMSCALE} * 0.18 = 0.17 \text{ in} \qquad \text{which gives DIMSCALE} = 0.94$$

Set DIMSCALE using:

```
AutoCAD <pick> DIM <pick> DIM VARS <pick> next <pick> DIMSCALE <pick>
Current value <1.0> New value: 0.94 <return>
```

5.6   Draw Circle Center Lines

Set the dimension variable DIMCEN to a negative value to draw center lines rather than center ticks (read Chap. 3, Sec. 3.7) and draw the center lines:

```
Previous <pick> DIMCEN <pick> Current value <0.09> New value: -0.09
<return> DIMMENU <pick> CENTER <pick> Select arc or circle: Digitize a point on
the circumference of the 2.125-unit-diameter center circle. <pick> <return>
```

Add center lines to the side circles also. When selecting the circle, digitize a point on the circumference of the 0.60-unit outside circle so that the center lines extend to the extent of that circle, as illustrated in Fig. 5.1. Exit the DIM command.

5.7   Horizontal Dimensions

Prior to dimensioning the top view it is necessary to change the size of the view on the screen to allow room to display the dimensions as they are drawn. The ZOOM Dynamic commands allow you to shrink or enlarge the displayed view in an interactive manner:

```
AutoCAD <pick> DISPLAY <pick> ZOOM <pick> All/Center/Dynamic/Extents/
Left/Previous/Window/<Scale(X)>: Dynamic <pick>
```

AutoCAD clears the screen and displays the dynamic zoom screen illustrated in Fig. 5.4. The Drawing Extents box (white) shows the larger of either the drawing limits or the actual area occupied by the drawing. The Generated Area box (red) indicates the portion of the drawing which AutoCAD can generate at high speed. Any views outside that area require a regeneration, which may take considerable time for a large complex drawing. The Current Display box is dotted (green).

The Pan View box has an X at its center and is initially the same size as the Current View. The box is panned by moving the mouse. Press the <pick> button and the Pan View box is replaced with the Zoom View

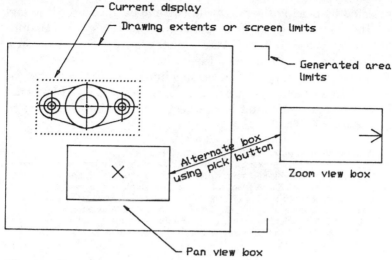

Figure 5.4 Dynamic zoom.

box. Move the mouse and the view box will be enlarged or decreased in size. If the <pick> button is pressed, the Pan View box is returned. When the desired view is framed with either view box, the <return> button or Enter key is pressed to view the framed area as the current screen. Frame the view as illustrated in Fig. 5.5 and press the Enter key.

The horizontal dimensions in the top view originate from a baseline at the center line of the circles on the right side of the view. When dimensioning from a center line, the dimension extension lines should originate from, and act as an extension to, the circle center line. That point

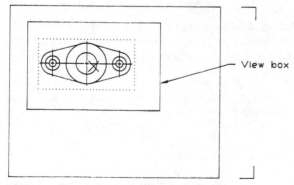

Figure 5.5 Frame for dimensioning top view.

can be selected by placing the cursor on the end of the center line and digitizing the point or by using a temporary object snap ENDpoint. ENDpoint, in response to AutoCAD's request for a point, turns on a temporary object snap and places a target box over the cursor.

When the object snap target is placed on a line, AutoCAD searches for the end of that line which is closest to the target. Since OSNAP: was not used, the object snap command is in effect only for the point located immediately after ENDpoint is entered.

AutoCAD <**pick**> DIM: <**pick**> LINEAR <**pick**> HORIZONTAL <**pick**> First extension line origin: * * * * <**pick**> ENDpoint <**pick**> of Place the target on the bottom end of the center line of the right side circle. <**pick**> Second extension line origin: * * * * <**pick**> ENDpoint <**pick**> of Place the target on the bottom of the center line of the center circle. <**pick**> Dimension line location: Digitize the location of dimension line. <**pick**> Dimension text <1.750>: **1.75** Type 1.75 since the default value is 1.750 <**return**> BASELINE <**pick**> Second extension line: * * * * <**pick**> ENDpoint <**pick**> of Place the target on the bottom end of the left side circle. <**pick**> Dimension text <3.500>: **3.5** <**return**>

5.8   Dimension Circles

If DIMCEN contains a value other than 0, AutoCAD places center ticks or lines in circles and arcs *as they are dimensioned.* Since we have already put the center marks in the circles and arcs, you should now enter a 0 in DIMCEN:

DIM VARS <**pick**> DIMCEN <**pick**> Current value <−0.09> New value: **0** <**return**>

Dimension the radius of the 0.6-unit right-side circle in the top view. Refer to Sec. 4.7 for the procedure if you need assistance.

The 1.125-unit-diameter center circle is dimensioned by using a leader (pointer) rather than the DIAMETER command. The DIAMETER command places a dimension line through the circle; in this case it is preferable to point to the circle with a leader instead. The circle diameter symbol is printed by using a special control code, c. AutoCAD is informed that the next character in the input is a control code by preceding the character with two percent symbols, as illustrated in the following:

DIMMENU <**pick**> LEADER <**pick**> Leader start: Digitize a point on the top right side of the circumference of the 1.125-unit-diameter circle. <**pick**> To point: Extend leader as desired by moving the cursor. Press the pick button for each bend point in the leader. Press Enter to end the leader. If the leader ends as a sloping line, AutoCAD will add a short horizontal line at the end of the leader line in the direction of the slope. <**return**> Dimension text <1.125>: **%%c1.125** <**return**> <**Ctrl-C**>

Add the "1.00 DEEP" text using the text command. In Sec. 5.5 the text height was calculated as 0.17 units to get ⅛-in text on the plotted drawing.

DRAW <**pick**> TEXT <**pick**> Starting point or Align/Center/Fit/Middle/Right/ Style: Digitize the start point of the text. <**pick**> Height <.20>: **0.17** (Since the default value 0.20 is not correct.) <**return**> Rotation angle <0>: Select default value of 0. <**return**> Text: **1.00 DEEP** <**return**>

Add the leader dimension text to the left circle and save the drawing. AutoCAD places the leader text on the side that the end point of the leader leans toward. To force the leader text to the other side, bend the end of the leader and extend a short leader in that direction.

5.9   Draw Front View

Use the ZOOM and DYNAMIC commands to zoom on the drawing from slightly above the horizontal center line in the top view and to the base of the drawing screen below it. This is done so that the front view will be as large as possible on the monitor and a sufficient amount of the top view will be displayed so that lines can be extended down to locate elements on the front view in relation to the top view.

The top left corner of the 2.125-unit-diameter shaft in the front view will have a Y coordinate (vertical) of 2, which is determined by visually locating the screen cursor at the approximate vertical position desired and reading the vertical coordinate of that position from the display at the top center of the monitor. The X coordinate (horizontal) is to be in line with the left side of the 2.125-unit-diameter circle in the top view.

5.9.1   X/Y/Z filters

When AutoCAD requests coordinates, they can be selectively entered by using *filters*. The top left corner of the front view is located as follows (the filters may be typed as illustrated or picked from the screen menu):

LINE <**pick**> From point: **.XZ** (For Release 10, or) **.X** (For Release 9 and Ver. 2.6) <**return**> of * * * * <**pick**> INTersec <**pick**> of Locate the object snap target on the left side intersection point of the 2.125-unit-diameter circle and the horizontal center line in the top view. <**pick**>

You have used an XZ or X filter to locate the x coordinate (do not forget the period in .XZ or .X). The INTersect object snap was also used to accurately select the intersection. With Release 10 you have actually located X and Z since it always works in 3-D. The Z coordinate happens to be 0. This is discussed in Chap. 10.

AutoCAD now requests the y coordinate, which we decided earlier was to be 2:

(need Y) **2** <**return**>

Continue drawing the front view as follows:

> To point: **@2.125<0** **<return>** To point: **@1.25<270** **<return>** To point: **@**
> **1.2875<0** **<return>** To point: **@0.45<270** **<return>** To point: **@4.7<180** **<return>**
> To point: **@0.45<90** **<return>** To point: **@1.2875<0** **<return>** To point: **c**
> **<return>**

Draw the 1.125-diameter hole in the 2.125-diameter shaft in the front view. The lines are to be continuous, rather than hidden, since the solid portion of the front view is to be hatched in Sec. 7.4. The hole is started as follows:

> LINE **<pick>** From point: **.XZ** (or **.X**) **<return>** * * * * **<pick>** INTersec **<pick>** of
> Place the object snap target on the left-side intersection point of the 1.125-diameter hole and
> the center line in the top view. **<pick>** (need Y) **2** **<return>** To point: (etc.)

When drawing the bolt and countersunk holes in the front view, it is important that the lines exactly meet object lines because of hatching to be done later. The NEARest object snap is used to *snap* onto a line, arc, or circle that is closest to the cursor object snap target as follows:

> DRAW **<pick>** LINE **<pick>** From point: **.XZ** (or **.X**) **<return>** of Place the target on the
> intersection of the side of the countersunk hole and the center line in the top view. **<pick>**
> (need Y) * * * * NEAR **<pick>** to Place the object snap target on the top of the plate in the
> front view where the countersunk hole is to start. **<pick>** To point:

The depth of the countersunk hole is drawn by eye. Continue the bolt holes in the front view. Use the .XZ (or .X) filter to locate the x coordinate in the top view, when required, and the NEAR object snap to ensure that the y coordinate is selected exactly on an object line. When the bolt hole is completed on one side, use the COPY command to copy it 3.5 in horizontally to the other side.

5.10 Fillets

Fillets may be added by editing the drawing. When using the FILLET command for the first time, you must set the radius by selecting the R (radius) option as illustrated below. Once the radius is selected, it need not be reselected unless the fillet radius is to be changed. Fillets are then drawn by recalling the FILLET command and digitizing the two lines that are to be joined by the fillet. When selecting the two intersecting lines to be filleted, remember that AutoCAD draws arcs in a counterclockwise direction.

> EDIT **<pick>** FILLET **<pick>** Polyline/Radius/<Select two lines>: **r** (Radius)
> **<return>** Enter fillet radius: **0.1** **<return>** FILLET **<pick>** Polyline/Ra-
> dius/<Select two lines>: Digitize two intersection lines at a corner where a fillet is
> desired. **<pick>**

To insert other fillets, recall the FILLET command by pressing Enter or the Space Bar, and select two points at the corner where the fillet is desired. The radius does not have to be reentered.

5.11 Dimension Front View

Prior to adding the horizontal dimensions to the front view, use the ZOOM and DYNAMIC commands to enlarge the front view, making it easier to select points.

When dimensioning, use the cursor to specify the extension line locations. When the location is a corner, the temporary object snap INTersec may be used. This will place a target around the cursor. When the target is placed over two intersecting lines, AutoCAD will then search for the intersection of the two points. The base dimension commands are:

AutoCAD <**pick**> DIM: <**pick**> LINEAR <**pick**> HORIZON <**pick**> First extension line origin: * * * * <**pick**> INTersec (intersection) <**pick**> of Place the target on the lower left corner of the front view. <**pick**> Second extension line origin: * * * * <**pick**> INTersec <**pick**> of Place the target over the lower right corner. <**return**> Dimension line location: Digitize a point indicating where you wish the dimension line to be located. <**pick**>

Insert vertical dimensions on the right side of the front view using the base of the object as a baseline (review Sec. 4.6.3). If the 0.44 dimension is located outside the dimension lines and is horizontal, enter UNDO to erase the dimension; then enter:

DIM <**pick**> DIMVARS <**pick**> next <**pick**> DIMTOH <**pick**> Current value <on> New value: **off** <**return**>

The preceding commands turn DIMTOH (DIMension Text Outside Horizontal) off. When DIMTOH is on (the default value), text which falls outside of the dimension lines is printed horizontally, which is not desired on this drawing. The dimension should now be redone, and it will be printed vertically (parallel with the dimension line). Since DIMTOH is now off, any other vertical dimension text which falls outside of the dimension lines will be printed parallel with the dimension line.

5.12 Text

Add the "ROUNDS AND FILLETS .10 R" text to the right side of the front view. The DTEXT (dynamic text) command will be used rather than TEXT (for versions earlier than 2.5 use TEXT):

AutoCAD <**pick**> DRAW <**pick**> DTEXT <**pick**> Start point or Align/Center/Fit/ Middle/Right/Style: Digitize the location where text is to start. <**pick**> Height

<0.17>: Select default value of 0.17 set earlier. <**return**> Rotation angle <0>: <**return**> Text: **ROUNDS AND** <**return**> Text:

Notice that the text appears on the drawing as it is being typed when DTEXT is used. Also note that the Text: prompt is reissued after you have entered the text, and the cursor is positioned at the start of the next line below the current line of text. The next line of text will use the same specifications (height and angle). (A similar procedure occurs when the TEXT command is recalled by pressing Enter or the Space Bar—use this for earlier versions of AutoCAD.) The DTEXT command is canceled by pressing Enter without entering text, as illustrated in the following:

Text: **FILLETS .10 R** <**return**> Text: <**return**>

Enter ZOOM and All to set the monitor to the drawing limits.

Add the "Conversion Chart" text heading to the top right side of the drawing. Prior to adding more text, move the cursor to the top far right of the drawing and read the coordinates of the location. If the chart, plus a small border, will exceed the current limits of 10,8, reset the LIMITS, providing a larger horizontal distance (possibly coordinates 11,8). Enter ZOOM and All to reset the monitor to the new limits.

The standard AutoCAD text font is TXT. This font is not desirable when printing tables since the space used for letters is not uniform, making it impossible to align characters, as illustrated in the chart in Fig. 5.1. The MONOTXT font uses the same space for each character and is to be used for the chart. Prior to changing the current text font, the STYLE command is used to create the text style definition:

AutoCAD <**pick**> SETTINGS <**pick**> next <**pick**> STYLE <**pick**> Text style name (or ?) <STANDARD>: **mono** <**return**> Font file <TXT>: **monotxt** <**return**> Height <0.00>: <**return**> Width factor <1.00>: <**return**> Obliquing angle <0>: <**return**> Backwards? <N>: <**return**> Upside-down? <N>: <**return**> Vertical? <N>: <**return**> MONO is now the current text style. DRAW <**pick**> DTEXT <**pick**> Start point or Align/Center/Fit/Middle/Right/Style: Pick the point where you wish to start the first column of numbers. <**pick**> Height <0.17>: <**return**> Rotation angle <0>: <**return**> Text: **0.10   2.5** <**return**> Text: **0.375   9.52** <**return**> etc.

To change the text style back to standard enter:

DTEXT <**pick**> Start point or Align/Center/Fit/Middle/Right/Style: **Style** <**pick**> Text style name (or ?) <**MONO**>: **Standard** <**return**> Existing style Font file <txt>: <**return**> Height<0.000>: <**return**> etc.

Use the END command to save the drawing and exit AutoCAD.

Layers

OBJECTIVE *Use LAYERs command for line type and colors in plot, HATCH command, set hatch and line type scale, align dimension text with dimension lines (DIMTOH and DIMTIH—off); replace dimension arrowheads with tick lines (DIMTAD—on), dimension and text practice, and SNAP command as a drawing aid.*

DRAWING *Boot up AutoCAD and begin a new drawing with the name* **b:proj-6**. *Draw the plot plan shown in Fig. 6.1, setting the screen limits to 0,0 and 70,50. Use decimal units with three digits to the right of the decimal point.*

6.1 Layers

The concept of layering in CAD may be paralleled with overlays used in texts, where various components are drawn on transparent sheets and may be viewed individually or with any number overlayed to view the interaction of the parts. In AutoCAD any number of layers may be used. The layers all have the same drawing limits, coordinate system, and units. Zoom factors apply to all layers in the drawing. Layers may be viewed individually or any number or sequence of layers may be viewed

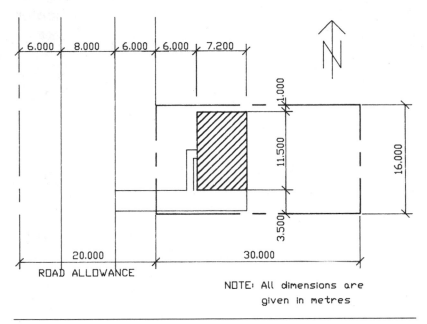

Figure 6.1 Project 6, lot plan.

at one time. Any one layer may be designated as the current layer on which new items drawn will reside.

The drafter designates a color and line type for each layer. All items on a layer will have the same color and line type. [There is a COLOR command in the Settings menu that can be used to set different colors for entities residing on the same layer. It is recommended, however, that you do not mix the two methods (colors by layer and also by entities), to prevent confusion.] The color of a layer is used by the plotter to select pens. When plotting, each color may be given a pen number. As the colors change, the plotter will select the pen number designated for that color. The pens may have different colors and/or nib widths. This provides the drafter with the ability to control the line widths and colors on a plotted drawing. The layer colors may be displayed with a color monitor.

The layer that an item resides on may be changed at any time. If an item is moved to a layer with a different line type, the item's line type will change to that of the new layer.

6.1.1   Line types

Each layer is associated with a specific line type. The standard library of line types supplied with AutoCAD is illustrated in Fig. 6.2. The default line type for a layer is continuous.

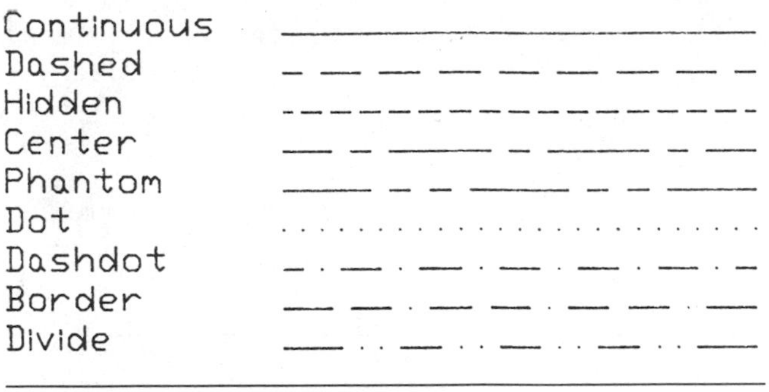

```
Continuous        _____
Dashed            _ __ __ __ __ __ __ __ __ _
Hidden            _._____.
Center            ___ _ _____ __ _____ _ ___
Phantom           _____ _ _ _____ __ _ ___
Dot               . . . . . . . . . . . . . . . . . . . . . . . .
Dashdot           _ . ___ . ___ . ___ ___ . ___ . _
Border            ___ __ . ___ __ . ___ __ . ___
Divide            ___ . . ___ . . ___ . ___ . . ___
```

Figure 6.2   AutoCAD line types.

6.1.2   Colors

Each layer is assigned a specific color number, an integer between 1 and 255. The first seven color numbers are associated with specific colors:

1   Red

2   Yellow

3   Green

4   Cyan

5   Blue

6   Magenta

7   White

The color numbers may have a different effect with some systems, therefore, you should refer to the *AutoCAD Installation and Performance Guide* for more information relating to your specific system.

Although the colors cannot be displayed with a monochrome monitor, you may wish to use specific color numbers for layers to control the selection of pens by the plotter. When plotting, each color number may be associated with a specific pen number (if the plotter has more than one pen). The pens may vary in color and/or nib widths, thereby giving you control over the lines on the plotted drawing.

The default color number for a layer is white (7).

6.1.3   Layer names

Each layer must be given an individual name. It may be up to 31 characters long and may contain letters, digits, and the special characters, $, _, and -. *Do not include spaces in the layer name.* It is better to pick descriptive names for a layer, such as roof, 1stfloor, etc.; however, the names may be as simple as 1, 2, 3, etc.

When AutoCAD is started, a layer named 0 is created with a continuous line type and a color number 7. This layer has specific properties, which will be discussed in Sec. 10.2, and it cannot be deleted or renamed as other layers can.

6.1.4 Layer commands

When the LAYER command is entered, the following options are displayed:

Command	Function
Make	Creates a new layer and makes it the current layer (a combination of New and Set).
New	Creates a new layer.
Set	Selects a current drawing layer.
On	Layers turned on are displayed on the monitor.
Off	Layers turned off are not displayed.
Color	Specifies a color number for specific layers.
Ltype	Specifies a line type for specific layers.
?	Lists layer data for specified layers.
Freeze	Frozen layers are ignored in the regeneration process, thereby speeding up the drawing regeneration (ADE-3 only). Freezing automatically turns a layer off.
Thaw	Used to turn the freeze state for a layer off (ADE-3 only).

6.2 Set Layer Specifications

The lot plan to be drawn is to have file layers with the following specifications:

Object	Name	Color	Line type
Road and walk	0	White	Continuous
Road allowance	Center	Blue	Center
House	House	Red	Continuous
Dimensions and text	Dimens	White	Continuous
Property	Property	Red	Center

The current layer name is displayed in the upper left corner of the monitor. Any new entities drawn will be displayed on that layer. Since the default layer set by AutoCAD is named layer 0, that name should be displayed in the upper left corner of the monitor.

6.2.1 Create the new layers

Prior to doing anything with the layers, they must be created. Layer 0 does not have to be created since it is the default layer created when

AutoCAD is booted. New layers can be created at any time during the drawing process. The layers may be created individually as they are required or together at the beginning of the drawing. We will create all of the required layers for this drawing now (noting that when the list of new layer names is typed in, the names are separated with a comma and there are no spaces in the list):

```
LAYER: <pick>?/Make/Set/New/On/Off/Color/Ltype/Freeze/Thaw: New <pick>
New layer name(s): center,house,dimens,property <return>
```

6.2.2   Set the line type for each layer

The line type for each layer may be defined now that the layers have been created. There are two line types to define for this drawing, center and continuous. The procedure for specifying a line type is to:

1. Enter the Ltype command from the Layer menu.
2. Specify the line type (see Fig. 6.2).
3. Specify the layers' names that have that line type.
4. Layers with the default continuous line type do not have to be defined.

The line type procedure is followed for each of the two line types (note that the LAYER command is still in effect):

```
Ltype <pick> Linetype (or ?) <CONTINUOUS>: center <pick> Layer name(s) for
lino type CENTER: center,property <return>
```

6.2.3   Set the color for each layer

The color of each layer will now be defined. Remember that even if you do not have a color monitor, the color command is useful since with it the plotter may be instructed to select a different pen for each color. The procedure for specifying the layer color is:

1. Enter the Color command from the Layer menu.
2. Specify the color.
3. Specify the layer name that is to have that color.
4. Layers with the default white color do not have to be defined.

```
Color <pick> New entity color (WHITE): Blue <pick> Layer name(s) for color 5
(blue): center <return> Color <pick> New entity color (BLUE): Red <pick>
Layer name(s) for color 1 (RED): house,property <return>
```

6.2.4   Display the layer specifications

To view the layer specifications as they currently stand, select the ? command from the Layer menu and then press Enter in response to the request for "Layer names <*>:." The default asterisk is a wildcard and is used when you want to display the specifications for all layers created. This is done as follows:

    ? <**pick**> Layer names for listing <*>: <**return**>

Compare the displayed list with that illustrated at the beginning of this section. If it is not the same, review the procedures outlined in the above sections and redo the necessary items.

If you are using Release 9 or 10, you can view and modify layers using the Modify Layer dialogue box. To display the box move the cursor to the top of the screen to the pull-down menu (see App. E) and select Settings. Then, select the Modify Layers option.

Press the F1 key to return to the drawing editor. Press Ctrl-C to eliminate any residue commands.

Note that the current layer is 0 as indicated in the upper left corner of the monitor.

6.3   SNAP Command

Decimal units have been set with three digits to the right of the decimal for this drawing. The precision of the drawing, however, requires only one digit to the right of the decimal (note the 7.200 and 11.500 dimensions in Fig. 6.1). Since the dimension precision is 0.1, it is preferred to have 0.1 as the smallest cursor movements on the monitor. The SNAP command is used to lock the cursor on an imaginary grid—in this case it is desired that the grid lines be 0.1 units apart. SNAP sets the fine movement of the cursor. Larger steps can still be made. Select the following:

    AUTOCAD <**pick**> SETTINGS <**pick**> next <**pick**> SNAP <**pick**>

The following will appear in the command line at the bottom of the screen:

    Snap spacing or ON/OFF/Aspect/Rotate/Style <default>:

The On and Off commands are entered to activate or deactivate SNAP. If a value is entered, it will set SNAP to that number and turn SNAP On. Enter:

0.1 <return>

As the cursor is moved about the screen, you will observe the coordinates vary in steps of 0.1, providing you have activated the coordinates with Ctrl-D.

The SNAP function, once set, may be switched on or off using Ctrl-B or the F9 function key.

Ctrl-O is a toggle switch to turn orthogonal mode on or off. When on, lines can only be drawn horizontally or vertically, thereby simplifying the selection of points on the monitor. Press Ctrl-O to turn orthogonal on.

6.4   Draw Road and Driveway

The road and driveway are to be drawn on layer 0 (see Sec. 6.2), which is the current layer as is indicated in the upper left corner of the screen. The line type for layer 0 is continuous; therefore, the lines will be drawn solid on the monitor.

The coordinates of the lower left corner of the road will be assumed as 7,8. The road is then drawn using:

DRAW <**pick**> LINE <**pick**> Line from point: **7,8** <**return**> To point : Move the cursor vertically to about point 7,45 and digitize the point. If the coordinate display at the top of the monitor does not change as the cursor is moved, press Ctrl-D. If the coordinate display shows relative distance <angle, press Ctrl-D again until it displays screen coordinates. <**pick**> To point: <**return**>

In the previous set of commands you should have noted that *during the line command*, Ctrl-D is a toggle switch that is used to:

1. Activate or deactivate the current coordinate display

2. Set the coordinate display to relative distance <angle

3. Set the coordinate display to current screen coordinates

The LINE command is next recalled to start a new line by pressing Enter or the Space Bar. The other side of the road is drawn using:

<**return**> Line from point: **15,8** <**return**> To point: Move the cursor vertically to about 15,45. <**pick**> To point: <**return**>

Draw the driveway. The coordinates of the lower left corner of the driveway are assumed as 15,16.5, and the driveway is 3 units wide:

<**return**> Line from point: **15,16.5** <**return**> To point: **@19.2<0** <**return**> To point: **@3<90** <**return**> To point: <**return**>

Draw the remainder of the driveway and walkway as illustrated in Fig. 6.3. *Do not place any driveway lines along house lines* since, when plotting this drawing (in Chap. 7), a different pen color will be used for the house and driveway.

6.5   Draw House on House Layer

Set House as the current drawing layer:

```
AutoCAD <pick> LAYERS <pick> LAYER: <pick>
?/Make/Set/New/On/Off/Color?Ltype/Freeze/Thaw: s (Set) <return> New cur-
rent layer: house <return><return>
```

Release 9 and 10 drafters may wish to use the Modify Layer dialogue box to set a new current layer. If so read Sec. E.2 of App. E.

The upper left corner of the monitor should now indicate that the House layer is set as the current layer. Presently both layers 0 and House are on; however, House is *set* as the layer any new items drawn will be placed on.

Draw the house lines starting at the top right end of the driveway shown as point A in Fig. 6.3.

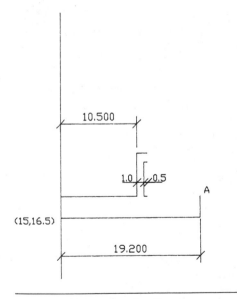

Figure 6.3 Driveway and walk.

6.6 Hatching

AutoCAD is supplied with a good library of hatch styles. Refer to your AutoCAD manual for a listing of the patterns available. You may also create specific hatch pattern libraries for use by AutoCAD. Pattern creation will not be discussed in this text.

Hatching uses a considerable amount of computer memory and you are cautioned to refrain from using a lot of hatching on a drawing unless your computer system has at least 640K of RAM.

If an object is to be hatched, the boundaries enclosing the hatching must be clearly defined using individual lines. As a result, hatching is not easily done on complex objects with AutoCAD. If the left side of the box illustrated in Fig. 6.4 is to be hatched, lines A, B, D, and E must be drawn individually. If lines A-C and D-F are drawn as a continuous line, AutoCAD may not hatch the left side of the box properly. In Chap. 7 a procedure for hatching complex objects will be discussed.

The house is hatched using the ANSI31 (American National Standards Institute) hatching pattern:

```
AUTOCAD <pick> DRAW <pick> HATCH <pick> Pattern (? or name/U,style):
ANSI31 <return>
```

If you want to see a listing of the styles available, enter ? rather than a pattern name. If you use ? to list the hatch styles, you will have to press the F1 key to return the screen to the drawing mode.

Release 9 and 10 drafters may use the Hatch Pattern dialogue box to visually select the desired hatching. To do so, move the cursor to the pull-down menu at the top of the screen (see Fig. E.1) and select Draw. Next, select Hatch from the menu and several hatch patterns will be displayed. The second pattern down from the top left is ANSI31.

The program will now ask for the scale. All AutoCAD scale factors are based on a factor of 1 unit per 1 in of plotted drawing; hence, the following formula may be used to determine any AutoCAD scale factor:

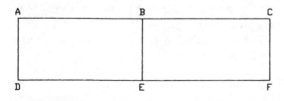

Figure 6.4 Hatch boundaries.

$$\text{Plot scale * factor} = 1 \text{ in * conversion} \qquad (6.1)$$

where plot scale = scale at which drawing is to be plotted
factor = scale factor
conversion = factor to convert inches to drawing units

This drawing is done in meter units and will be plotted using a scale of 1:300 to fit on an A-size sheet which is measured in millimeters at 280 by 216 mm (11 by 8.5 in). Using 1 in = 25.4 mm and 1 m = 1000 mm:

$$1/300 * F = 1 \text{ in * } (25.4 \text{ mm}/1 \text{ in * } 1 \text{ m}/1000 \text{ mm})$$
$$F = 7.62$$

A hatch scale of 7.62 is then used:

Scale for pattern <1>: **7.62<return>** Angle for pattern <0>: **0 <return>** Select objects: Digitize the four sides of the house, then press Enter to execute the command.

If you make a mistake, use the U (undo l) command and then retry the hatching.

If AutoCAD's architectural scale (Imperial units) is used and the drawing is to be plotted with a scale of 1/8 in = 1 ft 0 in, the hatch scale would be:

$$1/96 * F = 1 \text{ in * } \qquad \text{giving a factor of 96}$$

6.7   Draw Property Lines on Property Layer

Set the current drawing layer to Property. When the layer is set correctly, the upper left corner of the screen will show the layer name Property.

Refer to Sec. 6.5 for the procedure used to set a new current layer.

6.7.1   Set line type scale

The center line type is used for the property layer. Since this line type is not a solid line, it must be scaled to suit our drawing. The scale factor for line types (LTSCALE) is calculated using Eq. 6.2 (3/4 of the factor calculated by Eq. 6.1). The notations are the same as for Eq. 6.1.

$$\text{Plot Scale * LTSCALE} = 1 \text{ in * conversion * } \tfrac{3}{4} \qquad (6.2)$$
$$1/300 * \text{LTSCALE} = 1 \text{ in * } (25.4 \text{ mm } / 1 \text{ in * } 1 \text{ m } / 1000 \text{ mm}) * \tfrac{3}{4}$$
$$\text{LTSCALE} = 5.7$$

AUTOCAD <**pick**> SETTINGS <**pick**> LTSCALE Current value <1.0> New value: **5.7** <**return**>

Draw the property lines. The driveway is 3 m wide; therefore, the property line starts 0.5 m below the driveway since the distance from the edge of the house to the property line is 3.5 m.

6.8 Draw Road Allowances

The road allowances are to be drawn on the Center layer. Set **Center** as the current drawing layer. The line type scale does not have to be set again. Draw the road allowance as illustrated in Fig. 6.5. *Do not overlap the previously drawn property line* since a different color is used for the property line.

6.9 Dimension Drawing

Dimensioning is to be done on the Dimens layer. Set **Dimens** as the current drawing layer.

6.9.1 Calculate text height

The text and dimension text height will be calculated assuming that the drawing will be plotted on an A-size sheet (280 by 215 mm) using a scale

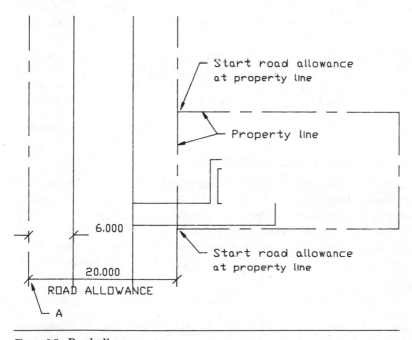

Figure 6.5 Road allowance.

of 1:300 (1 mm = 300 mm, or 0.3 m). The drawing units are meters, and the desired height for text on the plotted drawing is 3 mm.

The monitor text height (h) is then calculated as follows:

$$1/300 * h = 3 \text{ mm} \quad \text{giving } h = 900 \text{ mm, or } 0.9 \text{ m}$$

The dimension text variables scale, DIMSCALE, is calculated based on the default AutoCAD value for a dimension text height of 0.18 and the previous calculation from which we determined that the text height must be drawn 0.9 meters high to obtain a plotted text height of 3 mm when plotting the drawing using a scale of 1:300. DIMSCALE is calculated as follows:

$$\text{DIMSCALE} * 0.18 = 0.9 \quad \text{giving DIMSCALE} = 5$$

The dimension scale, DIMSCALE, is then set as follows:

```
DIM <pick> DIM VARS <pick> next <pick> DIMSCALE <pick> Current value
<1.000> New Value: 5 <return>
```

6.9.2   Change dimension arrows to ticks

The dimension variable DIMTSZ specifies the size of the dimension ticks. If the variable is a zero, arrows are drawn. If the variable is a number greater than zero, dimension ticks are used by AutoCAD instead of arrowheads. The default value is zero, hence AutoCAD normally draws dimension arrows.

DIMTSZ is to be changed to 0.1, giving dimension ticks about one-half of the dimension text height (DIMTXT, which specifies the height of dimension text, is 0.18). Both DIMTSZ and DIMTXT are scaled by DIMSCALE, which was set in Sec. 6.9.1 as 5.

```
next <pick> DIMTSZ <pick> Current value <0.000> New value: 0.1 <return>
```

6.9.3   Set orientation of vertical dimensions

Normally all dimensions are placed horizontally. Text printed outside of the dimension lines is controlled by DIMTOH (DIMension Text Outside Horizontal). Text printed inside of the dimension lines is controlled by DIMTIH (DIMension Text Inside Horizontal). The default value for both is on, which means that, by default, all dimension text is printed horizontally. To align dimensions with the dimension lines turn both off:

```
DIMTOH <pick> Current value <on> New value: off <return> previous <pick>
DIMTIH <pick> Current value <on> New value: off <return>
```

The dimension variable DIMTAD (DIMension Text Above Dimension line) controls the placement of text with respect to the dimension line. If

DIMTAD is off (default setting), the dimension lines are broken and the text is centered along the dimension line. To place the text above the dimension line turn DIMTAD on:

DIMTAD <**pick**> Current value <off> New value: **on** <**return**> DIMMENU <**pick**> To view the dimension variables select status.

6.10 Horizontal Dimensions

The horizontal text at the bottom of the drawing is added:

LINEAR <**pick**> HORIZON <**pick**> First extension line origin: * * * * <**pick**> NEAR <**pick**> to Digitize point A in Fig. 6.6. <**pick**> Second extension line origin: @20<0 <**return**> Dimension line location: @ <**return**> Dimension text <20.000>: <**return**> CONTINUE <**pick**> Second extension line: * * * * <**pick**> INTersec of Digitize point C in Fig. 6.6. <**pick**> Dimension text <30.000>: <**return**>

@ is a relative command—when no values are entered, this point is the same as the last point. We use it here since no extension line is desired. Notice how the second extension line origin and the dimension line location were made at the same point by using the relative @ command. By doing that, the size of the dimension extension line is reduced. There is a way to completely eliminate it, but that is discussed in a later project.

The horizontal text across the top of the drawing is added:

HORIZON <**pick**> First extension line location: * * * * <**pick**> NEAR <**pick**> to Place the target at point A in Fig. 6.7. <**pick**> Second extension line origin: @6<0 <**return**> Extension line location: @ <**return**> Dimension text <6.000>: <**return**>

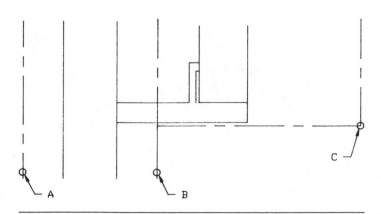

Figure 6.6 Horizontal dimension points.

Note: AutoCAD versions prior to Release 10 will have printed the text outside of the dimension lines because of the small space between the extension lines. If that has happened, use the UNDO command to undo the dimension.

With Release 10 AutoCAD usually places the dimensions within the extension lines when DIMTAD (DIMension Text Above Dimension lines) is on. If dimension text falls outside the dimension lines, set the dimension variable DIMTIX (DIMension Text Inside Extension line) on to force the text within the extension line. Continue the dimensions along the top of the plan as illustrated in Fig. 6.1 and then skip to Sec. 6.11.

With earlier versions, to "trick" AutoCAD, dimension lines will be added to the drawing without text, which will be added later. However, even if text is not entered in the 6.000-m span, AutoCAD will assume the space is insufficient and will not draw the dimension line solid. It will instead place the dimension line outside of the extension lines. To prevent this, skip the 6.000-m dimension and use the 6.000 + 8.000 = 14.000-m dimension line. The missing dimension tick at 6.000 will be added later (as will the text.)

Normally data may be entered by pressing either the Space Bar or the Enter key. When dimension text is asked for, it may be suppressed by pressing the Space Bar. This must then be followed by pressing the Enter key to enter the (suppressed) data. To undo your previous dimension, you would enter the following to place the dimensions within the dimension lines:

LAST <**pick**> HORIZON <**pick**> First extension line location: Digitize point *A* in Fig. 6.7. <**pick**> Second extension line location: @14<0 <**return**> Dimension line location: @ <**return**> Dimension text <14.000>: <**space bar**> <**return**> CONTINUE <**pick**> Second extension line location: Digitize point *B* in Fig. 6.7.

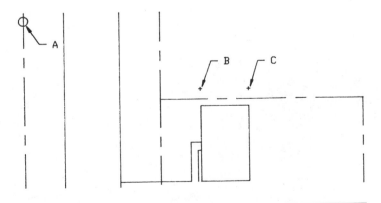

Figure 6.7 Horizontal dimension points.

```
<pick> Dimension text <12.000>: <space bar> <return> CONTINUE <pick>
Second extension line location: Digitize point C in Fig. 6.7. <pick> Dimension
text <7.200>: If the default is not 7.200, type 7.200. <return>
```

To add the missing dimension ticks, use the relative @ command and place the first extension line location, the second extension line location, and the dimension line location each on the same point. AutoCAD will then be tricked into adding a dimension tick at that point.

```
HORIZONTAL <pick> First extension line: * * * * <pick> INTersec <pick> of
Place the target over one of the missing tick locations. <pick> Second extension line
location: @ <return> Extension line location: @ <return> Dimension text
<0.000>: <space bar> <return>
```

Notice how AutoCAD added a dimension tick at the intersection point selected. Add other tick lines as required following the same procedure.

6.10.1 Add text to dimensions

The TEXT <return> C (centered) command will be used to add missing text to the dimension. In Sec. 6.9.1 the text height was calculated as 0.9 units. To add the missing dimension to any one of the dimension lines:

```
DRAW <pick> TEXT <pick> Start point or Align/Center/Fit/Middle/Right/
Style: c (Centered) <return> Center point: Digitize a point a small distance above the
dimension line at the center distance along the line. <pick> Height <0.20>: 0.9 <re-
turn> Rotation Angle <0>: <return> Text: Type in dimension text value desired.
<return>
```

6.11 Vertical Dimensions

Add the 16.000-m dimension to the right side of the property. The first and second extension line points are the top and bottom corners of the right side of the property line.

Some versions of AutoCAD will print the short dimension along the right side of the house outside the dimension lines. If that happens, a procedure similar to that used for the horizontal dimension string along the top of the drawing is used as follows.

```
VERTICAL <pick> First extension line: * * * * <pick> NEAR <pick> to Digitize
point A in Fig. 6.8. <pick> Second extension line: Digitize point B in Fig. 6.8. <pick>
Dimension line location: Digitize point C in a vertical line with point A. <pick>
Dimension text: <space bar> <return> <Ctrl-C> (To exit the DIM Command)
```

Use the ZOOM and Dynamic commands to display the right side of the house and the last dimension line.

Use the DRAW and LINE commands to add the missing extension and dimension lines shown in Fig. 6.8, and then add ticks at the junction points using the procedure outlined for the horizontal dimensions.

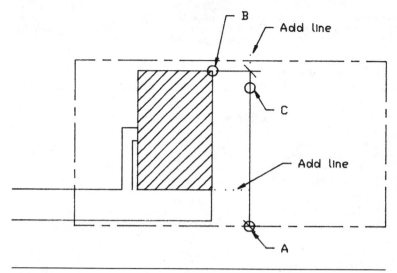

Figure 6.8   Vertical dimension points.

6.11.1   Add missing text
to vertical dimensions

When adding the missing text to the vertical dimension lines, use TEXT and R (right justified) to select the right side point for the 3.500-m dimension. The text angle will be 90 degrees since it is to be written vertically.

To add the midddle 11.500 text, use TEXT and C (center point) to locate the text by its center point. The angle of the text is 90 degrees.

The 1.000-text location is selected by TEXT and then by digitizing the start point.

6.12   North Arrow

TEXT <**pick**> Start point or Align/Center/Fit/Middle/Right/Style: Digitize the point where you wish the right side of the arrowhead for the north arrow to be. <**pick**> Height <1>: **4**<**return**> Rotation angle <90>: <**return**> Text: ><**return**> <**return**> DRAW <**pick**> LINE <**pick**> Draw a line for the arrow shaft. <**return**> TEXT <**pick**>   Start   point: or   Align/Center/Fit/Middle/Right/Style: **c** <**return**> Center point: Digitize the location of the bottom center of the N. <**pick**> Height <4>: <**return**> Rotation angle <90>: **0** <**return**> Text: **N** <**return**>

Configuring AutoCAD and Plotting

OBJECTIVE *Use the configuration program on AutoCAD to configure AutoCAD for specific hardware; plot a drawing using the default specifications; change plot specifications to vary line type and colors, set plot scale.*

DRAWING *Previously saved drawings will be plotted.*

7.1 Configuring AutoCAD

The configuration function is used to tailor AutoCAD to your hardware. For instance, if you wish to use a mouse to enter data and commands, you will have to configure your copy of AutoCAD to recognize that a mouse is part of the system. It will also require driver information which gives AutoCAD technical information about the type of mouse you are using.

Technical information about the usual hardware used with AutoCAD is on the .drv disk(s) provided with AutoCAD. That disk(s) will be required during the configuration process. If you are not sure of which disk(s) those files are on, list the directories of all your disks and look for a number of files with the .drv extension.

The configuration procedures discussed in this text will be limited to more common configurations. You should refer to the AutoCAD manual for configurations of a more complex nature.

To begin the configuration select task 5, "Configure AutoCAD" (task 4 on earlier AutoCAD versions), from the main menu—the menu displayed when AutoCAD is first booted up or after the QUIT or END command is entered.

The configuration task menu is displayed as:

```
Configuration menu
0. Exit to Main Menu
1. Show current configuration
2. Allow detailed configuration
3. Configure video display
4. Configure digitizer
5. Configure plotter
6. Configure printer plotter
7. Configure system console
8. Configure operating parameters
Enter selection:
```

A task is selected by typing the number associated with that task and pressing Enter. When the configuration is ended, AutoCAD returns to the Configuration menu. If you wish to cancel all changes made during a task, press Ctrl-C.

7.1.1   Exit to main menu

When the configuration process is completed, enter 0, "Exit to Main Menu." AutoCAD will ask if you wish to keep the configurations made. If you answer N, the original configuration will be used and the changes made will be deleted. A Y answer will cause AutoCAD to save the new configuration and use that configuration each time AutoCAD is booted.

7.1.2   Show current configuration

To see what AutoCAD is configured for, enter 1, "Show current configuration." AutoCAD will list the hardware that it is presently configured for.

7.1.3   Configure video display

This task is used to tailor AutoCAD to your particular video display components. The available displays will be listed and you will be asked to select one. AutoCAD is initially configured for a monochrome monitor. If you have a color monitor, you will have to configure AutoCAD to suit your monitor or the drawings will be done in black and white only unless the supplier configured your version for your system when you purchased it. This task is also used to tailor the system to a high-resolution board.

The "mode status line" is the line in the upper left corner of the monitor that indicates what layer is current. By default the status line is enabled. It may be disabled during this task.

The AXIS command displays a ruler line with specific tick spacings along the bottom and right side of the monitor. During this task you can choose whether the axis is to be inside or outside of the drawing area.

On some displays the screen menu on the right side of the monitor and the command prompt area along the bottom of the screen can be disabled—see your *AutoCAD Installation and Performance Guide* for instructions. That would also be done during this task.

7.1.3.1 Dot aspect ratio correction.

On many screens the dot density is not the same in the horizontal and vertical axis. The ratio of horizontal to vertical dots per inch is called the "dot aspect ratio." The display driver file contains a factor which should correct for the dot aspect ratio. If circles appear as ovals on your screen, you may have to make a further correction during the video display configuration task. AutoCAD will prompt:

```
If you have previously measured the height and width of a "square" on your
graphic screen, you may use these measurements to correct the aspect ratio.
Would you like to do so? <N>:_
```

The first time you configure AutoCAD enter N. Later, if circles are not round, draw a large square on the screen and measure the sides. Reconfigure AutoCAD and enter Y to the preceding question. The program will then ask for the horizontal and vertical measured dimensions of the square and will correct the aspect ratio.

7.1.4 Configure digitizer

A list of digitizers supported by AutoCAD will be displayed. The user will be asked to select one. If you do not have a digitizer, select "none."

7.1.5 Configure plotter

AutoCAD will list the supported plotters. The user will be asked to select one. If you do not have a plotter, select "none."

7.1.6 Configure printer plotter

This task is similar to Sec. 7.1.5 and is used to select the printer that you have on your system. If you do not have a printer, select "none."

7.1.7   Configure operating parameters

This task will display the following menu:

```
Operating parameters menu:
0. Exit to configuration menu
1. Alarm on error
2. Initial drawing setup
3. Default plot file name
4. Plot spooler directory
5. Placement of temporary files
6. Network node name
7. AutoLISP feature
Enter selection: ___
```

Selecting task 0 returns you to the configuration menu.

7.1.7.1   Alarm on error. This subtask allows you to set AutoCAD to buzz an audible alarm whenever an invalid entry is made.

7.1.7.2   Initial drawing setup. This subtask allows you to set default initial drawing conditions to be used by AutoCAD whenever the program is booted. In Vers. 2.1 and 2.5 this is used to specify a default prototype drawing.

7.2   Plotting Drawings

Drawings can be plotted from the drawing editor by entering the PLOT command or from the main menu by selecting task 3, "Plot a Drawing," or task 4, "Printer Plot a Drawing."

When PLOT is called from the drawing editor or from the main menu, you will be asked to choose the plotting device. The plotter (pen plotter) is discussed in this section. The use of a printer plotter is discussed in Sec. 7.3.

When the PLOT command is executed from the main menu or the drawing editor, options and plot specifications similar to the following will be displayed (values shown are for example purposes; your specifications may vary from those illustrated):

```
What to plot-Display, Extents, Limits, View, or Window <D>:___
```

The options available are:

Display (D)   Plots the view that is currently on the monitor when plot is called from the drawing editor; plots the last view saved when plot is called from the main menu.

Extents (E)   The plot will be the largest view of the drawing and available that contains all of the drawing entities.

Limits (L)   Plots the entire drawing area as defined by the drawing limits.

View (V)   Allows the user to print a named view. Naming views is dis-
                cussed in Chap. 15.

Window (W)   Allows the user to define the area to be plotted by defining a
                window around the area [similar to the ZOOM <return> W
                (window) command].

The option desired may be selected by entering the letter enclosed in
parentheses.

The next AutoCAD display will depend on the type of plotter you have.
The values shown are for example only.

```
Plot will NOT be written to a selected file
Sizes are in Inches
Plot origin is at (0.00,0.00)
Plotting area is 14.00 wide by 9.80 high (MAX size)
Plot is NOT rotated 90 degrees
Pen width is 0.010
Area fill will be adjusted for pen width
Hidden lines will NOT be removed
Plot will be scaled to fit available area

Do you want to change anything? <N>:_
```

If you do not wish to change any of the settings, enter N. To change a
setting enter Y. If Y is entered, the following will be displayed:

Layer	Pen	Line	Pen	Layer	Pen	Line	Pen
Color	No.	Type	Speed	Color	No.	Type	Speed
1 (red)	1	0	38	9	1	0	38
2 (yellow)	1	0	38	10	1	0	38
3 (green)	1	0	38	11	1	0	38
4 (cyan)	1	0	38	12	1	0	38
5 (blue)	1	0	38	13	1	0	38
6 (magenta)	1	0	38	14	1	0	38
7 (white)	1	0	38	15	1	0	38
8	1	0	38				

```
Line types: 0 = continuous line
            1 = ..................
            2 = . . . . . . . . . . .
            3 = --------------------
            4 = - - - - - - - - - -

Do you want to change any of these parameters?<N>:_
```

If you enter Y, AutoCAD will display the following:

```
Enter values.
blank=Next value, Cn=Color n, S=Show current values, X=Exit
```

If you are using only one color (7, white) on the drawing and the plot
specifications indicate "Pen No. 1" is used for color 7 and you are not
drawing with traces and solids, you would press Enter or the Space Bar

to select the default N. AutoCAD will then request that you position the paper in the plotter, and it will plot the drawing.

If you are using more than one color (layers) on the drawing or if any other data in the plot specifications requires changing, you would type Y and press Enter. AutoCAD will then prompt you for new values for each item in the specification. Each prompt will show the default value inside square brackets [ ]. If you do not wish to change the value, press Enter or the Space Bar. To change a value, type in the new data and press Enter or the Space Bar. To correct typing errors use the Backspace key. To cancel the entire plot press Ctrl-C.

7.2.1   Plot example

The following process would be used to plot the drawing from Chap. 6 using a two-pen plotter on an 280- by 215-mm sheet and a 1:300 scale. The drawing units for Chap. 6 were meters. The plot sheet units are in millimeters.

Boot AutoCAD and select task 3, "Plot a Drawing," from the main menu, and enter the drawing name. Prior to the plot specifications being displayed, you will be required to define what is to be plotted. The options available were discussed above. Press Enter to select the default D and plot the current display:

```
What to plot-Display, Extents, Limits, View, or Window <D>: <return>
```

AutoCAD will list the plot specifications, as illustrated in Sec. 7.2, and will request the following:

```
Do you want to change anything? <N>: y <return>
```

AutoCAD now displays the options available, as illustrated in Sec. 7.2, and asks if you wish to change any of the specifications. To change specifications, enter Y (do so for this example). To use the current specification enter N.

```
Do you want to change any of these parameters? <N>: y <return>
```

You may change the color specifications for each layer color. A request similar to that shown below will be displayed following the color specifications:

```
Enter values. blank=Next value, Cn=Color n, S = Show current choices, X =
Exit
```

For each color, AutoCAD will prompt you for a line type, pen number, and pen speed. Only colors 1 through 15 can be assigned pen numbers and line types. Colors greater than 15 plot the same as color 15.

Line types are to be selected during the drawing process by using layers as was done in Chap. 6. As a result, you should not use any line type other than continuous when plotting. The plotter will plot the line type used in the drawing. Since the default line type for plotting is 0 (continuous), we will not change any line types and AutoCAD will plot using the line type specified for the layer.

The default pen speed for all pens is 38 in/s. If you have a pen that skips at that speed, you may wish to reduce the pen speed. We will not change any pen speeds here.

In Sec. 6.1, layer colors 7 (white), 5 (blue), and 1 (red) were used. Assuming you have a two-pen plotter and that a black pen is in holder 1 and a red pen is in holder 2 of the plotter, the layer colors 7 (white) and 5 (blue) will be assigned to pen 1, and layer color 1 (red) will be assigned to pen 2.

Specifications are set as follows:

Layer color	Pen no.	Line type	Pen speed	
1	1	0	38	Pen Number <1>: **2** **<return>**
1	2	0	38	Line type <0<: **C5** **<return>**
5	2	0	38	Pen number <2>: **1** **<return>**
5	1	0	38	Line type <0>: **C7** **<return>**
7	1	0	38	Pen number <1>: **X** **<return>**

In the preceding, the red layer was set to use pen No. 2, then C5 was entered to skip to color No. 5, which was then set to use pen No. 1; then C7 was entered to skip to color No. 7. Since the white layer (No. 7) default pen was No. 1 as desired, x was entered to exit the layer specification.

If you enter S in response to any of the above, AutoCAD will list all of the color specifications and then return to the current prompt.

You can instruct AutoCAD to write the plot output to a file rather than to the plotter. The file can then be plotted with a utility program at a later time:

```
Write the plot to file? <default>: n <return>
```

If you enter Y, the file name will be requested:

```
Enter file name for plot <default>:_
```

The default value is the current drawing name. The plot file will be given the extension .plt (not to be entered with the file name by the user).

AutoCAD will now request the size units for the sheet on which you are plotting. Your response will govern the way other specifications are entered later and how AutoCAD relates to them (in particular scaling). The drawing in Chap. 6 was done in millimeter units.

```
Size units (Inches or Millimetres) <current>: m <return>
```

The drawing plot may start at any coordinate location on the sheet. The default value is 0,0, which is the lower left corner of the sheet (the plotter's "home" position; refer to your plotter manual). AutoCAD will request the plot origin in the units selected. The default value of 0,0 will be selected:

```
Plot origin in Millimetres <0.00,0.00>: <return>
```

If you wish to start the plot at some other location on the sheet, measure the x and y distance from the plotter's home position using the units specified, next enter the coordinates in the form x,y, and then press Enter or the Space Bar.

7.2.1.1 Plot size. AutoCAD now requests the plot size. The MAX is the maximum size plot for the plotter you have configured AutoCAD for. If you wish to see the options, enter ?. The following table illustrates (in inches) the drawing size and plot size used if MAX is selected (for plotters capable of plotting E-size drawings):

Size	Paper (in)		Plot (in)	
	Width	Height	Width	Height
A	11.00	8.50	10.50	8.00
B	17.00	11.00	16.00	10.00
C	24.00	18.00	21.00	16.00
D	36.00	24.00	33.00	21.00
E	48.00	36.00	43.00	33.00

The plot size will be set to an A-size sheet (11 by 8.5 in) converted to millimeters (280 by 215):

```
Enter the Size or Width,Height (in millimetres)<MAX>: 280,215 <return> Ro-
tate 2D plots 90 degrees clockwise? <N>: <return>
```

If SOLID or TRACE is used in the drawing to draw solid lines or objects, AutoCAD will require the pen width to assign pen movements when filling in the object. Since solid objects are in Chap. 7, the default value will be used:

```
Pen width <default>: <return>
```

You may choose to have the boundaries around filled areas adjusted 1/2-pen width. This is generally not necessary. The prompt is:

```
Adjust area fill boundaries for pen width? <N>: <return>
```

If the ADE-3 package is present, the next prompt is:

Remove hidden lines? <N>: **n** (No is entered since this drawing is not done in 3-D).
<**return**>

7.2.1.2   Scaling.   The program will next prompt you for the scale. The scaling process may seem a bit confusing when you review the following sections. In Chap. 12 a method of scaling on a special plot drawing that will simplify the procedure considerably will be discussed. AutoCAD will display the following prompt:

Specify scale by entering:

Plotted units=Drawing Units or Fit or ? <F>:_

If you wish AutoCAD to "fit" the drawing onto the sheet (not to scale), enter f. (Do *not* do so since a 1:300 scale is to be used.)

To plot to a particular scale you will have to relate your drawing units to the units being used on the plotted sheet. Table 7.1 illustrates the values to enter to obtain specific scales. When drawing units are set at the beginning of the drawing, architectural and engineering units show feet and inches; however, AutoCAD assumes the screen units are inches. If decimal units are selected, the drawing units may be assumed as any value.

Project 6 was drawn in decimal (meter) units and the plot is to be done in millimeter units using a 1:300 scale (1 mm of the plot equals 300 mm), which means that 1 mm on the plotted sheet equals 0.3 m on the monitor. The entry is then:

Specify scale by entering:
Plotted milimetres=Drawing Units or Fit or ? <F>: **1=0.3** <**return**>

TABLE 7.1   Plot Scales

Drawing	Plot Units	Scale	Enter
Decimal (ft)	Inches	1/4 in = 1.0 ft	1 = 4
Archit. (in)	Inches	1/4 in = 1 ft 0 in	1 = 48
Inches	Inches	3/4 (3/4 in = 1 in)	1 = 1.33
Decimal (ft)	Inches	1:100 (1 in = 100 ft)	1 = 100
Decimal (m)	Millimeters	1:20 (1 mm = .02 m)	1 = 0.02
Decimal (mm)	Millimeters	1:10 (1 mm = 10 mm)	1 = 10

AutoCAD will prompt you to place the paper in the plotter and to press Enter, as follows:

```
Position paper in plotter.
Press RETURN to continue or S to Stop for hardware setup. <return>
```

The drawing will then be plotted to scale.

7.3   Printer Plot a Drawing

Some versions of AutoCAD support a plot via a dot matrix line printer. If your version does, you will see the "Printer Plot a Drawing" option (4) in the main menu, or the option will be listed in the Plot submenu.

When item 4, "Printer Plot a Drawing," is selected from the main menu, the procedure to printer plot is as follows (Printer Plot called from the Plot submenu is similar except that the drawing name is not requested):

```
Enter name of drawing:_
```

Enter the name of the drawing to be plotted. Remember to precede the name with B if the drawing is stored on drive B.

```
Specify the part of the drawing to be plotted by entering:
Display, Extents, Limits, View, or Window <D>:_
```

Generally the last screen display saved is the view to be plotted. If so, enter D (for display) or just press Enter if D is the default value.

AutoCAD will now display the default values. The values shown are for example purposes only.

```
Sizes are in Inches.
Plot origin is at (0.00,0.00).
Plotting area is 8.00 inches wide by 11.00 inches high. (Max. size)
Plot is NOT rotated 90 degrees.
Hidden lines will NOT be removed.
Plot will be scaled to fit available area.

Do you want to change anything <N>:_
```

If you do not wish to change any of the default values, press Enter to select the default values. To change any default values enter Y.

7.3.1   Printer plot example

To obtain a printer plot of Proj-6 you would answer Y to the last question outlined in Sec. 7.3, "Do you want to change anything <N>:," so that the plot rotation may be changed and also to set a plot scale. If Y is entered,

AutoCAD will request the data beginning with the size units. Since Proj-6 was done in metric units, m is entered:

```
Size units (Inches or Millimetres) <current>: m <return>
```

The drawing plot may start at any coordinate location on the sheet. The default value is 0,0, which is the upper left corner of the sheet. Use the default value:

```
Plot origin in Millimetres <0.00,0.00>: <return>
```

AutoCAD will now display the "Standard value for plotting size" as (width, height) 8 by 11 in or 200 by 279.4 mm, which are the maximum sizes for most printers. Select Max.:

```
Enter size or Width,Height (in Millimetres) <Max>: <return>
```

You will next be asked if you wish the plot rotated 90 degrees clockwise. Usually you will want to do so to make the sheet rectangle match that of the monitor:

```
Rotate 2D plots 90 degrees clockwise <N>: y <return>
```

For three-dimensional plots (see Chap. 15) you may next opt to have hidden lines removed. Since that does not apply to two-dimensional drawings, press Enter. The scale will now be requested as follows:

```
Specify scale by entering:
Plot Inches = Drawing Units or Fit or ? <F>:_
```

If you wish AutoCAD to fit the drawing onto the sheet (no scale), enter f. Here a 1:300 scale is to be used.

When plotting to scale, the drawing units must be related to the units used for the plotted sheet. Table 7.1 illustrates the values to enter to obtain specific scales. When using AutoCAD's architectural or engineering units, remember that, although feet and inches are displayed on the monitor, AutoCAD works internally with inches for those two unit types.

Proj-6 was drawn in meter units and the plot is to be done in millimeter units using a scale of 1:300 (1 mm of the plot equals 300 mm). This means that 1 mm on the plotted sheet equals 0.3 m on the monitor. The entry is then:

```
Specify scale by entering
Plot millimetres = Drawing Units or Fit or ? <F>: 1=0.3 <return>
```

AutoCAD will now specify the plot area and request that you position the paper and press Return (Enter) to continue. Press Enter and the drawing will be plotted (on large drawings there is a delay while Auto-CAD converts the drawing vectors to plot data).

7.4   Hatch and Plot Proj-5

Select Task 2 from the main menu to edit Proj-5.

7.4.1   Hatch Project 5

Select Task 2 from the main menu to edit Proj-5. When Project 5 is displayed, create two new layers named **Hatch** and **Hatcho**. Make the color of layer Hatcho red and Hatch, yellow. Set layer Hatch as the current layer. The commands are:

```
LAYER: <pick> ?Make/Set/New/On/Off/Color/Ltype/Freeze/Thaw: New <pick>
New layer name(s): hatch,hatcho <return> Color <pick> Color: red <return>
Layer name(s) for color 1 (red): hatch <return> Color <pick> Color: yellow
<return> Layer name(s) for color 2 (yellow): hatcho <return>

?/Make/Set/On/Off/Color/Ltype/Freeze/Thaw: Set <pick> New current layer:
hatcho <return> <return>
```

The current layer name Hatcho should now be displayed in the upper left corner of the screen.

Use the ZOOM and W (window) commands to enlarge the front view of the object. You are to draw lines over the existing front view lines outlining the objects to be hatched, illustrated in Fig. 7.1. To facilitate locating the points, set a running INTersect object snap and pick off the corners of the areas to be hatched. When you come to a corner with a fillet, the INTersect object snap must be temporarily turned off by selecting the temporary object snap command: * * * * <pick> None <pick>. Then line up the horizontal and vertical cursor lines on the object lines and digitize the intersection point. Each hatch area must be drawn separately. The running object snap is set as follows:

```
AUTOCAD <pick> SETTINGS <pick> next <pick> OSNAP: <pick> INTersec <pick>
<return>
```

As indicated, the Return key must be pressed to complete the selection of the running object snap(s).

Trace over the three sections illustrated in Fig. 7.1. If the INTersect object snap cannot locate an intersection, there is probably a small gap where the lines are supposed to intersect. Use the Extend and Trim commands discussed in Sec. A1.1 (item no. 32) to fix the intersection.

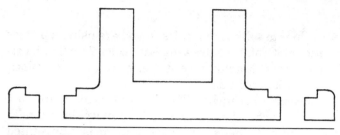

Figure 7.1 Hatch boundaries.

When all three sections have been drawn, turn layer 0 off. The view should appear as illustrated in Fig. 7.1; however, the corner will not be filleted.

Prior to filleting the corners, turn the running object snap off by following the same sequence of commands used when turning it on, but select None rather than INTersect from the object snap menu. Use the FILLET command to add the 0.1-radius fillets to the appropriate corners (see Sec. 5.8).

Set layer Hatch as the current layer. Do not continue until that layer is indicated as the current layer in the upper left corner of the monitor. Determine the hatch scale using Eq. 6.1. The drawing is to be plotted using a 3/4 scale for the limits set in Chapter 6:

Plot Scale * Factor = 1 (inch) * Conversion
    3/4 * Factor = 1 * 1
       Factor = 1.33

Hatch the object using the ANSI31 hatch type as follows:

DRAW <**pick**> HATCH <**pick**> Pattern (? or name/U, style): **ansi31** <**return**> Scale for pattern: **1.33** <**return**> Angle for pattern: **0** <**return**> Select objects: Window <**pick**> Digitize a window enclosing the three blocks.

AutoCAD will now hatch in the three blocks. If there is an error, use Erase Last to erase the hatching and then correct the error. If the hatching is not correct, check that all corners actually intersect by zooming on them.

Turn layer Hatcho off. The hatching only will now be displayed. Turn Layer 0 on and then enter the ZOOM and All commands. Use the END command to exit the drawing, saving the data.

7.4.2   Plot Proj-5

Change the default values to select inch units. If you are using a plotter (as opposed to a printer plot), plot the drawing with color 7 (main object) set to select pen 1 and color 1 (hatching) set to select pen 2. Use a black ink pen in 1 and a red ink pen in 2.

The plot units selected are to be inches. The plot scale is to be 1 in = 3/4 in. Consequently, .75 plot inch = 1 drawing unit, so you would enter .75 = 1. For a printer plot, Enter Y when asked if the drawing is to be rotated by 90 degrees.

8

Isometric Drawing

OBJECTIVE *Use SNAP mode and ellipse command to draw an isometric drawing; display a grid of reference points on the monitor; set drawing aids using the dialogue box; change isoplanes; locate intersection points, midpoints, and nearest points of lines with the temporary object snap mode, and edit with the TRIM command.*

DRAWING *Boot up AutoCAD and begin a new drawing named **B:Proj-8.** Set the screen limits to −6,−0.5 and 6,8.5 so that the coordinates of the lower front corner are 0,0. Use decimal units with two digits to the right of the decimal. The 4-unit by 4-unit "isobracket" illustrated in Fig. 8.1 is to be drawn.*

8.1 Snap Mode—Isometric Style

The SNAP command is used to align the cursor movements to an invisible grid. The snap resolution defines the spacing of the grid points. When SNAP is on, the smallest movement of the cursor is from grid point to grid point. The user has two snap styles to select from—standard and isometric. In the standard mode the invisible grid is on a rectangular *x,y* plane. In the isometric style the grid is rotated to a 30-degree isometric plane.

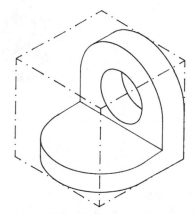

Figure 8.1 Isobracket.

When the snap style is set to isometric, the cursor movements vary depending on whether one is drawing on the top, front, or right side view of an object. When isometric snap is activated, the isoplane is "left" (the left side of the cube). As the cursor is moved about the drawing screen, the movements will be either in a vertical direction or along a line acting at 150 degrees to the horizontal, as illustrated in Fig. 8.2.

The isoplane may be changed by selecting a new plane from the screen menu or by pressing Ctrl-E. The new plane will be specified in the command line at the bottom of the drawing screen.

When isoplane "right" is activated, the cursor movements are in a vertical direction or along a line at 30 degrees to the horizontal, as

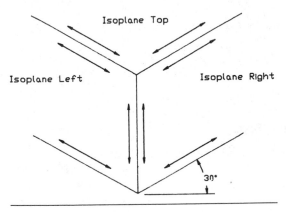

Figure 8.2 Isometric snap cursor movement.

illustrated in Fig. 8.2. In the isoplane top mode the cursor movements are along a line at 30 degrees to the horizontal or a line at 150 degrees to the horizontal, as illustrated in Fig. 8.2.

The isometric mode is used only to assist the drafter in drawing isometric views and has no other effect on the drawing. The user may reset AutoCAD to the standard mode at any time and continue drawing with the cursor movements acting along the standard horizontal and vertical lines.

The snap style is set to isometric as follows:

SETTINGS <pick> next <pick> SNAP <pick>

The snap options displayed are:

Snap spacing or ON/OFF/Aspect/Rotate/Style<current>:

The On or Off command may be selected to turn SNAP on or off; however, prior to turning SNAP on, a number which specifies the minimum movement step of the cursor must be entered. When a value is entered, SNAP is automatically turned on. If it is turned off, the previous snap step value becomes the default value when snap is turned on again. The Aspect command is used to set a different x and y snap. The Rotate command is used to rotate a rectangular grid at any angle from the horizontal or to set the snap grid's base point to some other coordinate than 0,0. The Style command is used to set the format of the snap grid to either standard or isometric.

As is usual for command options displayed in the command line, you may enter the desired command by digitizing the command in the screen menu or by entering the first letter of the command. The Screen Aids dialogue box may also be used to select the snap settings.

The Style command is selected from the screen menu to set the snap mode to isometric (30 degree) with a snap movement of 0.1 as follows:

Snap spacing or On/Off/Value/Aspect/Rotate/Style: Style <pick> Standard/ Isometric <S>: Iso <pick> Vertical spacing <1.00>: **0.1 <return>**

The current isoplane is the left plane. Move the cursor around the screen noting its movement on the isometric axis. Press Ctrl-E, and the command line will indicate that the plane has changed to top. Move the cursor around the top plane. Press Ctrl-E, and the plane will change to right. Move the cursor around the right plane. Press Ctrl-E to return to the left plane.

8.1.1 Drawing Aids dialogue box

The Release 9 and 10 Drawing Aids dialogue box may be displayed by selecting Settings and then Drawing Aids from the pull-down menu (see App. E) or by invoking the DDRMODES command in the screen SET-TINGS submenu. Select the following from the pull-down menu:

Settings <**pick**> Drawing Aids... <**pick**>

The Drawing Aids dialogue box is now displayed. The snap settings of Sec. 8.1 may be made *using the following entries in the dialogue box* (see App. E for procedure):

Snap—X Spacing <**pick**> 0.1 <**return**> Snap <**pick**> Isometric <**pick**> Isoplane—Right <**pick**>

Notice that the Y Spacing is set equal to the X Spacing if a value is not entered for Y. Leave the dialogue box displayed.

8.2 ORTHO Mode in Isometric

When the ORTHO mode is turned on, lines are snapped to the drawing planes. This means that if the snap mode is set to standard and ORTHO is *on*, all lines drawn will snap to either a horizontal or a vertical line—depending on which is closer considering the current cursor position and the previous position. In the isometric snap mode, the lines will snap along a vertical or 30 degree (or 150 degree) plane depending on the current isoplane. If a mouse or digitizing tablet is used and snap is set to isometric with ORTHO off (default setting), the cursor moved with the mouse or digitizing puck will not automatically move along the current isoplanes. To force the cursor along the isoplanes, turn ORTHO on. This is done by pressing Ctrl-O, which acts as a toggle switch to turn ORTHO mode on or off, or by selecting Ortho from the dialogue box. ORTHO may be turned on or off at any time during the drawing process as required. The current ORTHO setting is displayed in the upper left corner of the monitor.

8.3 GRID Command

The GRID command is used to display a reference grid of dots, with a specified spacing, on the drawing editor. The grid is visible on the monitor only and is not plotted with the drawing. The grid follows the snap style so that, when snap is set on isoplane, the grid is displayed in an isometric format. If the grid spacing specified is too dense, AutoCAD will display a message indicating so, and the grid will not be drawn.

When the GRID command is invoked, the following menu is displayed:

```
Grid spacing(X) or ON/OFF/Snap/Aspect <current>:
```

The On or Off command is used to turn the grid on or off; however, prior to turning the grid on, a number must be entered. When the value is entered the first time, the grid is automatically turned on. The grid will be set to every fifth snap position (0.5). If you are using the screen menu, the entries are:

AutoCAD <**pick**> SETTINGS <**pick**> GRID <**pick**> Grid Spacing(X) or ON/OFF/Snap
<0.00>: **0.5<return>**

If you are using the Drawing Aids dialogue box, set the following:

Grid−X Spacing <**pick**> **0.5** <**return**> Grid <**pick**> Ortho <**pick**> Ok <**pick**>

AutoCAD sets the Y Spacing equal to the X Spacing unless you specify a different Y Spacing. The dialogue box is cleared from the screen when Ok is selected. Redisplay the dialogue box and note the Grid x and y settings of 0.87 and 0.25, respectively. When in the isometric mode, the dialogue box displays the grid spacings for the standard snap mode, so it is showing the horizontal and vertical distance between grid points on the screen. The isometric grid spacing is still 0.5. Exit the dialogue box by picking Ok.

The grid may be turned on or off at any time using the Ctrl-G toggle switch.

The screen will now display a grid of dots 0.5 units c/c along an isometric plane.

8.4   Draw the Cube

The bracket object lines are to be drawn on layer 0 and the construction lines on layer Constr. Using the screen menu or the Modify Layer dialogue box, complete the following layer settings:

Object	Name	Color	Line type
Bracket object lines	0	White	Continuous
Construction lines	Constr	Yellow	Continuous

Set Constr as the current layer.

If the current isoplane is not the right-side plane, toggel Ctrl-E to set the isoplane. Ortho should be written in the upper left corner of the screen, indicating the Ortho mode is on. If it is not, press Ctrl-O. Also, press Ctrl-D to activate the current cursor location display. Draw the right side of the cube using the following commands—note that data may be entered via the keyboard as illustrated or by digitizing the points on the screen using the distance<angle coordinate position displayed at the top of the screen.

DRAW <**pick**> LINE <**pick**> From point: **0,0**<**return**> To point: **@4<30** <**return**> To point: **@4<90** <**return**> To point: **@4<210** <**return**> To point: **c** <**return**>

Note that when drawing on isoplane right, the cursor moves along a 30-degree and 90-degree line on the right side view.

Prior to drawing the lines for the left side of the cube, toggle Ctrl−E to set the snap plane to isoplane left. The current isoplane is specified in the command line at the bottom of the monitor.

The left side of the cube is drawn as follows:

LINE <**pick**> From point: * * * * <**pick**> INTersec <**pick**> of Place the intersection object snap on the lower front corner of the current right-side view. <**pick**> To point: **@4<150** <**return**> To point: **@4<90** <**return**> To point: * * * * <**pick**> INTersec <**pick**> of Close the left-side view by placing the object snap target on the top front corner of the right-side view. <**pick**> <**return**>

Use the Ctrl-E toggle switch to set the snap style on isoplane top, and draw the top view of the cube. Use the temporary object snap command to start the lines from a corner of the cube.

8.5   Ellipse Command

When drawing an ellipse, the center point of the ellipse must be entered. Toggle to isoplane left and draw the lines illustrated in Fig. 8.3 to locate the center of the back side of the cube—Ortho must be on:

LINE <**pick**> From point: * * * * <**pick**> MIDpoint <**pick**> of Place the target on one of the midpoints indicated in Fig. 8.3. To point: Draw the line as illustrated. To point: <**pick**> <**return**> <**return**> Line From point: Draw the next midpoint line.

Toggle to isoplane top and draw the construction lines to locate the center point of the bottom of the cube.

Prior to drawing the ellipses, set the current layer to 0. The first ellipse is drawn on the bottom of the cube as follows—the current plane should be isoplane top, and the layer should be 0:

ELLIPSE <**pick**> <Axis endpoint 1>/Center/Isocircle: Iso <**pick**> Center of circle: * * * * INTersec <**pick**> of Place the target on the midpoint intersecting lines in

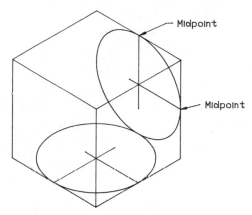

Figure 8.3 Ellipse.

the bottom view of the cube. <**pick**> <Circle Radius>/diameter: **2** (The radius of the ellipse) <**return**>

Toggle Ctrl-E until the isoplane is the left side and draw the ellipse on the back face of the cube.

The thickness of the back of the cube is 1 unit. The COPY command is used to draw a second ellipse 1 unit in front of the back of the cube:

EDIT <**pick**> COPY <**pick**> Select objects: Digitize a point on the circumference of the ellipse which is on the back of the cube. <**pick**> <**return**> <Base point or displacement>/Multiple: Pick a point on the ellipse. Second point of displacement: @1<**210** <**return**>

The bottom of the bracket is to be 0.75 units thick. Toggle to the top isoplane and copy the bottom ellipse 0.75 units above the base of the cube. Turn off 0 layer.

Use the dynamic zoom to enlarge a view as illustrated in Fig. 8.4. In isoplane left, draw line *a* in the upper left corner tangent to the two ellipses using the TANgent object snap to pick each point. If AutoCAD indicates a tangency could not be found, press Ctrl-C and redo the line, placing the TANgent object snap target closer to where the point of tangency should be. This may happen because the ellipse is drawn as a polyline (see Chap. 15) using four arc segments, and the tangent target may not be on the proper segment.

Toggle to isoplane right and draw lines *b* and *c* (Fig. 8.4) as follows:

LINE <**pick**> From point: * * * * <**pick**> TANgent <**pick**> to Digitize the TAN point for line *b*. @2<**270** <**return**> <**return**> <**return**> LINE From point * * * * <**pick**> TANgent <**pick**> to Digitize the TAN point for line *c*. <**pick**> To point: @2<**30** <**return**>

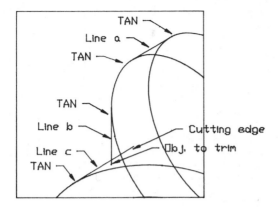

Figure 8.4 Tangent lines.

In the preceding the second point is entered from the keyboard because the orthogonal mode is disabled by AutoCAD when the TANgent object snap is used to select the first point.

8.6 Trimming Lines

The TRIM command is used to trim lines to a specified cutting edge. Lines *b* and *c* in Fig. 8.4 are to meet at a point; hence each line acts as a cutting edge for the other. The lines are trimmed as follows:

```
EDIT <pick> next <pick> TRIM <pick>
Select cutting edges.....
Select objects: Select the cutting edge for line b as illustrated in Fig. 8.4. <pick>
Select objects: <return> Select object to trim: Select the end of the line b to trim
as illustrated in Fig. 8.4. <return>
```

Repeat the TRIM command to trim line *c*. Line *b* is the cutting edge. When picking the object to be trimmed, remember to pick the side of line *c* that is to be trimmed off. If you make a mistake and trim the wrong side, use the U (undo 1) command to fix the mistake and try again.

Zoom the back- and right-side lower right corner of the cube and add in the necessary lines following the same procedures.

Sections of the ellipses must now be removed. Zoom on a view as illustrated in Fig. 8.5. To trim the ellipse on the front of the vertical portion of the bracket, two cutting edges are selected as illustrated in Fig. 8.5. The object to trim is then the bottom of the ellipse as shown. When trimming the ellipse at the back of the cube, the cutting edges are line *a* in Fig. 8.4 and the vertical line in the lower right corner of the back of the cube.

Complete the cube as illustrated in Fig. 8.1. The hole in the back upright is 2 units in diameter.

Turn the Constr layer off and plot the drawing using a scale of 1/2 = 1.

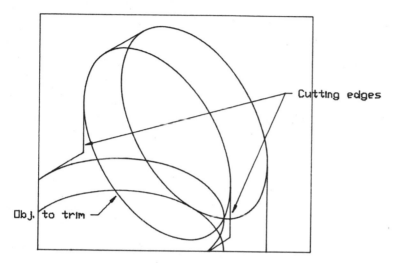

Figure 8.5 Trimming.

Entity Controls

OBJECTIVE *Use entity controls—MOVE COPY, ARRAY, and MIRROR; change layer an entity resides on; set grid and snap mode, set layers for separate drawing elements, and plot specific layers; locate circle center with object snap command.*

DRAWING *Draw and dimension the octagonal and rectangular plates illustrated in Fig. 9.1. Begin a new drawing named B:Proj-9. Initially set the screen limits to 0,0 and 13,9 [don't forget to use ZOOM and All]. Use decimal units with two digits to the right of the decimal.*

9.1 Define Layers

Four layers will be required with the following specifications:

Item	Name	Color	Line type
Construction in lines	0	White	Continuous
Objects	Object	White	Continuous
Center lines	Center	Red	Center
Dimensions and text	Dimens	Red	Continuous

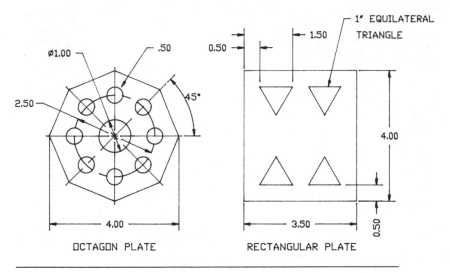

Figure 9.1   Project 9.

Set the layer specifications. Refer to Sec. 6.2 for the procedure.

Before continuing, display the layer settings from the layer command by selecting **?** <**pick**> * <**pick**>. If the layer specifications do not match the specifications outlined above, make the necessary changes by redefining any improper layer.

Press the **F1** key to return to drawing editor.

9.1.1   Set snap and grid

A 0.5-unit grid will be used and snap will be set at 0.1 units:

```
Ctrl-D
AUTOCAD <pick> SETTING <pick> GRID <pick> Grid spacing (X) or On/Off/Snap/
Aspect: 0.5 <return> LAST <pick> SNAP <pick> Snap spacing (X) or On/Off/
Aspect/Rotate/Style: 0.1 <return>
```

9.2   Set Line Type Scale Factor

Since a center line type is being used, the line type scale (LTSCALE) will have to be set to suit the final plot size of this drawing. It will be assumed that the drawing units are inches and that the final drawing will be plotted on an A-size sheet (8½ by 11 in) using a 3/4 scale. Using Eq. 6.2, the scale factor is calculated as:

$$\text{Plot scale} * \text{factor} = 1 \text{ in} * \text{conversion} * 3/4$$

$$3/4 * \text{factor} = 1 \text{ in} * 3/4$$

$$\text{factor} = 1$$

Set the line type scale, LTSCALE, using:

```
AUTOCAD <pick> SETTINGS <pick> LTSCALE <pick> New scale factor <1.0>: 1
<return>
```

9.3 Octagon Plate

To construct the octagon, a 4-unit-diameter circle with its center at coordinates 3.5,4.5 is to be drawn. Lines are then drawn through the circle at 45-degree intervals. The points where the lines intersect the circle will be the corners of the octagon. Later the layer that these construction lines reside on will be changed to place them on the center layer, which has a center line type. These lines will then change line type and become center lines.

The circle on this layer is for construction purposes and will not be displayed with the final drawing.

The current layer, indicated in the upper left corner of the monitor, should be *layer 0*.

Press Ctrl-D to display the cursor coordinates:

```
AUTOCAD <pick> DRAW <pick> CIRCLE <pick> CEN,DIA <pick> Center point:
3.5,4.5 <return> Radius (or D): Diameter: 4 <return>
```

9.3.1 Draw an array of lines

The construction lines crossing the circle will be drawn using the AR-RAY command.

The ARRAY command is used to draw a cluster of similar items. The array may be rectangular or circular. In a rectangular array, the items are repeated in rows and columns in a block or rectangular pattern, as illustrated in Fig. 9.2. That array has four columns and three rows. The original item is in the lower left corner of the array. The unit cell distance between rows is illustrated as a and the unit cell distance between columns is distance b. If the unit cell distances are entered as +'ve numbers, the array "grows" upward and to the right (+'ve cartesian coordinates). To replicate the objects to the left, enter a −'ve-unit cell distance for the columns. To replicate the objects downward, enter a −'ve-unit cell distance for the rows.

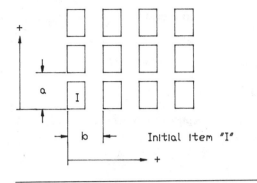

Figure 9.2 Rectangular array.

In a circular array the items are repeated along the circumference of a circle, as illustrated in Fig. 9.3. AutoCAD will ask if the items are to be rotated as they are copied. The items in Fig. 9.3a were not rotated whereas the items in Fig. 9.3b were rotated as they were copied. If the angle between items is entered as positive, AutoCAD copies the objects by rotating about the circle center in a counterclockwise direction.

If the entity to be repeated in a circular array is made up of a number of entities, such as the rectangle in Fig. 9.3b, and the entities are not to be rotated as they are copied, the entity will have to be saved as a block (see Chap. 10) before the array is constructed. That is necessary since AutoCAD will rotate each entity in the item about the center point of the array and, consequently, the relative position of the entities with respect to each other may change. If the entities are part of a block, the item becomes a single entity and the item does not become disjointed. This is not a problem when the items are rotated as they are copied.

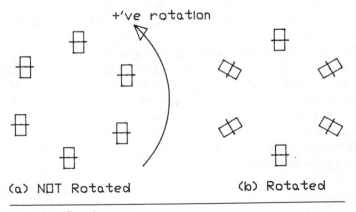

Figure 9.3 Circular array.

To use the ARRAY command a single item is drawn first. The ARRAY command is then invoked and a rectangular or circular pattern is selected. The items will then be repeated in the pattern selected and spaced as specified.

To begin the array a horizontal line will be first drawn across the center of the circle. The ARRAY command is next invoked to draw an array of lines around the circle at 45-degree intervals. The lines will have to be rotated as they are copied so that each line is at a 45-degree interval from the previous line and passes through the center of the circle, as illustrated in Fig. 9.4.

DRAW <**pick**> LINE <**pick**> From point: Using the cursor, draw a horizontal line across the center of the circle. Ensure that the line extends slightly past the circumference of the circle on each side.
EDIT <**pick**> ARRAY: <**pick**> Select objects: **1** (Last) <**return**> Select objects: <**return**> Rectangular or Polar array (R/P): Polar <**pick**> Center point: * * * * <**pick**> CENter (To invoke the center object snap) <**pick**> Center of: Place the object snap target anywhere on the circumference of the circle. <**pick**> Number of items: **4** <**return**> Angle to fill (+ =CCW, −CW)<360>: **0** (Zero is a no response, forcing a request for angle between items.) <**return**> Angle between items (+ =CCW, −CW): **45** <**return**> Rotate objects as they are copied <N>: **y** <**return**>

Note the use of the center object snap command to snap the cursor onto the center of the circle in the preceding set of commands.

9.3.2   Draw octagon

Set **Object** as the current layer. Do not continue until Object is the current layer.

Ver 2.18.   The corners of the octagon are at the intersection of the lines drawn at 45-degree intervals around the circle and the circle circumference. Use the LINE command and the INTersec object snap to draw the octagon.

Ver. 2.5 to Release 10.   The POLYGON command is used to draw the octagon (an eight-sided polygon) as follows:

AUTOCAD <**pick**> DRAW <**pick**> POLYGON <**pick**> Number of sides: **8** <**return**> Edge/<Center of polygon>: * * * * <**pick**> CENter <**pick**> of Place the target on the circumference of the circle. <**pick**> Inscribed in circle/Circumscribed about circle (I/C): **I** <**return**> Radius of circle: **2** <**return**>

The octagon is now to be rotated by 22.5 degrees:

EDIT <**pick**> ROTATE <**pick**> Select objects: **1** (Last) <**return**> Select objects: <**return**> Rotation angle/reference: **22.5** <**return**>

All versions.   Draw the 1.0-unit-diameter circle in the center of the octagon. When the center of the circle is asked for, use the Center object snap and place the target on the circumference of the previous circle.

9.3.3 Draw center lines

Set **Center** as the current layer.

The CHANGE command will be used to change the layer that the 45-degree lines crossing the circle center point reside on. If those lines are moved to the center layer, which has a Center line type, the lines will change to center lines. This command is invoked as follows:

EDIT **\<pick>** CHANGE **\<pick>** Select objects: Digitize points 1, 2, 3, and 4 in Fig. 9.4.
\<pick> Select objects: **\<return>**

The following entries are now made.

Ver. 2.1

Change point (or Layer or Elevation): **1** (Layer) **\<return>** New layer: **center**
\<return>

Ver. 2.5 to Release 10

Properties/\<Change point>: Properties **\<pick>** Change what property (Color/
Elev/LAyer/LType/Thickness)? LAyer **\<pick>** New layer: **center** **\<return>**

The lines will be erased and redrawn onto the Center layer by AutoCAD.

Now draw a circle with a diameter of 2.5 units. This circle forms the center line for the .5-unit-diameter circles which will be drawn later. Remember to use the Center object snap to pick the center of the main circle when asked for the location of the center of the 2.5-unit-diameter circle.

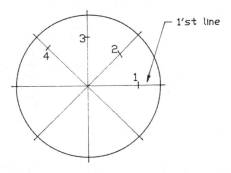

Figure 9.4 Circular array lines.

9.3.4   Draw array of 0.5-diameter circles

Set the current layer to **Object.**

   The circle which is to be used as the entity in the array is first drawn at the top of the octagon. Its center is at the intersection of the 2.5-unit-diameter center circle just drawn and the vertical center line. That point is located by using the INTersect object snap. Draw the circle with a diameter of 0.5 units:

    DRAW <**pick**> CIRCLE <**pick**> CEN,DIA <**pick**> Center point: * * * * <**pick**> CENter
    <**pick**> of Place target over the intersection point, as illustrated in Fig. 9.5. <**pick**>
    Diameter: **0.5** <**return**>

Draw the circular array of 0.5-diameter circles as follows:

    EDIT <**pick**> ARRAY <**pick**> Select objects: **1** (Last) <**return**> Select objects:
    <**return**> Rectangular or polar array (R/P): Polar <**pick**> Center point: * * * *
    <**pick**> CENter <**pick**> of Place the object snap target on the circumference of the large
    circle. <**pick**> Number of items: <**return**> Angle to fill (+=CCW, −=CW) <360>:
    Select default 360 <**return**> Angle between items (+=CCW, −=CW): **45** <**return**>
    Rotate objects as they are copied <Y>: <**return**>

Note the two different methods used to draw an array of items. For the lines, the number of items was entered, but an "Angle to fill" of 0 was used. This forced AutoCAD to ask for the angles between items. For the circles, since the number of items was not entered, the angle to fill (360 degrees) had to be entered.

   Turn the construction layer off:

    AUTOCAD <**pick**> LAYER: <**pick**> Off <**pick**> Layer names: **0** <**return**> <**return**>

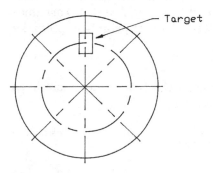

Figure 9.5 Intersection object snap target location.

9.3.5   Dimensions and text

Determine the text height and set the dimension scale:

The drawing units are inches. It is to be plotted at a 3/4 scale. Assume 1/8-in-high text is desired on the plotted drawing:

$$3/4 * h = 1/8 \quad \text{gives } h = 0.20$$

The dimension scale, DIMSCALE, is calculated using Eq. 4.2:

$$\text{DIMSCALE} * 0.18 = \text{text height}$$

$$\text{DIMSCALE} * 0.18 = 0.20 \quad \text{gives DIMSCALE} = 1.11$$

Set DIMSCALE as follows:

```
AUTOCAD <pick> DIM: <pick> DIMVARS <pick> DIMSCALE <pick> Dimension scale
factor <1>: 1.11 <return>
```

Before continuing, set Dimens as the current layer.

9.3.5.1   Angular dimensioning. The ANGULAR dimension subcommand is used to add the 45-degree dimension on the right side of the octagon plate as follows:

```
DIM <pick> ANGULAR <pick> Select first extension line: end (Endpoint) <re-
turn> of Place the object snap target on the right end of the horizontal line passing through
the center of the circle. <pick> Second line: end <return> of Place the target on the
end of the 45-degree center line. <pick> Enter dimension line arc location: Digitize
a point where you want the angular dimension line to be located. <pick> Dimension text:
45 <return> Enter text location: Digitize the point where you want the dimension text
to be located. <return>
```

When the dimension text is requested, you may enter a value of 45, as indicated above, or press the Enter key to accept the default value shown. If the Space Bar is pressed instead of the Enter key, AutoCAD assumes that you wish no text. If you do not want AutoCAD to print text, press the Space Bar, followed by the Enter key.

9.3.5.2   Diameter dimensioning. Dimension the 2.5-diameter circle as follows:

```
DIM <pick> DIAMETER <pick> Select arc or circle: Digitize point a illustrated in
Fig. 9.6. <pick> Dimension text <2.5>: <return>
```

With some versions the text is displayed inside the dimension line and across the center of the circle. It is preferable to use a leader and place

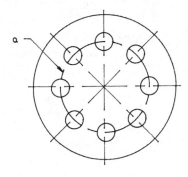

Figure 9.6 Diameter dimension location.

the text outside of the circle, as illustrated in Fig. 9.1. Use the UNDO command to erase the dimension:

UNDO <return>

Redo the dimension, pressing the Space Bar when the text is called for. This causes the computer to draw the dimension lines but suppress the text. The text can then be added using the LINE and TEXT commands. The commands are as follows:

```
DIM: <pick> DIAMETER <pick> Select arc or circle: Digitize point a. <pick>
Dimension text <.2.5>: Press the space bar to suppress the text <return> <Ctrl-C>
```

The line command is to be used to draw the leader line, and text is added as follows:

```
DRAW <pick> LINE <pick> From point: @ <return> To point: Extend the leader line
as desired. <pick> To point: <return> DRAW <pick> next <pick> TEXT <pick>
Starting point (or ACRS): r (To right-justify the text) <return> Digitize a point
locating the lower right corner of the text. <pick> Height: 0.20 <return> Rotation
angle <0>: <return> Text: 2.5%%c <return>
```

The two percent signs, %%, in the text indicates to AutoCAD that the next value is a code. The code c tells AutoCAD to print the circle diameter symbol.

9.4   Rectangular Plate

Set the current layer as **Object**. Using the LINE command draw the rectangular plate starting with the lower left corner at coordinates 7.5,2.5.

9.4.1   Draw and copy triangles

Draw one equilateral triangle in the upper left corner of the plate. The Point command will be used to locate the cursor on the upper left corner, and relative coordinates are then used to locate the top left corner of the triangle:

> DRAW <**pick**> POINT <**pick**> Point: **int** (INTersec) <**return**> of Digitize the target over the top left corner of the rectangle. <**pick**>
>
> LINE <**pick**> From point: @0.5−0.5 <**return**> To point: @1<0 <**return**> To point: @1<240 <**return**> To point: **c** <**return**>

Copy the triangle into the right corner of the plate as follows:

> EDIT <**pick**> COPY <**pick**> Select objects: **w** <**return**> Place a window around the triangle to be copied. <**pick**> Base point or displacement: Digitize a point anywhere on the monitor. <**pick**> Second point of displacement: @1.5<0 <**return**>

A copy of the first triangle will now appear on the monitor, 1.5 units to the right of the initial triangle. Note that the first displacement point was selected anywhere on the drawing. This is possible since the second point selected is relative to the first, defining the amount of movement and the direction rather than the location of the copied object.

9.4.2   Draw mirror image of triangles

The two bottom triangles will be drawn by having AutoCAD draw a mirror image of the two top triangles as follows:

> EDIT <**return**> MIRROR <**return**> Select objects: **w** <**return**> First point: Digitize the lower left corner of the window as illustrated in Fig. 9.7. <**pick**> Second point: Digitize the upper right corner of the window. <**return**> First point of mirror line:

The mirror line is a horizontal line through the midpoint of the rectangular plate. The MID (midpoint) object snap will be used to locate the midpoint of the side of the rectangle as illustrated in Fig. 9.7:

> **mid** (Midpoint) <**return**> of Locate target on the left side line. <**pick**> Second point: **mid** <**return**> of Locate target on the right side line. <**pick**> Delete old objects? <N>: **n** <**return**>

Since the top two triangles are not to be deleted, n (no) was entered in response to the last question.

9.4.3   Dimension rectangular plate

Set the Dimens layer as the current layer and dimension the rectangular plate, as illustrated in Fig. 9.1.

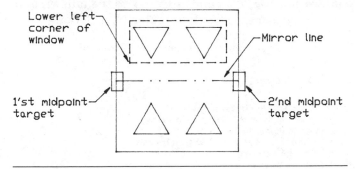

Figure 9.7 Mirror selection points.

9.5 Reset Limits

Using the cursors, check to see if the drawing exceeds the limits of 0,0 and 13,9 which were set at the start of the drawing. If the limits are exceeded, reset them.

9.6 END and PLOT

Use ZOOM and A (all) to set the monitor display to the drawing limits. Use END to save the drawing file and exit from the drawing.

Select task 3, "Plot a Drawing," from the main menu. The drawing will be plotted on an A-size sheet using a 3/4 scale. When the PLOT command is initiated, AutoCAD displays the stored plot specifications as illustrated in Sec. 7.2 and requests the input illustrated in the following.

The view that is to be plotted is the view that was displayed on the monitor when the drawing was saved. Enter **D** (Display) in response to the following:

```
What to plot-Display, Extents, Limits, View, or Window <D>: d <return>
```

The basic plot specifications are now displayed. The specifications displayed on your computer may be correct, i.e., drawing units are inches, plotting area is 11 by 8.5 in, and plot origin is at 0,0. Even if your specifications are correct, for the practice, indicate that they are to be changed:

```
Do you want to change anything <N>: y (yes) <return>
```

AutoCAD will display layer color, line type, and pen speed specifications that are similar to those illustrated in Sec. 7.2. If you wish to change any of the specifications, review Sec. 7.2.1 and answer Y to the following. If you do not wish to change the specifications, enter N, as follows:

```
Do you want to change any of the above parameters <N>: <return>
```

The plot options will be set as:

```
Write the plot to a file? <N> n <return> (Ver. 2.5 only)
Size units (Inches or Millimetres) <I>: i <return>
Plot origin in Inches <0.00,0.00>: <return>
Plot size (MAX, ?) or width in Inches <MAX>: 11 <return>
Plot Height <default>: 8.5 <return>
Rotate 2D plots 90 degrees clockwise? <N>: <return>
Pen width <default>: <return>
Adjust area fill boundaries for pen width? <N>: <return>
Save changes for future plots? <N>: <return>
Remove hidden lines? <N>: <return> (ADE-3 package)
```

AutoCAD will now request the scale, which is entered as illustrated for the various versions of AutoCAD. The drawing is 3/4 scale, which means that 3/4 of an inch on the plot = 1 in on the drawing:

```
Specify scale by entering:
Plotted inches=Drawing Units or Fit or ? <F>: .75=1 <return>
Position paper in plotter.
Press RETURN to continue or S to Stop for hardware setup: <return>
```

10

Blocks

OBJECTIVE *Create block files to be inserted as components in another drawing, use coordinate and dynamic insertion, LAYERS command; SOLID command, drawing regeneration. Complete an electronic circuit drawing.*

DRAWING *Create a block drawing file for each of the electrical components. Complete the electronic circuit drawing illustrated in Fig. 10.1 by inserting the electronic component block files into the circuit drawing.*

10.1 Blocks

Blocks are entities grouped together to form a complex object which is then defined as one entity. If the block is repeated in a number of locations on the drawing, there is a considerable saving in disk space since the block entities are not redefined with each use. The use of blocks also speeds up the drawing process by allowing the insertion of complex block units into the drawing.

Making revisions to components on drawings is often very tedious. If a component was drawn as a block, all copies of the component are altered by revising the original block, with a considerable saving of time.

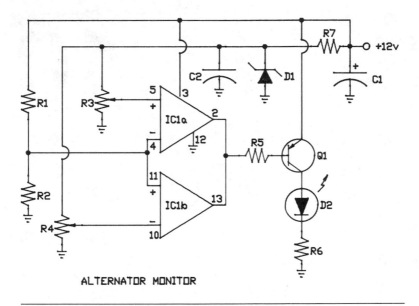

ALTERNATOR MONITOR

Figure 10.1 Project 10, electronics drawing.

When a block is created, AutoCAD asks the user for an insertion point for the block. The operator then specifies a point on the block which is to be used as the point of insertion for that block on any subsequent drawings. Often the lower left corner of the block or coordinate 0,0 is selected as the insertion point.

When blocks are inserted into drawings, AutoCAD asks for x and y scale factors. This allows the drafter to input multipliers of the x and y axes, modifying the x and y dimensions of the block being inserted. The program also asks for the rotation angle for the block, allowing the drafter to draw the block at any angle. The drag mode can be used for any of these items, allowing the drafter to visually insert the component into the drawing.

If components are to be stored in a drawing file for insertion into different drawings or if the component may have different x-y dimensions on the drawing, a useful convention is to draw the component in a 1- by 1-unit block. When the block is inserted into the drawing, the x and y scale factors then become the actual dimensions in drawing units.

After a block is initially defined on a drawing and saved as a block, it is erased by AutoCAD. If the initial location of the block is desired, it can be recalled into that location by immediately using the oops command.

When a block is created, it is defined as a block on the current drawing only. To create a drawing file of the block for utilization on other drawings, the WBLOCK (write block) command must be used. The electronic components used on this project will be stored as drawing files for utilization on other drawings. If the blocks are to be stored on the data disk in drive B, you must remember to *use B: in front of the file name.*

Block names may be up to 31 characters long and may contain letters, digits, and the characters - and _. File names for blocks are subject to the same restrictions as are drawing file names (eight characters maximum). If a block is to be stored as a file, you will usually wish to use the same block and file name; hence, the more stringent restrictions of the file name will be used when naming the block.

Blocks may be composed of other blocks. This is referred to as "nesting" of blocks.

10.2 Blocks and Layers

Information about the layer on which the entities of a block were initially drawn are part of the block information that is stored with the block on the disk. When the block is inserted into a drawing, the entities of the block remain on their original layer regardless of what layer the block is inserted into on the drawing.

One exception to the layer rule for blocks is that entities that were drawn on layer 0 in a block will become part of the layer that is set when the block is inserted into the drawing.

10.3 Draw Resistor Block

Each of the electronic components shown in Fig. 10.2 is to be drawn as a block and stored as a file for later insertion into a drawing. Draw each component as a 1- by 1-unit block to allow modification of the size as desired when the block is inserted into the drawing. The insertion point should be selected on the left side of the component at a point where it would be connected to the electronic circuit. The following procedure is used to draw the resistor.

Start a new drawing named **B:Proj-10**. Use the default screen limits of 0,0 and 12,9.

Set the units to decimal with two digits to the right of the decimal.

The GRID command is very useful when working with blocks. The *blocks should be drawn in a grid that will be used in the final drawing.* Points on the block entities will then coincide with the grid on the final drawing, facilitating the connection of entities on the main drawing. This procedure is illustrated in this chapter.

Set SNAP to 0.1 and set the grid to 0.2:

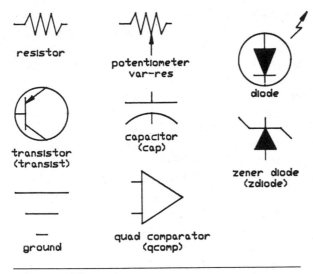

Figure 10.2 Electronic components.

```
AutoCAD <pick> SETTINGS (or MODES) <pick> SNAP <pick> Snap spacing (x) or
On/Off/Aspect?rotate/Style: 0.1 <return> _LAST_ <pick> GRID <pick> Grid
spacing (x) or On/Off/Snap/Aspect: 0.2<return>
```

The blocks will be drawn in a 1-square-unit box starting at coordinate 1,1. Zoom on a box around 1,1 and 2,2:

```
AutoCAD <pick> DISPLAY <pick> ZOOM <pick> All/Center/Dynamic/Extents/
Left/Previous/Window/<Scale>: w <return> First corner: 0.2,0.2 <return>
Next corner: 2.8,2.8 <return>
```

Draw the resistor 1 unit long using the cursor snap and the grid, as illustrated in Fig. 10.3.

10.3.1   Save resistor as a block

Designate the resistor as a block (remember that the left end of the resistor lead is coordinate 1,1):

```
AutoCAD <pick> Blocks <pick> BLOCK <pick> Block name (or?): resistor <re-
turn> Insertion base point: 1,1 <return> Select object: w <return> Place a
window around the resistor. <return>
```

The resistor will be erased from the screen. If you wish to have the resistor returned to the screen, the oops command may be used. That is not desired now, however.

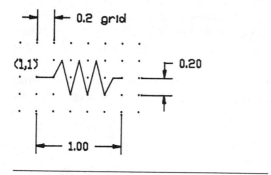

Figure 10.3 Resistor.

The block may be recalled to this drawing at any time with the INSERT command. If you want to use this block in other drawings, it must be saved in a *drawing file* using the WBLOCK command. If the block is to be used only in the current drawing, it should *not* be saved in a file using the WBLOCK command since that would be a waste of disk space. To write the block to a disk file, enter the following commands:

LAST **<pick>** WBLOCK **<pick>** File Name: **b:resistor <return>** Block name: = **<return>**

Note the use of B: in the file name to store the file on the data disk in drive B. The block name is entered as = to specify that the block name is the same as the file name. Note that the block name refers to the name used when creating the block. The file name and block name do not have to be the same.

If you wish to clean up the drawing, use the REDRAW command.

10.4   Draw Potentiometer Block

Use the INSERT command to recall the resistor block:

INSERT **<pick>** Block name (or?): **resistor <return>** Insertion point: **1,1 <return>** X scale factor <1>/Corner/XYZ: Select the default 1 value. **<return>** Y scale factor (default = X): Select the default *x* value, 1. **<return>** Rotation angle <0>: Select the default value 0. **<return>**

Note that B: was not required in front of the block name since the resistor block is part of the current block and does not have to be read from the disk file.

Create a variable resistor (potentiometer) by adding an arrow to the resistor using the DIM <return> LEADER commands. When the initial line of the leader is drawn, press Ctrl-C to cancel the remainder of the leader. If AutoCAD does not place an arrowhead on the leader, the leader line is too short. Use the UNDO command to delete the leader and then draw a slightly longer one. The BREAK command can be used to later shorten the leader.

Save the block using the name **Var-res**. Write the block to a drawing file using the same name. Remember to use B: when entering the *file name*.

10.5   Draw LED Block

The LED will be drawn, as illustrated in Fig. 10.4 with the grid shown. The SOLID command is used to fill in the arrowhead in the block as follows:

DRAW <**pick**> SOLID <**pick**> First point: Place the cursor on the tip of the arrowhead in the LED. <**pick**> Second point: Place the cursor on a corner of the arrowhead. <**pick**> Third point: Place the target on the next corner. <**pick**> Fourth point: <**return**>

Note how useful the GRID and SNAP commands are when locating points on the monitor.

Save the LED as a block and then write it to file using the WBLOCK command.

Draw the remaining blocks and write each one to file. The insertion point for each block should be a point on the block where the component connects to the electronic circuit line.

10.6   Block Modifications

Regardless of a block's complexity, it is treated as a single entity on a drawing. As such, components in the block cannot be altered. To tran-

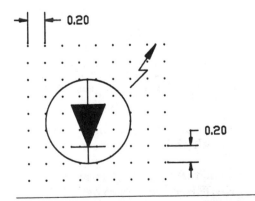

Figure 10.4   LED

scribe a block and retain its separate entities, precede the block name
with an asterisk, *:

INSERT <**pick**> Block name (or?): ***var-res** <**return**> etc.

When the Var-res block is loaded, you will be able to erase or otherwise
modify its entities.

If you attempt to load blocks which were created in a previous drawing
and stored on disk with the *... format, you would expect to enter the
block name as B:*.... AutoCAD will indicate that an error was made,
however, and will not load the file. The procedure used to load a block file
named Resistor from drive B:, and to transcribe the block's separate
entities, is as follows:

INSERT <**pick**> Block name (or ?): **b:resistor** <**return**> Insertion Point:

Exit the command by pressing Ctrl-C and continue as follows:

<Ctrl-C> INSERT <**pick**> Block name (or ?): ***resistor** <**return**> etc.

10.7   Circuit Drawing

Use the ZOOM and A (all) commands to zoom to the full screen limits of
0,0 and 12,9.

Prior to starting the drawing, familiarize yourself with the block
insert command that follows:

INSERT <**pick**> Block name: **var-res** <**return**>

Insertion point: The insertion point can be entered as a coordinate, as a relative
coordinate (@), by digitizing a point, or by typing drag and dragging the point to the proper
location.

X scale factor <1>/Corner/XYZ: To use the default value 1, press the Enter key. Any
value entered will be a multiplier of the x dimension of the resistor. To visually drag the x and
y dimensions of the resistor, type **drag** and press Enter. Use the cursor to drag the length and
height of the resistor to that which is desired. Note that an invalid entry will result if you
attempt to drag only one axis of the entity by moving the cursor only horizontally or only
vertically, which implies that the orthogonal multiplier is 0, an impossible value.

Y scale factor (default=X): Use the same scale as that for the x dimension and press
the Enter key. Any value entered will be a multiplier of the y dimension of the resistor.

Rotation angle <0>: Press Enter to select the default angle 0. To rotate the resistor, enter
the angle desired where 0 degrees is horizontal. To drag the resistor to the desired angle, type
drag and press the Enter key.

If a block from drive B is inserted, the file name must be preceded with
B: the first time the block is inserted into the drawing. If a fixed disk is
used, the file name will have to be preceded by the file path if the block
file does not reside in the same menu as AutoCAD. Further insertions do
not require that the drive letter or path precede the file name.

Try the various methods of inserting the Var-res block into the drawing. Use the ERASE <return> LAST commands to erase the Var-res block and begin the circuit drawing.

Prior to beginning the circuit drawing, draw a 0.1-unit-diameter circle as a block for the circuit connections. Use the center of the circle as the insertion point. To fill the circle use the hatch command, ANSI31. Use a .02 scale for the hatch. The SOLID command, which is used to fill objects, is only for use with quadrilateral or rectangular sections and cannot be used to fill a circle. The ADE-3 package has a DONUT command which can be used to draw a solid dot. The procedure is illustrated in Chap. 16.

This block does not have to be stored on file using the WBLOCK command since these intersection points will be used only on this drawing.

Complete the circuit drawing, as illustrated in Fig. 10.1. Use the object snaps INT (intersect) and END (end point) as required to make the drawing production easier. Use the COPY command to copy segments of the drawing as required; for instance, the resistor connected to a ground is used twice—draw one and then copy it to the next location. The same procedure should be used for the var-res ground and the capacitor ground. Occasionally it is easiest to insert the block close to where it is desired and then use the MOVE command to move it to the desired position, making use of temporary object snaps such as END (end point). This is especially useful when a block is to be rotated.

Do not worry about where to start the drawing. Remember that you can use the MOVE command at any time to move the entire drawing to a new location. If the drawing exceeds the drawing limits, change them.

Most items will be inserted using an x and y scale factor of 1. When inserting the QCOMP (quad comparator), use a scale factor of 2 (1.5 might appear okay; however, the points on the comparator would not fall on the snap lines, making it more difficult to connect lines to those points). The ground should be inserted using an x and y scale factor of .25. If you insert an object and wish to reinsert it at a different scale, use the ERASE <return> L (last) commands and then reinsert the item.

10.8 Drawing Modifications

You may call up the block files using the * name command to modify them at any time (see Sec. 10.5). If a block has been inserted into a drawing and its block file is later modified, all of its copies on the current drawing into which it was inserted may be modified using the following procedure. Assume Resistor has been inserted into the current drawing and was later modified. The copies of Resistor on the current drawing are now to be modified to comply with the revised block file:

AUTOCAD <**pick**> BLOCKS <**pick**> INSERT: <**pick**> Block name (or ?): **resistor** =**b:resistor** <**return**> Insertion point: <**Ctrl-C**>

All copies of Resistor in the drawing will be replaced with the updated block. If the modified Resistor file is stored on the currently logged drive, i.e., A, do not enter the drive letter B: in front of the file name. If you are using a fixed drive system and the block file is in another file, the file path will have to precede the file name. For instance, if the block file is in subfile Acad, the block name entered would be Resistor= \acad\resistor.

11

Custom Menu

OBJECTIVE *Create a customized menu to simplify drawing construction; use a line editor (EDLIN).*

11.1 Menu Files

An AutoCAD menu file is a text file with the extension .mnu. The customized file is created with any text editor or word processor that does not place extra coding characters in the text. An ideal text editor to use is EDLIN, which is on the MS-DOS or PC-DOS disk.

The menu file may contain one AutoCAD command or a string of commands. The file is loaded into the drawing editor with the MENU command, which will request the name of the menu file. The standard AutoCAD menu file is named Acad.mnu. When the file is called, the extension .mnu is not specified as part of the name by the user since AutoCAD assumes the extension and inserts it automatically after the name.

11.2 Example Screen Menu

The following menu could be used to draw only lines and circles, and it allows erasing:

```
LINE
CIRCLE
TRACE .3
FILL
ERASE W
ERASE L
OOPS
QUIT
END
```

The TRACE command allows solid or parallel lines of a specific width to be drawn. If FILL is on, a solid line is drawn. If FILL is off, two parallel lines are drawn. FILL is turned on or off by the FILL command.

In this menu the third line is called a macro since the command line performs more than one function. When TRACE is called, AutoCAD normally requests the width (or spacing) of the line. In this menu the width of .3 drawing units is inserted as part of the command sequence and will be inserted automatically when TRACE is selected by the user.

The menu also includes two ERASE commands—one for erasing by placing a window around the item and the other to erase the last item drawn.

If a menu string exceeds a monitor line length and must continue on the next line or if for clarity the line is shortened and is carried onto the next line, a plus (+) sign is placed at the end of the line to be continued to indicate it continues on the next line.

11.3   Screen Menu—Item Titles

Only the first eight characters of a menu can appear in the title displayed on the monitor. If SNAP 0.001 were placed in the menu, it would appear as SNAP 0.0. The user may resolve this problem by using a short title that illustrates the command. If the short title is not a standard AutoCAD command, it must be enclosed in square brackets [ ]. The SNAP command may appear as follows in the menu:

```
[FINE]SNAP 0.001
[COARSE]SNAP 0.1
```

The monitor would display the preceding commands as:

```
FINE
COARSE
```

11.4   Submenus

The maximum number of menu items that can be displayed on the monitor is limited by the number of lines the monitor can display.

Longer menus must be broken up into submenus. Submenus are also used to clarify menu selections as is done, for instance, in the Acad menu, where a Root menu is used to call submenus which replace the Root menu on the screen. Submenus may be nested.

A submenu is started with a submenu label using the format **name.

The name is a string of up to 31 characters containing letters, digits, and the characters $, -, and __. The submenu name must *not* contain any embedded blanks.

Screen submenus are called by the command $S = submenu name. When submenus are used, the main screen menu is indicated as ***SCREEN.

An example of a screen menu with a submenu is as follows:

```
***SCREEN
[DRAW  ]$S=draw
[REVISE]$S=erase
[FINISH]$S=finish
[ ]
[ ]
[ ]
**draw
LINE
CIRCLE
[TRACE]TRACE .3
FILL
[REVISE]$S=erase
[-MAIN-]$S=SCREEN
**erase
ERASE W
ERASE L
ERASE
OOPS
[-PREV-]$S=
[-MAIN-]$S=SCREEN
**finish
[DONE ]END
[GIVE UP]QUIT
[-MAIN-]$S=SCREEN
```

The spaces used in the menu heading blocks, [ ], are not required and are used here only to improve the readability of the file.

The blank lines are inserted so that each grouping has the same number of lines. When a submenu is called, the items are listed on the monitor from the top down. If the submenu does not have as many lines as the previous menu displayed, the lines not replaced by the new submenu will remain on the screen. The blank lines ensure that the lines are not displayed. Note that there may be times when you would like lines from the previous menu to be displayed. You can use items from an earlier menu that are on the monitor.

The main menu will be displayed as follows:

```
DRAW
REVISE
FINISH
```

If the Revise menu item is selected, the menu displayed is:

```
ERASE W
ERASE L
ERASE
OOPS
-PREV-
-MAIN-
```

If —PREV— is selected from the Revise menu, the previous menu displayed will be recalled. This is accomplished with the $S = command without placing a submenu name after the =.

11.4.1 Embedding keyboard input

To allow keyboard input in the middle of a menu list, place a backslash character (\) at the location where the keyboard input is required.

The following CIRCLE-2 command will request the center point of the circle from the user and will then read the radius of 2 units from the menu rather than ask the user for the radius:

```
[CIRCLE-2]circle \2
```

11.4.2 Embedding Enter key

The Enter key is embedded in a menu list by placing a semicolon (;) or a space at the location where the Enter key is required. The following macro command will write a .2-unit-high address at an angle of 0 degrees at a location specified by the user:

```
[ADDRESS] text \.2;0;CAMBRIAN COLLEGE;;;+
1400 Barrydowne Rd.;;;Sudbury, Ontario;
```

When ADDRESS is selected, it calls the AutoCAD TEXT command. When the TEXT command is selected, it must be followed by pressing the Enter key. This is included in the macro as the single space following the TEXT command.

The TEXT command requires input when it is invoked. The first information required is the text starting point. The backslash (\) in the macro sends control to the user, who must specify the starting point either by locating the cursor or by entering the coordinates. The user must press Enter to input the information so there must not be a space or semicolon in the macro after the backslash.

The next information required by the TEXT command is the text height, which is read from the menu macro as .2 units and is followed by a semicolon to invoke the Enter key. The angle is then read as 0 degrees and is also followed by a semicolon, invoking the Enter key.

The next item in the macro is the text "CAMBRIAN COLLEGE." The semicolon must be used to invoke the Enter key at the end of the text since AutoCAD would interpret a blank space as part of the text. The plus sign (+) indicates that the macro continues on the next line.

The semicolon at the beginning of the second line of the macro invokes the Enter key again, which repeats the text command and places the next text directly below the previous text (see Sec. 5.10), printing "1400 Barrydowne Rd."

The first semicolon following the text enters the text, and the next semicolon recalls the TEXT command, which prints the remaining text. The text is followed by a semicolon to enter the text.

Note that although the Enter key may be embedded in the macro with either a space or a semicolon, there are times when a semicolon must be used instead of a space. The space may always be replaced with a semicolon.

The + is inserted to indicate to AutoCAD that the commands extend onto the next line.

11.5 MENU Command

The MENU command is used to load a new menu. The following is used to load a menu named Proj-11.mnu:

```
MENU <return> File name: B:Proj-11 <return>
```

11.6 EDLIN

To create AutoCAD menu files a text editor or word processor that does not place extra code characters in the text must be used. EDLIN is a simple text editor on the MS-DOS disk that suits this purpose. List the files in the hard drive root directory to see if EDLIN is available.

```
C:\>dir\w <return>
```

If EDLIN.COM is not listed, insert your MS-DOS disk in drive A and enter the following:

```
C:\>copy a:edlin.com <return>
```

EDLIN may now be loaded by typing **EDLIN**, followed by the file name with the extension .mnu added. Menu file names are subject to the same restrictions as are drawing file names. If the file is to be stored on the disk in drive B, add B: to the front of the file name. To load EDLIN and create a menu file called Proj-11 to be stored on the disk in drive B, enter:

```
C:\>edlin b:Proj-11.mnu
```

If you store your drawing files on a fixed drive, read App. D.

EDLIN will respond that Proj-11.mnu is the new file and will wait for a command. The following is displayed:

```
New file
*_
```

The asterisk (*) is the EDLIN command prompt that indicates that you may enter an EDLIN command. *The asterisk will not be included in the file listing.*

11.6.1   EDLIN commands

Most EDLIN commands are single letters. The following is a discussion of a few of the commands that may be required to create menu files. For a more thorough explanation and listing of the commands refer to your MS-DOS or PC-DOS manual.

11.6.1.1   Insert.   To begin a new file enter **i**. EDLIN will respond with:

```
1:*_
```

The 1: is not part of the data and is displayed only to make reading of EDLIN lines easier. The *_ is the command prompt and is also not part of the data. The Enter key should be pressed at the end of each line entry. It is not shown in the commands. You may now type in one line of the menu:

```
1:****SCREEN
```

Note that although four asterisks are displayed, only three are part of the data. The first is the EDLIN command prompt.

When Enter is pressed, EDLIN will move to the next line and display:

```
2:*
```

Type in the next line:

```
2: *[DRAW ]$S=draw (Include the error, })
```

Add the remaining lines to the menu file as illustrated in Sec. 11.4. If you make an error, don't worry about it. Continue to add the remaining entries. The entry errors may be edited after the file is complete. The blank lines in the file are added by pressing Enter for those lines without typing in any values.

11.6.1.2   Ending entries. To stop adding lines to the file, press Ctrl-C. EDLIN will then display the command prompt:

    *_

11.6.1.3   Listing the file. To list the file enter L (list) in response to the command prompt *_. To list the file starting at line 5, type:

    *5l

11.6.1.4   Inserting lines in a file. Lines may be inserted anywhere in an existing file by preceding the I (insert) command with a line number. To insert a blank line at line 3, respond to the command prompt with the following:

    *3i
    3: *Press Enter key
    4: *Press Ctrl-C (This will appear as ^C)
    *_

List the file and note that a blank line has been added at line 3 and the previous line 3 has become line 4, etc. Leave this blank line in your file. We will delete it soon.

11.6.1.5   Deleting lines. Delete a line by typing the line number followed by d. To delete the blank line inserted at line 3, type:

    *3d
    *_

List the file and observe that the blank line at 3 is now deleted and that the lines following 3 have moved up to close the gap.

11.6.1.6   Editing a line. To edit a line, type the line number and press Enter. For example, to change } to] in line 2 below use:

    *2

EDLIN will list the line and allow editing of the line below it. To move the cursor to the }, use the right arrow key on the numeric keyboard:

```
2:*[DRAW]$S = draw
2:*[DRAW]
```

Type the square bracket] and move the cursor to the end of the line and press Enter.

To insert characters into an existing line, press the Ins key (do not type "ins"). Any keys pressed thereafter will be inserted into the location of the cursor. Press Ins again to stop the insert.

To delete a character in a line, press the Del key. The Del key deletes only one character at a time.

11.6.1.7   Ending EDLIN.   To end EDLIN and save the file, respond to the command prompt with e:

```
*e
```

DOS responds with the system prompt:

```
C:\>_
```

11.6.1.8   Editing an existing .mnu file.   To load an existing file respond to the DOS prompt with:

C:\>**edlin b:xxxxx.mnu**

The xxxxx represents the appropriate file name. The B: in front of the file name is not required if the file is in drive C (the current logged drive). On a fixed disk system, you will have to include the file path in front of the file name.

11.6.1.9   Aborting an editing session.   If you have made changes to an existing file and wish to cancel the changes, end the editing session by responding to the EDLIN command prompt with q:

```
*q
```

EDLIN will ask you to confirm the q (quit) command.

11.7   Testing Menu

To test the file, boot AutoCAD and start a new drawing called B:Proj-11. When the command line appears, use the MENU command to call the Proj-11.mnu created with EDLIN:

AUTOCAD <**pick**> UTILITY <**pick**> MENU <**pick**> File name: **b:Proj-11** <**return**>

AutoCAD will load your menu file. Try the menu. If you find that some of the commands do not work, exit AutoCAD and load EDLIN from DOS and edit the file. Compare what you have with that shown in Sec. 12.4. EDLIN can be loaded from the drawing editor by entering the command EDIT. If you wish to do this, first copy EDLIN.COM into the same directory as your ACAD files.

If you modify a menu that was previously loaded into a drawing, you will have to reload the menu into the drawing using the MENU command in order to replace the previously loaded menu.

11.8 Button and Pull-Down Menus

Insert the following lines into the end of your Proj-11.mnu file using EDLIN:

```
*** BUTTONS
;
^C ^C REDRAW
```

Exit EDLIN. If you loaded EDLIN from inside of AutoCAD using the EDIT command, invoke the MENU command and reload the PROJ-11 menu to load the latest version. If you exited AutoCAD to load EDLIN, the latest version of the menu is read when AutoCAD is booted and the drawing file is edited.

Reload the drawing and try the modified PROJ-11 menu. You will observe that the pick button on the mouse has not been changed. The second button on the mouse is now Return as specified by the semicolon in the menu. The third mouse button invokes two Ctrl-C's and RE-DRAW.

For a discussion of Pull-Down menus refer to App. E.

Attributes

OBJECTIVE *Use blocks with attributes to
construct a custom menu to draw borders
and title blocks for drawings; insert
drawings to scale into a border plot drawing.*

12.1 Attributes

Attributes are used to tag information to graphical drawing elements
which are stored as blocks. The information may be constants, such as
heat loss coefficients tagged with window blocks, or variable information requested from the user by AutoCAD as the block is being inserted
into the drawing.

Attribute information may be displayed on the drawing with the
graphic block, or the information can be collected on a disk for later
processing to create, for instance, a bill of material. Such information
can be collected from the disk by other software such as dBase II.

The procedure for using attributes is as follows:

1. Create an Attribute Definition using the ATTDEF command.

2. Create a block which includes the desired graphic information and
   the Attribute Definition.

The block, including the Attribute Definition, may be part of the current drawing only or may be saved as a separate file using the WBLOCK command and inserted into any other drawing. The block will always retain the attribute information tagged to it.

A block can have more than one attribute associated with it. AutoCAD will prompt the user for the value of each attribute when the block is inserted.

12.2   ATTDEF Command

The Attribute Definition is created with the ATTDEF command. This command is listed in the block submenu.

When ATTDEF is called, the following will be displayed in the Auto-CAD command line:

```
Attribute modes—Invisible:N Constant:N Verify:N Preset:N Enter (ICVP) to
change, RETURN when done:
```

You may turn on any or all of the four modes by entering I (invisible), C (constant), V (verify), or P (preset).

The four optional modes—invisible, constant, verify, and preset—are initially off, as indicated by the letter N (no) beside each mode name in the command line. If I, C, V, or P is entered, the mode line will be redisplayed with a Y (yes) beside that mode name, indicating that the mode is turned on. Each time the mode line is redisplayed, a mode may be turned on or off by entering the first letter in the mode name.

The modes perform the following functions:

Invisible.   When the invisible mode is turned on (Y), information relevant to that attribute is not displayed on the drawing with the block it is tagged to. For instance, if you wish to tag building window blocks with heat loss factors, you may not wish that information to be displayed on the drawing. The information is stored in the drawing file, however, and can be retrieved from the file by another program which might perform heat loss calculations. When the invisible mode is off (N), attribute information tagged to a block is displayed on the drawing with the block.

Constant.   When the Constant mode is off (N), the attribute tagged to the block is variable, and data is requested from the user by AutoCAD when the block is inserted. If the constant mode is on (Y), the attribute information tagged with the block is inserted when the block is created and cannot be changed when the block is inserted into a drawing.

Verify. If verify is on, any variable information entered by the user when the block is inserted will be redisplayed and the user will be given an opportunity to modify the entry. If verify is off (N), the information will be accepted immediately as it is entered, and the user will not be given an opportunity to modify it.

Preset. This mode allows you to create attributes that are variable but are not requested during block insertion.

When the mode switches are set correctly, the Enter key is pressed to move to the next attribute control.

12.2.1 Attribute Tag

When the modes are set, AutoCAD responds with:

```
Attribute tag.
```

The attribute tag is any name that you wish to use to identify the attribute. *This tag name must not include blank spaces and must not be a null value.* It is printed on the drawing when the attribute is created and *disappears* when the block is created. It is *not* printed on a drawing when the block is inserted. Generally, the attribute tag should be a short identifier name.

12.2.2 Attribute prompt

When the attribute tag is entered AutoCAD responds with:

```
Attribute prompt:
```

You may now enter a prompt line that is to be displayed in the command line when the block containing this attribute is inserted into a drawing. The prompt is not displayed on the block during the creation of the attribute.

The prompt is any text that you wish displayed to prompt the user to input the attribute value when the block is inserted into a drawing. If you wish AutoCAD to use the attribute tag as the prompt line, enter a null value by pressing Enter.

If you specified a constant mode for the attribute (see Sec. 12.2), AutoCAD will not request a prompt.

12.2.3 Default attribute value

If you specified a variable mode (constant, N) for the attribute, AutoCAD will now request any default value for the attribute in the form:

```
Default Attribute value:
```

If you enter a null value for the attribute when the block is being inserted, the default value will be used by AutoCAD.

12.2.4   Attribute value

If you specified a constant mode (Y) for the attribute, AutoCAD will now request the value of the constant:

```
Attribute value:
```

12.2.5   Attribute location

After the preceding information has been entered, AutoCAD will request the location of the attribute on the drawing using the TEXT command:

```
Start point or Align/Center/Fit/Middle/Right/Style:
Height <default>:
Rotation angle <default>:
```

This information is entered in a similar manner to that used for text.

12.3   Border and Title Block with Attributes

As an example, a standard border and title block will be constructed for an A-size (8.5 by 11 in or 215 by 280 mm) drawing and stored as a block. Attributes will be used to add the text information to the title block when the block is inserted into a drawing.

12.3.1   Border and title block construction

In this example metric units will be used on an A-size sheet; therefore, the screen limits will be set at 280 by 215 mm. A 20-mm border will be provided on the top long-side of the page, and 15 mm will be provided on the other side. The drawing border line will be started at coordinates 0,15 (for a Hewlett Packard HP 7470A Graphics Plotter), and the sides will then be 250 by 175 mm long.

The border dimensions and the start point are dependent on the plotter you are using. You can determine the proper values for your plotter by drawing the border as outlined in Sec. 12.3.2, but use the LINE command rather than the TRACE command. Then plot the display. If any of the border lines are not plotted, use the plot sheet to estimate where the line should be, and move the line on the screen using the MOVE command. Plot the display again, and relocate lines if necessary. You may also have to move the entire border so that it fits properly on the sheet. When your border is plotting properly, use the ID command and the INTersec object snap to locate the start point and the LIST command to specify the border line lengths. Then erase the lines. Replace the values in the following section with those for your plotter.

12.3.2 Commands

Start a new drawing named b:x and set the drawing limits at 0,0 and 280,215. Use the ZOOM and A (all) commands to set the screen to the limits.

The border will be drawn on a layer called Border. That layer name should not be used on any of your drawings:

```
AutoCAD <pick> LAYER: <pick> ?/Make/Set/New/On/Off/Color/Freeze/Thaw: n
(New) <return> New layer name: border <return> Set <return> New current layer
<0>: border <return> <return>
```

The border lines will be drawn solid by using a 0.2 TRACE line. The commands to draw the border are:

```
DRAW <pick> TRACE <pick> Trace width: 0.2 <return> From point: 0,15 <return>
To point: @250<0 <return> To point: @175<90 <return> To point: @250<180
<return> To point: 0,15 <return> To point: <return>
```

A 125- by 30 mm title block (see Fig. 12.1) is now drawn in the lower right corner of the drawing using:

```
TRACE <pick> Trace width: 0.2 <return> From point: 125,15 <return> To point:
@30<90 <return> To point: @125<0 <return> To point: <return><return>

From point: 150,15 <return> To point: @30<90 <return> To point: <return>
<return> From point: 150,37 <return> To point: @100<0 <return> To point:
<return>
```

12.3.3 Title block headings

The following commands are used to insert the headings into the title block illustrated in Fig. 12.1:

```
DRAW <pick> next <pick> TEXT <pick> Start point or align/Center/Fit/Mid-
dle/Right/Style: c (Center) <return> Center point: 200,39 Use the cursor to verify
this point on the monitor. <return> Height <0.18>: 4 <return> Rotation angle
<0>: <return> Text: CAMBRIAN COLLEGE <return> TEXT <return> Start
point or align/Center/Fit/Middle/Right/Style: 152,32 <return> Height
<4>: 3 <return> Rotation angle <0>: <return> Text: PROJECT: <return>
```

Add the remaining text using a space of 2 units between the text and a text height of 3 units.

The logo was drawn as a block and saved with the WBLOCK command. It was then inserted into the drawing. If you wish to draw the logo using a different color pen, draw it onto a new layer.

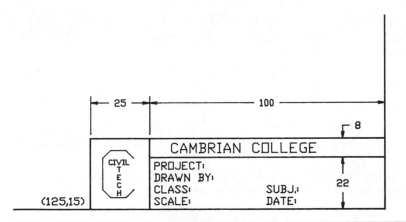

Figure 12.1 Title block dimensions and headings.

12.3.4 Create attributes

Attributes will be used to insert variable text into the title block. The commands are as follows (for Ver. 2.1, ATTDEF is in the Attribute menu):

```
AUTOCAD <pick> BLOCKS <pick> ATTDEF <pick>
```

The command line will list the modes with their settings:

```
Attribute Modes-Invisible:N Constant:N Verify:N Preset:N
Enter (ICVP) to change, RETURN when done:
```

The verify mode will be set to on so that the user will be asked to verify any attribute text entered. To do so, enter:

v (Verify) **<return>**

The command line will be repeated showing a Y beside verify:

```
Invisible:N Constant:N Verify:Y Preset:N
Enter (ICVP) to change, RETURN when done:
```

Since there are no other settings to change, press Enter.

The command line will now request the attribute tag. The tag Project will be used:

```
Attribute tag: Project <return>
```

AutoCAD next requests the prompt which will be used to request the attribute text from the user when the block is inserted into the drawing.

Any prompt text may be entered. If you wish the prompt to be the same as the attribute tag, enter a null value by pressing Enter. The following will be used:

Attribute Prompt: **Proj. name (21 letters max.)** <**return**>

The "21 letters max." is to inform the user that the name cannot exceed 21 letters or it will extend beyond the drawing border.

AutoCAD will now ask if there is a default value to be entered for the attribute. The default value will be printed if the user enters a null value when requested for the attribute.

Default Attribute value: <**return**>

AutoCAD will then request the text data as follows:

Start point or Align/Center/Fit/Middle/Right/Style: **175,32** Use the cursor to verify this point on the monitor. <**return**> Height: **3** <**return**> Rotation angle <0>: <**return**>

When the text specifications are entered, AutoCAD will insert the attribute tag, project, in the text location on the monitor. This tag will be replaced by the text entered by the user when the block is inserted into a drawing.

Add the attributes for the remaining title text *individually*. Do not use the Enter key or Space Bar to recall ATTDEF. If that is done, AutoCAD will not ask for the text location and will place the text directly below the last attribute text. While this may often be desirable, in this drawing each attribute location must be specified individually since the data must fit into a specific location in the title block. The text height is 3 units and the spacing between text lines is 2 units. Use a default value of NTS (not to scale) for the scale attribute.

The final title block illustrating the attribute tags used by the author is shown as Fig. 12.2.

If you wish to change an attribute prior to the attribute being saved with the block it is tagged to, data may be edited by erasing the attribute tag from the monitor and reentering the attribute.

12.3.5 Create the block

The entire drawing is to be saved as a block for insertion into other drawings. The block name will be Am-hbdr (A-size drawing, metric, horizontal border):

AUTOCAD <**pick**> BLOCKS <**pick**> BLOCK <**pick**> Block name: **am-hbdr** <**return**> Insertion base point: **0,0** <**return**> Select objects: **w** <**return**> First point **-1,-1** <**return**> Second point: **281,216** Placing a window around the entire drawing. <**return**>

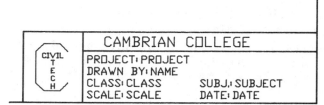

Figure 12.2   Title block attribute tags.

AutoCAD will erase the entire block from the screen. Write the block to a drawing file on the disk in drive B using a file name that is the same as the block name (refer to Sec. 10.3.1):

WBLOCK <**pick**> File name: **b:am-hbdr** <**return**> Block name: = <**return**>

You have now saved a drawing file named Am-hbdr on the disk in drive B. (If you are using a fixed disk, replace the B: with the path to the file desired.) The drawing you are presently working on is no longer required. Exit AutoCAD with the QUIT command:

QUIT <**pick**> Really want to discard all changes to drawing: **y** <**return**>

You could have started this drawing with the name B:Am-hbdr, rather than the name B:X, and used the END command to exit. As a matter of fact, that procedure would have required a few less steps; however, this project is about blocks, so the author wanted to demonstrate one. The drawing would then be used as a block in the same manner in the following sections. There is no difference between a drawing and a block once it is written to the file.

12.3.6   Test Am-hbdr file

The Am-hbdr file will be used to draw a border and title block. Data prompted from the user will be inserted into the title block. Prior to continuing, test the file by starting a new drawing called B:Test1 with limits of 0,0 and 280,215. Remember to use ZOOM and All to set the monitor to the limits. Insert the block using:

```
AUTOCAD <pick> BLOCKS <pick> INSERT <pick> Block name: b:am-hbdr <return>
Insertion point: 0,0 <return> X scale factor <1>: <return> Y scale factor
<1>: <return> Rotation angle <0>: <return>
```

AutoCAD will then prompt the user, using the prompts entered with the attribute, to enter data for each variable attribute:

```
Proj. name (21 letters max): TESTING <return> Your name: J. D. Smith <re-
turn> Class: CVTY 11 <return> Scale <NTS>: <return> Subject #: CAD 1000-3
<return> Date: 1986-03-02 <return>
```

Since the verify mode was turned on when setting ATTDEF, the prompts will be redisplayed showing the variable data entered. You may change the data if desired or simply press Enter for each one.

The drawing border and title block will be drawn with the text information inserted into the title block.

If your attributes do not perform correctly, use the QUIT command to exit the current drawing and then, from the main menu, edit an existing drawing by typing B:Am-hbdr. That file will be drawn with the attribute tags displayed. Remember to set layer Border as the current layer and then erase any problem attributes (by erasing their tags) and redo them. *Save the revised drawing using the END command.* Do not to use the BLOCK command, as outlined in the previous section, since you would be creating a block with the same name as the drawing you are currently working on; hence, the block would reference itself and could not be inserted into a drawing. Retry the test drawing as specified at the beginning of this section.

Quit the Test1 drawing; do *not* save the changes. Exit AutoCAD to DOS.

12.4 Editing Attributes

The AutoCAD ATTEDIT command may be used to edit attributes after they have been inserted. The reader should refer to the *AutoCAD Reference Manual* for a further discussion of that command.

To edit attributes prior to their insertion, load the block containing the attributes and retain all of the individual parts of the block by placing an asterisk, *, in front of the file name. Another method is to load the attribute file as a drawing, make the revisions to the attributes, and use the END command to save the drawing (do not use the BLOCK command since the block would have the same name as the drawing and would be referencing itself).

The block, or drawing, will be drawn with the attribute tag displayed. The user may then erase the attribute, redo it, and resave the block with the revised attribute.

12.5   Create a Special Border Menu

When you tested the Am-hbdr.dwg file, you were required to set limits and use the INSERT command. A special menu will now be created for a drawing called Border.dwg which will be used to draw borders and title blocks automatically.

The border drawing will be used to set up a plot drawing. A plot drawing has its limits set to the size of the sheet on which the drawing is to be plotted. Am-hbdr.dwg is inserted into the plot drawing and drawings to be plotted are then inserted to scale as blocks into the plot drawing. A number of drawing files may be inserted onto the plot drawings, each at a different scale.

The procedure is illustrated in Fig. 12.3 where the Border drawing is loaded. Am-hbdr is then inserted into the Border drawing, providing a border and title block. Next, a drawing named Proj-5 is inserted into the Border drawing, using a 3/4 scale. The Border drawing is then saved with the drawing name of Plot-5. Plot-5 may now be plotted using a 1:1 scale to provide a hard copy drawing.

12.5.1   Create menu file using EDLIN

Place your data disk in drive B. EDLIN will be used to create a menu file called Border.mnu on the disk in drive B. Review the EDLIN commands in Sec. 11.10. Start EDLIN using:

```
C:\>edlin b:border.mnu
```

The EDLIN prompt will now be displayed:

```
New file
*_
```

Use the I (insert) command to begin a new file:

```
*i <return>
1:*_
```

The following menu commands are then entered. Press Enter at the end of each line.

```
1: ***SCREEN
2: [-TITLE-]
3: [-BLOCK-]
4: [A-HOR-M]LIMITS;0,0;280,215;ZOOM;A;+
5: INSERT;B:AM-HBDR;0,0;;;;
6: INSERT
7: MOVE
8: ERASE
9: LTSCALE
```

```
10: PLOT
11: PRPLOT
12: [SAVE-END]SAVE;\QUIT;Y
13: ***BUTTONS
14: ;
15: ^C^C
16: Press Ctrl-C
```

The Ctrl-C exits the I (insert) command and displays the EDLIN prompt, *_. List the text by entering **L**. If the file is not exactly as entered, make changes as required, referring to the edit commands in Chap. 11. When the text is correct, exit EDLIN and save the file by responding to the EDLIN command prompt (*_) with **E**:

*E <return>

When the preceding menu file is loaded into a drawing file, the standard Acad.mnu file will be replaced by this Border.mnu file. Lines 2 and 3 of the file are used only to display the file name.

When line 4 is selected, the drawing limits will be set to 0,0 and 280,215. The ZOOM and All commands are then called to set the monitor to the limits. The plus sign indicates that the macro carries onto the next line, line 5.

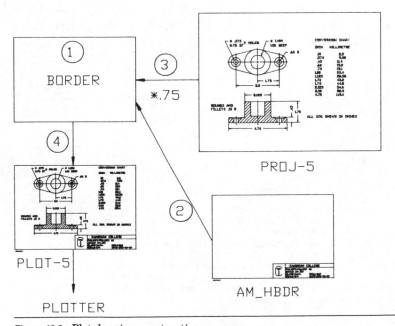

Figure 12.3 Plot drawing construction sequence.

On line 5 (which is a continuation of line 4) the INSERT command is invoked and the block file Am-hbdr is inserted with a base point of 0,0 and the default x and y multipliers of 1. The default rotation angle of 0 is used.

Line 6 is used to INSERT another drawing into the border drawing. You will be asked for the name of the drawing to be inserted and the insertion point, which is usually 0,0. Next, you will be asked for "X scale factor:." Assuming that the limits on the plot drawing are set to inches for Imperial measurement drawings and millimeters for SI (metric) measurement drawings, the value you are to enter is the scale factor listed in Table 12.1.

Since the border is created in metric (millimeter) units, if an imperial unit drawing is inserted, the scale will have to include a conversion factor to convert the drawing units to millimeters. A drawing done in inches and plotted using a 3/4 scale would then have a scale factor of 3/4 * 25.4 = 19.05.

Line 7 calls the MOVE command and allows you to move the entity inserted into the border drawing into a more satisfactory position. The inserted drawing is a single entity.

Line 8 calls the ERASE command.

Line 9 of the drawing is required to allow you to enter a line-type scale if the inserted drawing uses layers with line types other than continuous. When a block is inserted into a drawing, the LTSCALE of the recipient drawing predominates. This makes sense if you consider a number of blocks, each with a different LTYPE scale, being inserted into a drawing. Since a drawing can have only one line-type scale, the

TABLE 12.1   Plot-Drawing Scale Factors[1]

Dwg. units	Scale	X scale factor
Feet (architect)	$\frac{1}{8}'' = 1'0''$	.0104167[2]
Feet (architect)	$\frac{1}{4}'' = 1'0''$	.0208333[2]
Inches (decimal)	$\frac{3}{4}$	.75
Feet (engineer)	$1'' = 50'0''$	.0016667[3]
Meters (decimal)	1:100	10[4]
Millimeters (decimal)	1:100	.01

[1]See Table B.1 for a complete listing of plot-drawing scale factors.

[2]When using AutoCAD's architectural units, the drawing units are always inches even though the coordinates are displayed on the monitor in feet and inches. The scale factor is then 1/(N*12). For 1/8 in = 1 ft the scale factor is 1/(8*12) = 0.0104167.

[3]AutoCAD's engineering units are in inches even though the monitor displays feet and inches. The scale factor is then 1/(N*12). For 1 in = 50 ft the scale factor is 1/(50*12) = 0.0016667.

[4]The units used to draw the border are millimeters, and the units used for the drawing are meters. The scale 1:100 means that 1 mm = 100 mm or 1 mm = 0.1 m. The scale factor is then 1/0.1 = 10.

recipient LTSCALE governs. After the blocks are inserted, you will then have to enter an LTSCALE that will govern for the entire drawing.

Line 12 of the menu is used to call the SAVE command and then to request keyboard input of the file name. The file name entered is to be a *new* drawing name that is used to store the plot drawing. It should be preceded with a B: if the drawing is to be stored on the disk in drive B or a path if a fixed disk is used. When the file name is entered, the QUIT command is automatically called, and Y is entered automatically in response to "Really want to discard all changes to drawing?" This line saves the border and title block under a new file name and exits Auto-CAD without changing the current file.

Note: Lines 10 and 11 are used to plot or printer plot the drawing. The procedure to be followed when plotting is discussed in Sec. 12.7.

Do not type the END command to end a drawing when using the Border.dwg file. This file is to be used each time you prepare a plot drawing, and you do not want to save any other drawings on this file. Line 12 *must* be used to exit this drawing and save a border drawing on file.

Line 12 will create a slight problem if the plot drawing you are working on was previously saved. In such cases, when the SAVE command is entered, the sequence is as follows (assuming you are saving a drawing named Plot-5 on drive B):

```
SAVE <return> File name: b:plot-5 <return> A drawing with this file name
exists. Do you want to replace it <N>:
```

At this point in line 12 AutoCAD reads "QUIT" from the macro and responds with:

```
Please answer yes or no:
```

It then reads the "Y" from the macro and replaces the current file with the new file—but the macro is now finished and the QUIT command was not executed. To exit the drawing you will have to type in QUIT. Since the drawing was saved, you may exit without resaving it.

Line 13 is the heading for a Button menu. The pick button is unchanged but buttons 1 and 2 are RETURN (;) and CANCEL (^C^C), respectively.

12.5.2 Creating Border.dwg file

Boot up AutoCAD and start a new drawing called **B:Border**. Limits and units do not have to be set since this file is to be used only as an initialization file for other border files. Change the menu to the Border menu file developed in Sec. 12.5 by using:

AUTOCAD <pick> UTILITY <pick> MENU: <pick> File name: **b:border** <return>

Use the END command to save this drawing file, which will be used to create border and title block files for other drawings, and exit the drawing editor:

end <return>

12.6   Creating a Plot.dwg File

The border drawing file on the disk in drive B is designed to create drawing "plot-files" which contain the drawing border, title block, and scaled drawing file(s). The procedure used to insert that drawing into the border drawing and create a plot drawing is illustrated in the following example.

12.6.1   Plot Proj-5.dwg with a border and title block

Select item 2, "Edit an Existing Drawing," from the main menu to edit drawing B:Border.

Select the A-HOR-M command from the menu. AutoCAD will then proceed to draw the border and title block and will prompt you for data for each variable attribute.

Drawing Proj-5 was drawn in inch units and should be plotted at a 3/4 scale to fit on an 8.5- by 11-in A-size sheet. When the scale is requested in the attributes, enter 3/4.

When inserting the Proj-5.dwg drawing into the Border.dwg drawing, you must take into account that Border.dwg was drawn using millimeter units; therefore, the scale becomes 3/4 * 25.4 = 19.05. Select INSERT from the menu:

INSERT <pick> Block name: **b:proj-5** <return> Insertion point: **0,0** <return>
X–Scale factor <1>: **19.05** <return> Y–Scale factor <19.05>: <return> Rotation angle: **0** <return> <return>

Use the MOVE command to put the entity into a better location on the drawing. The entire Proj-5 drawing is now a single entity since it was inserted as a block. To move it using the MOVE command, use the following:

MOVE <pick> Select objects: **l** (Last) <return> <return> Base point or displacement: Digitize a convenient point on the Proj-5 entity to act as a first point during the move. <pick> Second point: Digitize a point on the monitor where you would like the first point to be moved to. <pick>

The entire Proj-5 entity will now be moved from the first to the second point. You can move the entity as often as desired. The DRAG command may be entered in response to "Second point:," and the entity may be dragged into location.

12.7 Plotting a Plot Drawing

Use the PLOT command to plot the drawing. The scale to be selected is 1:1 since the drawing was scaled when it was inserted into the plot drawing on the monitor. The plot sequence is as follows:

```
PLOT <pick>
```

The following prompt is displayed:

```
What to plot-Display, Extents, Limits, or Window: d (Display) <return>
```

AutoCAD will list the plot specifications which were illustrated in Sec. 7.2, and the following prompt is displayed:

```
Do you want to change anything?: y <return>
```

AutoCAD now displays the pen options available:

```
Do you want to change any of these parameters?<N>: <return>
Write plot to a file? <N>: n <return>
Size units (Inches or Millimetres): m <return>
Plot origin in millimetres <0.00,0.00>: <return>
Plot size (Max,?) or Width,Height (in millimetres): 280,215 <return>
Rotate 2D plots 90 degrees clockwise?<N>: <return>
Pen width <default>: <return>
Adjust area fill boundaries for pen width?<N>: <return>
Specify scale by entering:
Plotted millimetres=Drawing units or Fit or?: 1=1 <return>
Position paper in plotter:
Press ENTER to continue or S to Stop for hardware changes: <return>
```

The drawing will be plotted as specified. Select SAVE-END from the menu to save the file. AutoCAD will prompt you to enter a file name. Enter a new name along with a drive specification; for instance, to create a border for the drawing in Chap. 5, use the name B:Plot-5. AutoCAD will save the file and exit to the main menu. *Never type the END command when using the border drawing.* If you use the END command, the drawing which was inserted into the border drawing will be saved in the Border.dwg file, and you will not be able to use that file to create borders for other drawings. Always exit by using the SAVE-END command from the Border.mnu created, which calls the QUIT command to exit.

The drawing cannot be modified on the plot drawing since it was inserted onto that drawing as a block. If the drawing is to be modified, it is changed on the original drawing and the block definition is updated, following the procedure illustrated in Sec. 10.6.

12.7.1   Plot Proj-6.dwg

Use a similar procedure to plot the Proj-6.dwg drawing. That drawing was done in meter units and will be inserted into a plot drawing using a scale of 1 mm = 300 mm. The x and y insertion scale factor will be 1/300 * 1000 = 3.33 (since the drawing was in meters and the border is in millimeters, the 1000 multiplier converts the drawing units from meters to millimeters). Insert Proj-6.dwg into Border.dwg and use the MOVE command to locate it into position.

12.7.2   LTSCALE

When a block is inserted into a drawing, it uses the line-type scale (LTSCALE) of the current drawing. This is because there is only one LTSCALE setting for a drawing. After Proj-6 is inserted into the border drawing, the line-type scale is set using the LTSCALE command in our menu since different line types were used for layers in the drawing. The LTYPE scale used in Sec. 6.7 was 5.7. This value must be multiplied by the x, y insertion scale factor of 3.33, giving an LTSCALE of 19:

```
LTSCALE <return> New scale factor <1>: 19 <return>
```

The drawing will be regenerated with the new line-type scale.

Use the PLOT command to plot the drawing. You must select the option to change the plot specifications. The pen selection is as follows:

Layer color	Pen no.	Line type	Pen speed	
1 (red)	1	0	36	Pen number <1>: 2 <return>
1 (red)	2	0	36	Line type <0>: c5 <return>
5 (blue)	2	0	36	Pen number <2>: 1 <return>
5 (blue)	1	0	36	Line type <0>: c7 <return>
7 (white)	1	0	36	Pen number <1>: 3 <return>
7 (white)	3	0	36	Line type <0>: x <return>

The size units for the plotted drawing are millimeters. The plot origin is 0,0 and the plot size is 280 by 215.

Plot the drawing using a scale of 1 = 1.

12.7.3   Assignment

Create a border and title block for a B-size (11 by 17 in) drawing in both SI and Imperial units. The easiest way to do this is to edit the Border.dwg already created. Erase the borders—do *not* erase the title block. Use the BLOCK command to save the title block as a block with the insertion point at the lower right hand corner of the title block (name it **Title**). Write it to file using the WBLOCK command. Use the QUIT command to exit the drawing without changing the original Border drawing.

To create the Imperial units' B-size block, begin a new drawing named **B:Bi_Hbdr** (B size, Imperial units, horizontal border). Set the limits at 0,0 and 17,11. Make a new layer named **border** and set it as the current layer. Draw the border in. Plot the drawing and use the MOVE command to get the border in the proper location. When you are satisfied, insert the title block preceding the file name with an asterisk to transcribe its separate entities, as follows:

INSERT <**pick**> Block name: **b:title** <**return**> Insertion point: <**Ctrl-C**> <**re-turn**> Block name: ***title*** <**return**> Insertion point: **int** <**return**> of Place the intersection target over the lower right corner of the border. <**return**>

Since the original title block was drawn in SI units, the insertion scale will have to be 0.0394 (1/25.4) to convert the block to Imperial units.

Use the END command to exit the drawing and save it to file. It will later be inserted as a block from the Border drawing. Since it was saved as a drawing, its insertion point will be the lower left corner.

Add appropriate lines to the Border.mnu file, using EDLIN, to expand the file for the B-size drawing. Edit the Border drawing to incorporate the updated menu.

Now, create a SI B-size border and title block file and an A-size Imperial unit border and title block file, adding them both to the Border.mnu file on the Border drawing.

Chapter 13

Oblique Pipe Drawing

OBJECTIVE *Construct a custom menu and pipe fitting blocks to facilitate the drafting of an oblique piping drawing.*

DRAWING *The final pipe drawing is illustrated in Fig. 13.1. The drawing will be done using a custom menu, and will be made up of blocks, illustrated in Fig. 13.2. In this chapter the drawing instructions are not as specific as they were in previous chapters. A number of hints are given, and you should read the entire chapter before attempting the drawing. Review the menu, Pipe.mnu, and Sec. 13.1.1, "Menu Analysis," together.*

This chapter does not demonstrate the most efficient way to use CAD for piping drawings. For instance, pipe flanges are not inserted with the pipe elbows and have to be added separately. If you are drafting piping drawings on a continuous basis, you should create a block drawing for each of the pipe fittings and include in the block drawing all of the components (flanges, etc.) of that particular fitting. This project demonstrates how to build entities, such as pipe fittings, from a combination of block and menu macros. It also provides more drawing practice than would a similar project which used complete blocks for all of the pipe fittings.

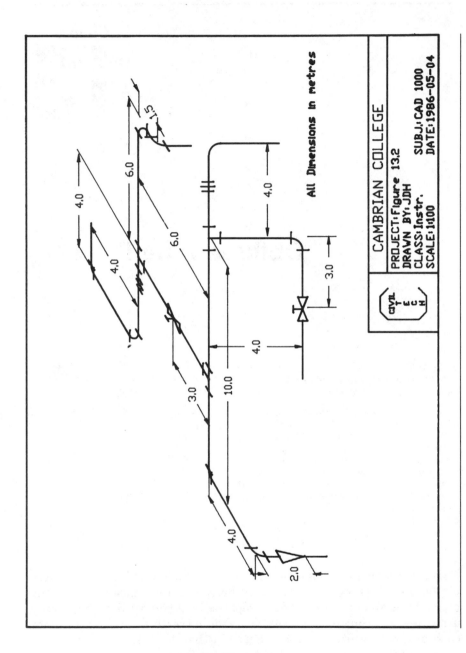

Figure 13.1 Project 13, pipe drawing.

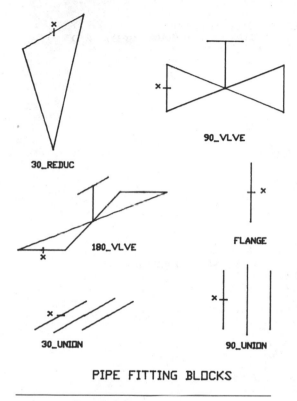

PIPE FITTING BLOCKS

Figure 13.2 Pipe fitting components.

13.1 Custom Menu

Boot up MS-DOS and insert the drawing data disk in drive B. Load **EDLIN** and start an AutoCAD menu file called **Pipe.mnu** as follows:

    C:\<edlin b:pipe.mnu <return>

Review the EDLIN commands in Sec. 11.6, and create the following file. The number and colon at the beginning of each line are part of the EDLIN prompt and are not to be typed in. The backslashes (\) in the file are menu-embedded keyboard input commands (see Sec. 11.4.1). Note that a space is used to represent menu-embedded Enter key commands, rather than a semicolon (;), in most of the macros—it is easier to type this way, and both the space and semicolon are acceptable to AutoCAD.

    1: ***Screen
    2: [MAIN_MNU]

```
 3: LIMITS
 4: [DIMSCALE]DIM DIMASO off DIMSCALE \EXIT
 5: [ISO _MODE]SNAP STYLE ISOMETRIC \ISOPLANE RIGHT GRID
 6: [STD _MODE]SNAP STYLE STANDARD \GRID
 7: [DRAW]$S=DRAW
 8: [EDIT]$S=EDIT
 9: [DIM]$S=DIM
10:
11: ZOOM W
12: ZOOM A
13: ZOOM P
14:
15: LAYER
16: PRPLOT
17: PLOT
18: SAVE
19: QUIT
20: END
21: **DRAW
22: LINE
23: endpoint
24: intersect
25: [POINT]SETVAR PDMODE 1 POINT \SETVAR PRDMODE Ø
26: [30_ELBOW]FILLET R .25 FILLET
27: [90_ELBOW]FILLET R .5 FILLET
28: [120ELBOW]FILLET R .8 FILLET
29: [30_REDUC]INSERT B:30_REDUC \\1 0
30: [90_VLVE ]INSERT B:90_VLVE \\1 0
31: [180_VLVE]INSERT B:180_VLVE \1 1 0
32: [0_FLG ]INSERT B:FLANGE \1 1 90
33: [30_FLG ]INSERT B:FLANGE \1 1 -60
34: [90_FLG ]INSERT B:FLANGE \1 1 0
35: [30_UNION]INSERT B:30_UNION \1 1 0
36: [90_UNION]INSERT B:90_UNION \1 1 0
37:
38: [DIM ]$S=DIM
39: [MAIN_MNU]$S=SCREEN
40: [EDIT ]$S=EDIT
41: **EDIT
42: ERASE
43: ERASE L;;
44: ERASE W
45: OOPS
46: BREAK
47:
48: [DIM ]$S=DIM
49: [DRAW] $S=DRAW
50: [MAIN_MNU]$S=SCREEN
51:
52: ZOOM W
53: ZOOM A
54: ZOOM P
55:
56: REDRAW
57:
58:
59:
60:
61: **DIM
62: [EXT_LINE]LINE \ @1<\^C
63: endpoint
64: intersect
```

```
65: near
66: [ALIG_DIM]DIM DIMSE1 ON DIMSE2 ON ALIGNED \\@ \EXIT
67: [H_DIM_ + X]DIM DIMSE1 OFF DIMSE2 OFF +
68: HORIZONTAL \\\\EXIT
69: [V_DIM_ + X]DIM DIMSE1 OFF DIMSE2 OFF VERTICAL \\\\EXIT
70: [H_DIM_-X]DIM DIMSE1 ON DIMSE2 ON HORIZONTAL +
71: \\@\ EXIT
72: [V_DIM_-X]DIM DIMSE1 ON DIMSE2 ON VERTICAL;\\@ \EXIT
73: TEXT
74: 'ZOOM D
75: 'ZOOM P
76: [MAIN_MNU]$S=SCREEN
77: [EDIT ]$S=EDIT
78: [DRAW ]$S=DRAW
79:
80: [ISO_MODE]SNAP STYLE ISOMETRIC \ISOPLANE RIGHT GRID
81: [STD_MODE]SNAP STYLE STANDARD \GRID
82:
83: ***BUTTONS
84: ;
85: ^C^C
86: CTRL-C
```

The Ctrl-C in line 86 is used to exit the I (insert) command and is not part of the menu (it will appear as ^C on the monitor). Review the menu you typed in, and make sure that it matches the one above. If you have to make corrections to your menu, review the procedure in Chap. 11.

When the menu is complete and correct, press **E** to exit from EDLIN.

13.1.1 Menu analysis

The menu contains a main menu and three submenus. Commands on a line are normally separated with a blank space, which invokes the Enter key. When the Enter key is not required, for instance, after the embedded keyboard input \, a blank space is not used. The following is a summary of the function and format required for commands in each line of the menu:

Line 1. When submenus are used, the first line of the main menu must begin with ***SCREEN.

Line 2. This line is a screen heading only.

Line 3. Used to call the LIMIT command.

Line 4. DIMSCALE will be displayed in the menu. This macro invokes DIM and DIMASO commands to turn associative dimensioning off. Then DIMSCALE is invoked and the embedded keyboard input \ returns control to the user to allow input of the dimension scale. The EXIT command is used to exit from the DIM command. Note that there is no space between \ and EXIT. Normally the space is used between commands to invoke the Enter key. In this case the user will press Enter after typing in the dimension scale.

Lines 5 and 6. These lines are used to set either the standard or isometric mode. The embedded keyboard input \ allows the user to enter the snap spacing. The user will also be requested to enter the grid spacing after the GRID command is invoked.

Line 7. Calls the DRAW submenu (line 21).

Line 8. Calls the EDIT submenu (line 41).

Line 9. Calls the DIM submenu (line 61).

Line 10. This is a blank line. The main menu and each submenu have 20 lines. If space is available, blank lines are used in the menu to separate groups and clarify the menu listing.

Lines 11–13. Calls ZOOM.

Lines 15–20. Standard AutoCAD commands.

Line 21. DRAW submenu heading.

Line 22. Calls LINE command.

Lines 23 and 24. Used to invoke a temporary object snap.

Line 25. Invokes the SETVAR command to set a system variable PDMODE to 1 (see App. F.4), and invokes the POINT command. This command is useful when drawing. For instance, if an item is to be drawn a specific distance from an intersection, the POINT command is invoked, followed by the INT (intersect) object snap command. The user then places the object snap target over the intersection and presses the Enter key. The last position of the cursor will have been the intersection where the point was drawn. A relative distance<angle entry may then be used from the intersection to locate the position of the item to be drawn.

Lines 26–28. The pipes are initially drawn from point to point without elbows. Elbows are later inserted using these three macros, which use the FILLET command to draw the elbows. When the angle between the pipes at the elbow is less than 90 degrees, a smaller fillet radius is used to reduce the cutoff at the intersection for the fillet. Try a .5R fillet with a 30-degree pipe intersection to see why. Note the use of a larger fillet radius (0.8) for the larger 120-degree elbow. These macros do not draw the flanges at the elbows. Flanges are input with the FLG command later.

Lines 29–31. Used to insert the pipe valves (blocks which will be created later in this chapter). When the command is called, the user will be asked to enter the insertion location for the block (by the first embedded input command \ in the macro). The user will next be asked to enter the *x* scale by the second \ in the macro). Normally a value of 1 is entered by the user for the *x* scale. If the user wishes to insert the valve block in the reverse direction to which the block was originally drawn, −1 is entered for the *x* scale.

Lines 32–34.   Used to insert pipe flanges. Note that only one block called Flange is created (Fig. 13.2). This block is then inserted at varying angles (90, −60, and 0 degrees), as required. When the block is called, the user will be requested to enter the insertion location. The macro specifies the *x* and *y* scales as 1; it also specifies the specific angle of insertion for each pipe flange.

Lines 35 and 36.   Used to insert the pipe unions.

Lines 38–40.   Used to call the submenus.

Line 41.   EDIT submenu heading.

Line 61.   DIM submenu heading.

Line 62.   AutoCAD always draws dimension extension lines and dimension lines at right angles to each other. In isometric drawings this is often not desired. Lines 66, 70, and 72 in the menu will draw dimension lines without extension lines (see below for the discussion of those lines). Prior to those lines the user draws the extension lines with line 62, which invokes the LINE command, requests the first point (\), inserts the @1 relative distance, and requests the user to enter the angle of the extension line (the second \). Each time a line is drawn with the LINE command, AutoCAD remains in control of the LINE command so that the line may be continued. The LINE command is exited with Ctrl-C, which is embedded in the menu line as ^C. The EXIT command will not cancel the LINE command at this stage.

Lines 63 to 65.   Used to call temporary object snaps.

Line 66.   Calls DIM, turns on DIMSE1 (DIMension Suppress Extension line 1), which suppresses the first extension line, turns on DIMSE2 to suppress the second extension line, calls the ALIGNED dimension command, requests the location of the first point (where the start arrow is to be placed), requests the end point, inserts a relative @ for the location of the dimension line (same location as last point), returns to the user for input of the dimension, and then exits the DIM command. If extension lines are required, the user adds them to the drawing with the EXT_LINE command prior to using this command.

Line 67.   Used to add horizontal dimensions with extension lines to the drawing. Calls DIM, turns off the suppressant of the extension lines 1 and 2, and invokes the HORIZONTAL dimension command. The plus (+) sign indicates that the macro continues on the next line, line 68.

Line 68. This is a continuation of the macro on line 67. The first backslash (\) returns control to the user for keyboard input of the location of the first extension line. The next three keyboard inputs (\\\) are used to get the input of the second extension line location, the dimension line location, and the dimension text. The EXIT command is used to exit from the DIM command. Note that there are no embedded spaces where the keyboard input is requested since the user must enter the data and then press the Enter key.

Line 69. Used to add vertical dimensions with extension lines. The format is similar to line 67.

Line 70. Adds horizontal dimensions without extension lines. The format is similar to line 66.

Line 72. Adds vertical dimension lines without extension lines.

Lines 74 and 75. Transparent zoom commands.

Line 83. The heading for a button menu.

13.2 Pipe Drawing

Boot up AutoCAD and start a new drawing named **B:Proj-13.** Insert the pipe menu using:

AutoCAD <**pick**> UTILITY <**pick**> MENU <**pick**> File name: **b:pipe** <**return**>

Set the drawing limits as **0,0** and **24,16.** Type units to call the UNIT command (it is not in our menu) and set decimal units with one digit to the right of the decimal. Press **F1** to return to the drawing editor screen.

Invoke the LAYER command and create the following new layers:

Name	Color	Line type
0	White	Continuous
Pipe	White	Continuous
Dim	Red	Continuous

13.3 Pipe Fitting Blocks

Invoke the ZOOM <return> W command and zoom in on a window with the coordinates **0,0** and **4,4.**

Draw the blocks illustrated in Fig. 13.2. The reducers and valves are drawn to fit into a 1-unit gap in the pipe line. The short line located beside *x* in the block diagrams is used to indicate the insertion point for the block and is *not* to be drawn as part of the block.

Use either the isometric or standard mode as you see fit to draw each of the blocks. You may find it best to alternate from one mode to the other while drawing. Set GRID at 0.1 and SNAP at 0.05 to facilitate the drawing of the blocks.

When drawing each block, use the POINT command to locate the cursor at a construction position. Then use relative distance<angle commands to draw the block lines. After each block is drawn, it is saved with the BLOCK command and selected using the W (window) command.

Review the discussion on blocks in Chap. 10. Unless the blocks are to be inserted into other drawings, they do not have to be written to file with the WBLOCK command. The blocks are to be drawn on layer 0 so that they will be inserted into the current layer when used.

13.4   Piping Drawing

Invoke ZOOM <return> A to zoom on all of the drawing. Set the LAYER to **Pipe**.

Complete the oblique piping drawing illustrated in Fig. 13.1, using the commands in the Pipe menu. The following hints will be helpful:

- When drawing the pipes, alternate between the isometric and standard modes as you see fit. Use a snap spacing of 0.05 and a grid of 0.5. Use relative distance<angle commands to draw the pipe line (@dist < angle). The isometric lines are at 30 degrees to the horizontal.

- Do not draw the elbows until the pipe lines and dimensions have been drawn.

- Insert the elbows prior to their flanges. To locate the flanges, use the "ENDpoint" object snap and set the target near the end of the pipe line framing into the elbow. The object snap will locate the end of the line framing into the elbow.

- Insert the reducers and valves while drawing the pipes. When the end of the pipe line being drawn is at the location of a reducer or valve, use Ctrl-C to exit the line command, and insert the reducer or valve by selecting it from the screen menu. The insertion point is entered by using the relative @ command (last point). After the reducer or valve is inserted, the pipe line is continued by invoking the LINE command. Since all of the pipe fitting blocks were drawn 1 unit long, the start point of the pipe line is 1 unit away from the insertion point of the reducer or valve lock. The line start point is then entered using the relative distance<angle command (@1<angle). Actually you could leave any size gap for the block and then use the DRAG command

when asked for the block x and y distances to make the block fit the gap.

- If blocks are inserted incorrectly, use the ERASE L command to delete them and then reinsert them.
- Unions are inserted after all the pipes are drawn.
- Tee flanges are drawn by using the POINT and INT (intersect) commands to locate the cursor on the intersection. Flanges may then be inserted 0.5 units from the intersection in each direction using the relative distance<angle command (@1<angle).
- If the pipe lines extend beyond the drawing limits, the limits will have to be reset.
- If you wish to move the pipe drawing on the monitor, type move to invoke the MOVE command and relocate the entire drawing as desired. Use a window to designate the items to be moved.

13.5   Dimensioning

Set the LAYER to **Dim**.

DIMSCALE is calculated to provide 3-mm text when the drawing is plotted on a 280- by 215-mm sheet, using a scale of 1:100. Since the pipe line was drawn in meter units, the text height of 3 mm is used as 0.003 meters (3/1000). The text height, h, to be used on the monitor is then determined as:

$$1/100 * h = 0.003 \qquad \text{gives } h = 0.3$$

DIMSCALE is calculated by Eq. 4.2:

$$\text{DIMSCALE} * 0.18 = h$$
$$\text{DIMSCALE} * 0.18 = 0.3 \qquad \text{gives DIMSCALE} = 1.7$$

Set DIMSCALE as 1.7.

The dimensions are added to the drawing using the Dim submenu. Dimensions that require extension lines, where the extension lines and dimension lines are perpendicular to the object being dimensioned, are drawn using the V_DIM_+X or H_DIM_+X commands in the menu.

Dimensions that are drawn between pipes require no extension lines. Those dimension lines are drawn using the ALIG_DIM or H_DIM_-X or V_DIM_-X commands.

Dimensions that require extension lines which are not perpendicular to the dimension line are drawn using the EXT_LINE and ALIG_DIM commands in lines 62 and 66, respectively. The EXT_LINE command is used to draw 1-unit-long extension lines at any angle. After the extension lines are drawn, the ALIG_DIM command is used to add an aligned dimension line and dimension text. Note that DIMSE1 and DIMSE2 are both turned on in line 62 so that extension lines (which would be perpendicular to the dimension lines) are not drawn.

When dimensioning without extension lines, the NEAR object snap in line 65 is used to make it easier to snap onto a line *nearest to the cursor.*

A *transparent* ZOOM with the Dynamic option (Sec. 5.7) is used in line 74. Transparent commands, introduced with Ver. 2.62, allow the entry of commands such as ZOOM, PAN, REDRAW, and HELP while another command is in progress. Transparent commands are invoked by preceding the command with an apostrophe. When asked to pick a dimension point in a crowded area of the drawing, selecting 'ZOOM D from the menu will invoke a dynamic zoom without exiting the DIM command. Use the dynamic zoom to zoom on the area, select the point, and then select ZOOM P (line 75) to return to the previous screen. Try typing other transparent commands, such as 'REDRAW, while another command is in progress.

When dimensions are placed outside the extension line, use the ERASE L command to erase the dimension and then use the TEXT command to write the dimension in between the extension lines.

When all dimensions have been added, check the drawing extents and modify the drawing limits as required. Remember to use ZOOM < return > A to reset the drawing to the new limits if the limits have been modified.

When the drawing is complete, use the END command to save the drawing and return to the main menu.

Prepare a plot-drawing by using the Border file, as outlined in Chap. 12. The drawing scale is to be 1:100 if it is plotted on an A-size sheet (280 by 215 mm).

When inserting Proj-13 onto the border sheet, the x and y multipliers are calculated for a scale of 1:100 with the drawing in meters and the border drawing in millimeters. This gives a multiplier of 10 (1/100 * 1000 = 10).

Plot the drawing using different color pens, or different nib widths, for the pipe and dimension lines.

Multiscale Drawings

OBJECTIVE *Create a "proto-drawing" to be used as a preliminary drawing border; plot a building floor plan to one scale and, on the same sheet, plot different scale details maintaining uniform text and dimension variable sizes.*

DRAWING *The final plotted drawing is illustrated in Fig. 14.1. The steps required to complete that drawing are outlined in the following text.*

14.1 Scaling Drawings

When drawing with AutoCAD, items are drawn full scale using the drawing editor. The scaling takes place during the plotting of the drawing or on a plot drawing as outlined in Chap. 12.

To create a multiscale drawing, the items for each scale will have to be drawn full size on a separate drawing and later inserted into a final plot drawing using the scale desired for that item.

The procedure is illustrated in Fig. 14.2, where entities 1 and 2 are to reside on the same final drawing, but each is to be drawn using a different scale. Entities 1 and 2 are first drawn full scale as separate drawing files. In the final hard copy drawing, entity 1 is to be drawn at a scale of 1/4 in = 1 ft 0 in and entity 2 is to be drawn at a scale of 1/2 in = 1 ft

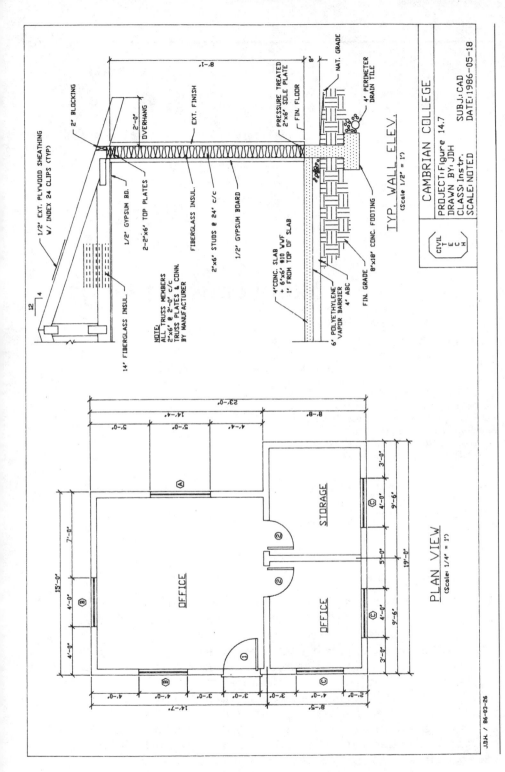

Figure 14.1 Project 8, office plan.

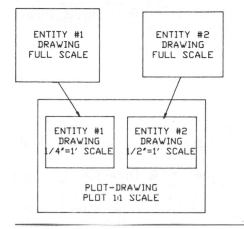

Figure 14.2 Multiscale drawing construction.

0 in. This is done by loading the Border.dwg file and inserting entity 1 using an x and y factor of 0.020833 [1/(4 * 12)] and entity 2 using an x and y factor of 0.0416667 [1/(2 * 12)] into the drawing. The drawing is then saved with a new file name and plotted using a scale of 1:1.

The scale factors are illustrated in Table 12.1 and Table B.1 in Appendix B.

You also have to ensure that the text height, dimension variables, and hatch scale factors are set for each entity drawing to provide a consistent size on the composite drawing. If the text height desired on the plotted drawing is 1/8 in, the text height on drawing entity 1, which is to be plotted at a scale of 1/4 in = 1 ft 0 in, will have to be 6 in [1/(4 * 12) * H = 1/8]. The text height on drawing entity 2, which is to be plotted at a scale of 1/2 in = 1 ft 0 in, will have to be 12 in [1/(2 * 12) * H = 1/8]. This same ratio must be used for the dimension variables and the hatch scale.

14.2 Creating a Proto-Drawing

The purpose of the proto-drawing is to provide a preliminary drawing sheet on which to develop drawings that will later be inserted into a plot-drawing. The proto-drawing dimensions are the reverse of the plot drawing, i.e., the limits are based on the full-scale size of the object. The title block and border is inserted into the drawing, providing a real-size drawing area for the object.

This project will be drawn on a B-size sheet (17 by 11 in) with a drawing area assumed to be 15 by 9.5 in, allowing for borders. For the drawing to be plotted using an architectural scale of 1/4 in = 1 ft 0 in, the limits will have to be set at 0,0 and 720,456 (15 * 4 / 1 * 12 and 9.5 * 4 / 1 * 12).

A Proto.mnu will be created to set the drawing size, draw the border, and insert the title block.

14.2.1   Create the Title.dwg block

The title block will be adopted from the title block created in Chap. 12. Boot AutoCAD and edit an existing drawing named **B:Am___hbdr** (which you drew in Chap. 12).

Use the ERASE command to erase the outside border lines by selecting each of them using the cursor.

Create a new layer Border 1. Zoom in on the title block and then use the CHANGE command as follows to transfer the title block to layer Border1:

ZOOM <**pick**> W <**return**> Place a window around the title block.

Ver. 2.1

EDIT <**pick**> CHANGE <**pick**> Select objects or Window or Last : **w** <**return**> Place a window around the title block. <**return**> Change point (or Layer or Elevation) : **1** (Last) <**return**> New layer : **border1** <**return**>

Ver. 2.5 to Release 10

EDIT <**pick**> CHANGE <**pick**> Select objects : **w (Window)** <**return**> Place a window around the title block. <**return**> Properties/<Change point>: **p** (Properties) <**return**> Change what property (Color/Elev/LAyer/LType/Thickness)? **la** (LAyer) <**return**> New layer : **border1** <**return**>

All versions.   Set the current layer to **Border1**. Convert the title into a block and write the block to a disk file:

BLOCKS <**pick**> BLOCK: <**pick**> Block name (or ?) : **title** <**return**> Insertion base point : Digitize the bottom right corner of the title block. <**pick**> Select objects : **w** <**return**> Place a window around the entire title block. <**return**>
WBLOCK <**pick**> File name : **b:title** <**return**> Block name : **=** <**return**>

Use the QUIT command to exit AutoCAD (do *not* use END).

14.2.2   Create the Proto.mnu file

Exit to DOS and create the following file using EDLIN:

```
C:\>edlin b:proto.mnu
1: ***screen
2: [-PROTO-]
3: [-MENU-]
4: [B_HOR-I]layer;new;border1;set;border1;;+
5: limits;0,0;15,9.5;zoom;all;+
```

```
 6: line;0,0;15,0;15,9.5;0,9.5;c;insert;b:title;15,0;+
 7: 0.039;;;\\\\\\\\\\\\block;b2;0,0;c;0,0;15,9.5;;$s=ib
 8: [acad_mnu]menu;acad;
 9: quit
10: end
11: save
12:
13:
14:
15:
16:
17: **ib
18: [-SCALE-]
19: [-arch-]
20. [1/8" =1']limits;0,0;1440,912;insert;b2,0,0;90;;;
21: [1/4" =1']limits;0,0;720,456;insert;b2;0,0;48;;;
22: [1/2" =1']limits;0,0;360,228;insert;b2;0,0;24;;;
23: [3/4" =1']limits;0,0;240,152;insert;b2;0,0;16;;;
24: [1" = 1']limits;0,0;180,114;insert;b2;0,0;12;;;
25: [1:N ]limits;0,0;\insert;b2;0,0;\;
26:
27: [ROOTMENU]$s=screen
28:
29: [ZOOM-ALL]zoom;all;layer;set;0;;menu;acad;
```

The function of each menu line is as follows:

Line 4. Creates a new layer named Border1, sets it as the current layer, and exits from the LAYER command. The plus sign (+) indicates that the macro continues on the next line.

Line 5. This is a continuation of the macro on line 4. The LIMIT command is called and the drawing limits are set at 0,0 and 15,9.5 (the drawing area available on a 17- by 11-in sheet). The ZOOM <return> A (all) commands are invoked to set the monitor to the drawing limits. The plus sign extends the macro to line 6.

Line 6. This is a continuation of the macro from lines 4 and 5. The LINE command is entered and a line is drawn around the perimeter of the screen. Next the INSERT command is invoked and the B:Title block is inserted with an insertion point of 15,0. The plus symbol extends the macro to line 7.

Line 7. The inserted block's x scale is set as 0.039 (conversion from millimeters to inches = 1/25.4). The second semicolon enters the y scale = x scale, followed by another semicolon to accept the default rotation of 0. The 12 backslashes are required to accept keyboard input of 6 attribute values in the title block plus a verification of each. The drawing is then saved as a block named B2, and transfer is made to a submenu named Ib.

Line 20. This line is in submenu Ib. The drawing limits are changed to 0,0 and 1440,912. The limits are based on a drawing area of 15 by 9.5

in and a scale of 1/8 in = 1 ft 0 in. The *x* limit is then (15 * 8 / 1 * 12) 1440 in, and the *y* limit is (9.5 * 8 / 1 * 12) 912 in. Block B2 is inserted into the drawing at coordinate 0,0 with an *x* and *y* scale factor of 96 (8 / 1 * 12).

Line 25.   Line 25 is similar to line 20; however, the user is required to enter the drawing limits and the scale factor for block B2.

Line 29.   When a scale is selected, such as in line 20, the drawing limits are changed, and block B2 is inserted into the drawing. The drawing will then have to be zoomed to the new limits. This line activates a ZOOM <return> A (all) command, sets the current drawing layer to layer 0, and then loads the standard Acad menu.

14.2.3   Creating the drawing

When creating a proto-drawing, first begin a new drawing from the AutoCAD main menu. Then, from the AutoCAD drawing editor, use the MENU command to load the Proto menu, which is stored on the disk in drive B:.

From the Proto menu, select the drawing size to be used (in this case B__HOR-I) and enter the attribute information when requested by the macro. The drawing border and title block will be drawn and then stored as a block B2 and consequently removed from the monitor.

Next, select the drawing scale desired from the menu.

Finally, select the ZOOM__ALL command from the menu. This macro will load the Acad menu, which will be used to continue the drawing.

14.3   Floor-Plan Drawing

Start a new drawing named **B:Proj-14a.** When the drawing editor is loaded, load the Proto.mnu file:

> UTILITY <**pick**> MENU <**pick**> File name: **b:proto** <**return**> B__HOR-I <**pick**> Enter the attribute data as requested.

The floor plan is to be drawn using a scale of 1/4 in = 1 ft 0 in. First, select that scale from the menu. Next, select the ZOOM__ALL command from the menu.

The limits were set by the proto-drawing. The units are to be set to architectural:

> SETTINGS (or UTILITY) <**pick**> UNITS <**pick**> **4** (architectural) <**return**> Denominator of smallest fraction to display (1,2,4,8,16,32 or 64): **1** <**return**> System of angle measurement: **1** (decimal degrees) <**return**> Number of fractional places for display of angles (0 to 8) : **0** <**return**>

Press the **F1** key to return to the drawing editor.

A 12- by 12-in reference grid will be set; set the cursor snap set to 2 in as follows:

```
SETTINGS (or MODE) <pick> GRID <pick> 12 <return> SNAP <pick> 2 <return>
```

Press **Ctrl-D** to turn on the cursor coordinate display. The grid may be toggled on and off with Ctrl-G, and the cursor snap may be toggled on and off with Ctrl-B.

Item	Name	Color	Line type
Object lines	Plan	White (7)	Continuous
Dimensions	Dim	Red (1)	Continuous
Text	Text	Red (1)	Continuous
Doors and windows	Details	Blue (5)	Continuous

Layer 0 is created automatically and layer Bordor1 was created when the border and title block were inserted.

Set the current layer as **Plan**.

Draw the walls of the house, as illustrated in Fig. 14.3 (the current layer should be Plan). Use the grid and the cursor snap and also observe the line lengths and angles in the coordinate display at the top of the screen.

Notice that when using the architectural or engineering mode, dimensions may be entered in inches with no units symbol displayed, i.e., 228, or in feet with the foot symbol displayed, i.e., 19′6 (do not include the inch symbol).

```
LINE <pick> Line from point: Digitize the location of the front left corner of the
building. <return> To point: @19′<0 <return> To point: @8′8<90 <return>
```

Ver. 2.1. Draw the inside wall line spaced 6 in from the outside wall line. If a mouse or digitizing puck is used, the cursor control keys may be easier to use for this input by setting the cursor on the corner of the building and moving it three steps with the fine cursor movement to get 6 in (SNAP is set at 2 in).

Ver. 2.5 to Release 10. To draw the inside wall of the house the OFFSET command will be used to offset the outside wall inward by 6 in. The corners are then trimmed by selecting Fillet 0 command:

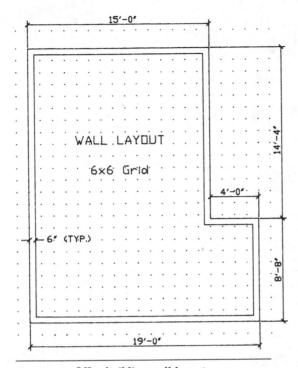

Figure 14.3 Office building wall layout.

DRAW <**pick**> OFFSET <**pick**> Offset distance or Through <0>: **6** <**return**> Select object to offset: Digitize one of the outside walls. <**pick**> Side to offset: Digitize a point on the inside of the wall selected. <**pick**> Select object to offset: Repeat the selection for each wall.

EDIT <**pick**> FILLET: <**pick**> Fillet 0 <**pick**> Select two objects: Digitize two of the inside walls at a corner. The Fillet 0 will join the two lines with a 0-radius fillet. Recall the FILLET command and repeat the procedure for each inside wall.

14.3.1 Text and dimension scales

The floor plan is to be plotted using a scale of 1/4 = 1 ft 0 in. For the plotted text to be about 3/32 in high, the text height on the monitor is calculated as follows:

$$1/(4*12) * H = 3/32 \text{ in}$$
$$H = 4.5 \text{ in} \qquad \text{use } H = 4 \text{ in}$$

The text height is made relatively small since the mechanically made letters will be quite legible and the smaller-dimension text will fit more easily into the space between the extension lines.

DIMSCALE is calculated using Eq. 4.2:

DIMSCALE * 0.18 = text height
DIMSCALE * 0.18 = 4   gives DIMSCALE = 22.22

The following dimension variables will also be set:

- DIMTAD on to place the DIMension Text Above the Dimension line

- DIMTSZ 0.09 to draw DIMension Ticks (SiZe) about 1/2 of the height of the dimension text (the default dimension text height is 0.18)

- DIMTIH off so that DIMension Text placed Inside the dimension ticks is not placed Horizontal

- DIMZIN 3 (on for Ver. 2.5) so that DIMension Zero INch editing is enabled to display 0 in for even feet dimensions (see Sec. 14.3.2)

- Ver. 2.6—Release 10: DIMASO off, to turn associative dimensioning off (see App. A1.1)

```
DIM <pick> DIM VARS <pick> next <pick> DIMSCALE <pick> 22.22 <return>
DIMTAD <pick> on <return> DIMTSZ <pick> 0.09 <return> DIMTIH <pick> off
<return> DIMZIN <return> 3 (on for Ver. 2.5) <return>
```

Press **Ctrl-C** to cancel the DIM command. Use the ZOOM <return> W (window) commands to enlarge the front wall of the building so that it will be easier to dimension.

14.3.2 Dimensioning the drawing

Set the current layer to **Dim**. When doing a large drawing, you often have to view specific sections a number of times throughout the drawing construction. The VIEW command allows you to name views and later recall those views quickly. The front wall will be named F, the back wall, B, the right side wall, R, and the left side wall, L. There should currently be an enlarged view of the front wall on the monitor:

```
AutoCAD <pick> DISPLAY <pick> VIEW <pick> ?/Delete/Restore/Save/Window:
s (Save) <return> View Name: F <return>
```

Zoom on each of the other walls and name the views. To see a view, initiate the VIEW command, enter R (restore), and then the name of the view desired. The current view should be view F (front wall).

Dimensions will be added to the building before drawing doors and

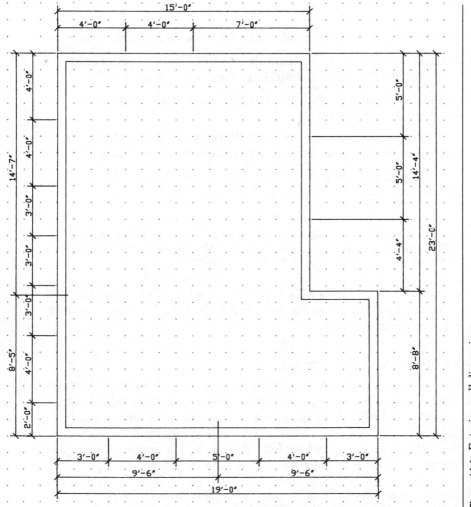

Figure 14.4 Exterior wall dimensions.

windows. This way those items are located by the dimensions and may be easily inserted as blocks. An example of the commands to draw Fig. 14.4 is:

AutoCAD <**pick**> SETTINGS or MODES <**pick**> SNAP<**pick**> **6** <**return**>
AutoCAD <**pick**> DIM <**pick**> LINEAR <**pick**> HORIZONTAL <**pick**> First extension
line origin: **int** <**return**> of Place target on lower left corner of building. <**pick**>
Second extension line origin: Digitize a 3-ft 0-in distance on the grid. <**pick**>
Dimension line location: Digitize a point three snap points, 1 ft 6 in, in front of the wall.
<**pick**> Dimension text. <3′-0″> <**return**>

For Ver. 2.1, notice that, by default, even foot dimensions would be printed without the inches. The text, therefore, is to be entered from the keyboard.

CONTINUE <**pick**> Second extension line origin: Digitize a point 4 ft 0 in to the right
using the grid as a reference. <**pick**> Dimension text <4′>: **4′-0″** <**return**> CONTINUE
<**pick**> etc.

When all dimensions are added to the front wall, use the VIEW command to view the left side wall (view name is L) for dimensioning.

If the left side wall dimensions are started from the lower left corner, you may find that AutoCAD prints the text, 2′-0″, outside of the dimension lines. If so, use Ctrl-D to exit the DIM command, then type ZOOM <return> W <return>, and zoom in on the dimension. Next, use the EDIT <return> ERASE commands to erase all of the dimension except for the lower extension line and the dimension tick that goes with it, as illustrated in Fig. 14.5.

Use ZOOM <return> L to zoom on the previous view and restart the dimensions from point a in Fig. 14.5. After the side wall dimensions are complete, use the LINE command to add the missing dimension line to the 2-ft 0-in dimension and add the text with the TEXT command.

Complete the dimensions illustrated in Fig. 14.4. Remember to adjust SNAP as required to make it easier to locate points. Also use the INT object snap and transparent zooms (see Sec. 13.5) where possible.

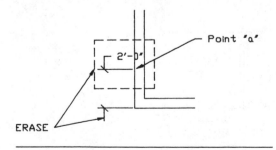

Figure 14.5 Window dimensioning modifications.

14.3.3   Window and door blocks

Set the current drawing layer to **Details**. Use the ZOOM command to enlarge an area about 6 ft 0 in by 6 ft 0 in, and draw the windows and doors illustrated in Fig. 14.6. As each is drawn, use the BLOCK command to save it as a block and, if desired, use WBLOCK to save the block to file for use in other drawings. Use the block names illustrated in Fig. 14.6. The ATTRIBUTE command will not be used to tag information to the windows and doors; however, consider the possibilities—a program could be written to read the door files and then create a door schedule, etc.

When drawing the doors and windows, use the SNAP command to alternate snap as required to facilitate the drawing.

14.3.4   Inserting the windows and doors

Set the current layer as **Plan**. When the blocks are inserted, they will retain their identity on layer Details (which they were drawn on) and will not reside on layer Plan even though that is the current drawing layer. If the blocks had been drawn on layer 0, when inserted, they would reside on the current layer (Plan).

Prior to inserting the blocks, draw the internal 6-in partition walls. Use the dimension lines and SNAP to locate the walls. Press Ctrl-O to turn on the orthogonal mode to facilitate the drawing of the horizontal and vertical wall lines. To turn the orthogonal mode off, press Ctrl-O again. Do not provide door openings yet.

An opening for the window is made and then the window is inserted into the left end of the front wall as follows:

AutoCAD <**pick**> DISPLAY <**pick**> VIEW <**pick**> ?/Delete/Restore/Save/Window:
r (Restore) <**return**> View name: **F** <**return**> _LAST_ <**pick**> ZOOM <**pick**> **w** <**return**> Place a window around the left window area. <**pick**> EDIT <**pick**> BREAK <**pick**>
Select object: Digitize the left side of the window—in line with the dimension line—on
the outside face of the wall. <**pick**> Second point (or F): **@48<0** <**return**> <**return**>
Select object: **@6<90** <**return**> Second point (or F): **@48<180** <**return**> DRAW
<**pick**> LINE <**pick**> From point: **@<return**> To point: **@6<270<return**> To

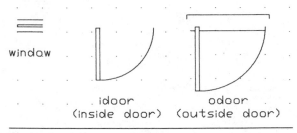

window

idoor   odoor
(inside door)   (outside door)

Figure 14.6   Window and door blocks.

point: **<return> <return>** From point: @48<0 **<return>** To point: @6<90 **<return><return>** AutoCAD **<pick>** BLOCK **<pick>** INSERT **<pick>** Block name (or?): **window <return>** Insertion point: **int** (INTersect) **<return>** of Place target over lower left corner of window opening. **<pick>** X scale factor: **4 <return>** Y scale factor (4): **1 <return>** Rotation angle <0>: **<return>** AutoCAD **<pick>** DISPLAY **<pick>** ZOOM **<pick> p** (Previous) **<return>**

The front wall is redisplayed. Add the window to the right side of the front wall. Use a similar procedure to insert all of the windows and doors. To insert a "mirror" image of the door block (see doors referenced as 2 in Fig. 14.1), use a negative value for the x scale factor when inserting the block.

14.3.4.1 Door and window reference symbol blocks.

The door reference symbol is inserted by creating a block drawing of a hexagon, with the reference symbol tagged to the block as a variable visible attribute. This information is drawn on the text layer.

Zoom on an area 4 ft 0 in by 4 ft 0 in and draw the block using the following commands:

AutoCAD **<pick>** LAYERS **<pick>** LAYER: **<pick> s** (Set) **<return>** Layer name: **text <return>** DRAW **<pick>** LINE **<pick>** From point: Digitize lower left corner of hexagon **<pick>** To point: @4<0 **<return>** To point: @4<60 **<return>** To point: @4<120 **<return>** To point: @4<180 **<return>** To point: @4<240 **<return>** To point: **c <return>**
AutoCAD **<pick>** BLOCKS **<pick>** ATTDEF **<pick>**
Attribute mode Invisible:N Constant:N Verify:N Preset:N
Enter (ICVP) to change, RETURN when done: **<return>**
Attribute tag: **A <return>** Attribute prompt: **Letter <return>** Default attribute value: **<return>** Starting point or (ACRS): **c <return>** Center point: Digitize the bottom center point of the text in the hexagon. **<pick>** Height: **4 <return>** Rotation angle: **0 <return>**
BLOCK: **<pick>** Block name: **hex <return>** Insertion point: Digitize the insertion point as the bottom center of the hex. **<pick>** Select objects: **w <return>** Place a window around the hexagon. **<return>**

If you wish, write the Hex block to file using the WBLOCK command.

Using a similar procedure, draw a circle and tag attribute information to it to create the door reference symbol block.

Insert the window and door reference blocks into the drawing.

Set the current layer to Text and add the text to the drawing.

14.3.5 Test plot-drawing and save file

Check that the floor plan is located on the drawing where you would like it located on the final plot. If not, use the MOVE command to relocate the floor.

Plot the drawing to visually ensure that the floor plan is complete. The drawing was done on the proto-drawing border for a B-size sheet (17 by 11 in, giving a plot area of 15 by 9.5 in), and is plotted using a scale of 1/4 in

= 1 ft 0 in, so the plot width is 720 in (4 * 12 * 15) and the height is 456 in (4 * 12 * 9.5). The plot scale will be 1 = 48 (or 1 = 4').

When the drawing is complete, set the current layer to Plan and *turn the Border1 layer off.* Use the END command to save the file and exit to the main menu.

14.4   Wall Detail Drawing

Start a new drawing named **B:Proj-14b**. When the drawing editor is loaded, use the MENU command to load the Proto menu (see Sec. 14.3). The wall drawing is to be done using an architectural scale of 1/2 in = 1 ft 0 in.

```
UTILITY <pick> MENU <pick> File name: b:proto <return> B _HOR-I <pick>
Enter attribute data requested.
ARCH <pick> 1/2" = 1'-0" <pick> ZOOM _ALL <pick>
```

The AutoCAD menu will now be loaded. Use the LAYER command to set the following layers:

Object	Name	Color	Line type
Wall	Elev1	White (7)	Continuous
Text	Text	Red (1)	Continuous
Dimensions	Dim	Red (1)	Continuous
Details	Details	Blue (5)	Continuous
Hatch border	Hatcho	White (7)	Continuous
Hatching	Hatch	Yellow (2)	Continuous
Construction lines	Const	White (1)	Continuous

Set **Elev1** as the current drawing layer.
Select architectural units with 1 as the smallest fraction.
Set GRID to 12 and SNAP to 6.

14.4.1   Text and Dimension Scale

The floor plan previously drawn is to be plotted using a scale of 1/4 in = 1 ft 0 in. In Sec. 14.3.1 the text height was calculated as 4 in. Since the wall detail is to be plotted using a scale of 1/2 in = 1 ft 0 in and since the two plots are to reside on the same drawing, the text height for the detail drawing is calculated as follows:

$$H = 4 * (1/4)/(1/2) \qquad \text{giving } H = 2$$

DIMSCALE was set as 22.22 for the floor plan. For the wall DIMSCALE is calculated as follows:

$$\text{DIMSCALE} = 22.22 * (1/4)/(1/2) \qquad \text{giving DIMSCALE} = 11.11$$

The dimension variables are set similarly to those used for the floor plan:

AutoCAD **<pick>** DIM **<pick>** DIM VARS **<pick>** DIMSCALE **<pick>** 11.11 **<return>**
DIMTAD **<pick> on <return>** DIMTSZ **<pick>** 0.09 **<return>** DIMTIH **<pick> off**
<return> DIMZIN **<return>** 3 (**on** for Ver. 2.5) **<return>**

14.4.2 Wall

The current layer should be **Elev1**. Draw the wall footing on the right side of the drawing area using the grid. The footing wall was drawn 18 in high. This is unsatisfactory in northern climates, but, remember, this is a CAD, not a building design, exercise. Use break lines in the footing if you wish.

Set the current layer to **Const**. Draw construction lines representing the face of the wall, the 2-ft 0-in roof overhang, and the bottom of the roof beam:

DRAW **<pick>** LINE **<pick>** From point: **int <return>** of Place the target on the top right corner of the footing wall. **<pick>** To point: @8'1<90 **<return>** To point: **<return> <return>** Line From point: @2'<0 **<return>** To point: @1'<270 **<return>** To point: **<return>**

The roof slope is 4/12, which means a 4-in rise for every 12-in (1 ft 0 in) run. For the 15-ft 0-in width section of the building the rise will be $4 * 15 / 2 = 30$ in (2 ft 6 in). The construction line for the bottom of the roof is drawn as follows (see Fig. 14.7):

Vers. 2.1 and 2.5

POINT **<pick>** Point: **end <return>** of Place the target on the top of the wall construction line, point a. **<pick> _LAST_ <pick>** LINE **<pick>** From point: @-7'6,2'6 (7 ft 6 in to the left of a and 2 ft 6 in above a) **<return>** To point: Extend the line to the right and down so that it touches the top of the wall construction line and extends out to the 2-ft 0-in roof extension cutoff line. **<pick>** To point: **<return>**

Vers. 2.6 to Release 10

POINT **<pick>** Point: **end <return>** of Place the target on the top of the wall construction line, point a. **<pick> _LAST_ <pick>** LINE **<pick>** From point: @7'6,2'6 (7'-6" to the left of a and 2'-6" above a) **<return>** To point: **end <return>** of Place the target on the top of the wall construction line, point a. **<pick>** To point: **<return>** EDIT **<pick>** EXTEND **<pick>** Select boundary edge(s) ... Select objects: Digitize the vertical line 2 ft from the wall that defines the roof edge. **<pick> <return>** Select object to extend: Pick the roof line. **<pick> <return>**

The grid will now be rotated so that it aligns with the roof slope, and then SNAP will be set to the roof joist thickness of 6 in:

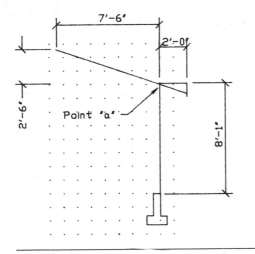

Figure 14.7 Wall elevation.

AutoCAD <**pick**> SETTINGS (or MODES) <**pick**> SNAP <**pick**> Snap spacing or ON/
OFF/Aspect/Rotate/Style: **r** (rotate) <**return**> Base point: **int** <**return**> of Place
target on the intersection point of the roof and the wall. <**pick**> Rotation Angle: **end**
(endpoint) <**return**> of Place the target on the left end of the roof line. <**pick**> <**return**>
Snap spacing or ON/OFF/Aspect/Rotate/Style: **6** <**return**>

Now press **Ctrl-O** to turn the orthogonal mode on. Draw a copy of the previous line 6 in above it:

EDIT <**pick**> COPY <**pick**> Select objects: Digitize the current roof line. <**pick**>
<**return**> Base point or displacement: Digitize a point on the current roof line.
<**pick**> Second point of displacement: Digitize a point one snap step above the
previous roof line. <**pick**>

Return grid to original snap plane, and set SNAP to 2 in:

AutoCAD <**pick**> SETTINGS (or MODES) <**pick**> SNAP <**pick**>

Snap spacing or ON/OFF/Aspect/Rotate/Style: **r** (Rotate) <**return**> Base point:
0,0 <**return**> Rotation angle: **0** <**return**>
<**return**> Snap spacing or ON/OFF/Aspect/Rotate/style: **2** <**return**>

Move the top line of the roof to align with the 2-ft 0-in overhang:

EDIT <**pick**> MOVE <**pick**> Select objects: **l** (Last) <**return**> <**return**> Base point
or displacement: **end** <**return**> of Place the target on the right side end of the top roof
line. <**pick**> Second point: Digitize a horizontal line extending from the previous point
to the 2-ft 0-in overhang. <**pick**>

Use the CHANGE command to transfer the roof beam and wall line to the Elev1 layer:

Ver. 2.1

LAST <**pick**> EDIT <**pick**> CHANGE <**pick**> Select objects: Digitize the two roof lines and the wall line. <**pick**> Change point (or Layer or Elevation): l (Layer) <**return**> New layer: **elev1** <**return**>

Ver. 2.5 to Release 10

EDIT <**pick**> CHANGE <**pick**> Select objects: Digitize the two roof lines and the wall line. <**return**> Properties/<Change point>: LAyer <**pick**> New layer: **elev1** <**return**>

Now turn the Const layer off and set Elev1 as the current layer:

AutoCAD <**pick**> LAYERS <**pick**> LAYER: <**pick**> set <**pick**> New current layer: **elev1** <**return**> off <**pick**> Layer names: **const** <**return**> <**return**>

Draw the remaining roof lines. Do not draw the 2- by 6-in members individually—draw one as a block and then use the INSERT command to insert the others where required.

The insulation is first drawn as a 1-ft 0-in block, see Fig. 14.8. One block is inserted at the base of the wall. The ARRAY command is then used to repeat the entity seven times. To make up the missing piece at the top, the last insulation unit is inserted as a block with its name preceded by an asterisk (*) to retain its entities so that the parts running into other members may be erased.

14.4.3   Hatching

The hatch scale is calculated using Eq. 6.1:

$$\text{Plot scale} * \text{factor} = 1 \text{ in} * \text{conversion}$$
$$1/2 * \text{factor} = 1 * 12$$
$$\text{Factor} = 24$$

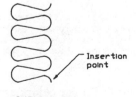

INSUL
(INSULATION BLOCK)

Figure 14.8 Insulation block.

Set the current layer to **Hatch**. Hatch the wall and floor separately using the dots hatch style. Select the boundaries by digitizing each boundary line.

The earth hatch requires a boundary line. Set the current layer to **Hatcho** and draw a lower boundary for the earth hatching and a boundary for the fiberglass hatching.

Set the current layer to **Hatch** and use the earth hatch style for the earth, and the insul hatch style for the insulation. When the hatching is complete, turn layer **Hatcho** off.

14.4.4   Text and dimensions

Set the current layer to **Dim** and add the dimensions. Set the current layer to **Text** and add the text to the drawing.

14.4.5   Test plot and save file

Test plot the drawing on a B-size sheet using a scale of 1/2 in = 1 ft 0 in. The plot units are inches. For a 15- by 9.5-in plot, based on the scale of 1/2 in = 1 ft (12 in), the plot width is 360 in (2 * 12 * 15) and plot height is 228 in (2 * 12 * 9.5). The scale is 1 = 24.

Make necessary corrections to the drawing and then turn layer **Border1** off and FREEZE it.

Use the END command to save the file and exit to the main menu.

14.5   Creating the Plot Drawing

From the AutoCAD main menu select to edit an existing drawing named B:Border (created in Chap. 12).

Select the B—HOR-I command from the menu. AutoCAD will then draw the border and the title block and will prompt you for the variable attribute information. When the scale is requested enter **NOTED**. Use the INSERT command to insert each of the drawings:

```
INSERT <pick> Block name: b:proj-14a <return> Insertion point: 0.0 <return> X
Scale factor: 0.0208 [1/(4*12)] <return> Y Scale factor <0.02>: <return> Rotation
angle: 0 <return> <return> Block name: b:proj-14b <return> Insertion point:
0.0 <return> X Scale factor: 0.0417 [1/(2*12)] <return> Y Scale factor: <return>
Rotation angle: 0 <return>
```

List the layers to ensure that border1 is off and the layer colors are as desired.

Use the MOVE command to move entities as required to fit the drawing better. Save the file:

SAVE__END <**pick**> File name: **b:plot-14** <**return**>

Plot the drawing from the main menu. Refer to the example in Chap. 12, Sec. 12.7. The plot data is:

- Units = inches
- Width = 17 in
- Height = 11 in
- Scale is 1 = 1

Three-Dimensional Drawing

OBJECTIVE *To construct and view three-dimensional drawings using commands from Vers. 2.5 and 2.6 and Release 10 of AutoCAD; drawing and editing Polylines.*

15.1 THICKNESS and ELEVATION Commands

Rudimentary three-dimensional capabilities were added to AutoCAD in Ver. 2.5 with the introduction of the THICKNESS and ELEVATION commands. These commands allow the assignment of an elevation and thickness (height) to any two-dimensional object, thereby producing an extruded plane. With Vers. 2.5 and 2.6 the only points on the extruded plane visible to AutoCAD are on the initial elevation, which may make it difficult to connect other entities to the extruded lines or their intersections. This is rectified in Release 9, in which all points on the extruded plane are visible. Since extruded planes may lie only in the z, z axis, they present limited capabilities to draw three-dimensional entities.

15.2 Convert Proj-4 Drawing to Three Dimensions

Boot up AutoCAD and "Edit an EXISTING Drawing:," **Proj-4**.
    When Proj-4 was drawn, all of the entities were on layer 0. Since the

objective of this exercise is to create a three-dimensional view of the object, the CHANGE command will be used to change the layer on which the object resides. The dimensions and text will be left on layer 0, which will be turned off. Also, since layer 0 will not be used for this drawing, you will FREEZE it. When a layer is frozen, it is turned off and the items on that layer are ignored by AutoCAD when the drawing is regenerated. If the layer is quite complex and it is not to be displayed, freezing it speeds up the regeneration process considerably. In this case the layer is not complex and there is little regeneration speed gained by freezing the layer. It is done to demonstrate the command. To turn a frozen layer on, the THAW command is used.

Using the LAYER and MAKE commands, make a new layer named **Object** and set it as the current layer. The CHANGE command is then used to transfer the drawing to the new layer as follows:

AUTOCAD <**pick**> EDIT <**pick**> CHANGE <**pick**> Select objects: Digitize each of the object lines in Proj-4, including the circle. Do *not* digitize any of the text or dimension lines. <**return**> Properties/<Change point>: Property <**pick**> Change what property (Color/Elev/LAyer/LType/Thickness): Layer <**pick**> New layer: **Object** <**return**>
AUTOCAD <**pick**> LAYER: <**pick**> ?/Make/Set/New/ON/OFF/Color/Ltype/Freeze/ Freeze/Thaw: Freeze <**pick**> Layer name: **0** <**return**> <**return**>

15.2.1   Adding three dimensions to two-dimensional entities

Two-dimensional objects are drawn on a flat plane using an x,y axis. For an entity to be a three-dimensional extruded plane, it must reside on a specific elevation (x,y axis) and have thickness along the z axis. If an object was initially drawn with two-dimensional entities, the CHANGE command may be used to specify an elevation for each of the entities and to define the depth in the z axis, making the entity three dimensional. For this project, the base of the object will be set as elevation 0 (any value may be used, even a -'ve elevation). The thickness of the object will be assumed to be 6 units.

The circle (hole) in the object will be given a base elevation of 3 units and a thickness of 3 units. This will place the top of the hole at the top of the object (i.e., at elevation 6) and it will extend 3 units into the object. A similar effect could be obtained by setting the elevation of the object and circle as 0 and then defining the thickness of the object as −6 and the thickness of the circle as −3:

EDIT <**pick**> CHANGE <**pick**> Select objects: Digitize each of the lines forming the object—do not digitize the circle. <**return**> Property/<Change point>: Property <**pick**> Change what property: Elev <**pick**> Elevation: **0** <**return**> New thickness: **6** <**return**>

Recall the CHANGE command and set the circle elevation and thickness:

> \<return\> Select objects: Digitize the circle. \<return\> Property/\<Change point\>:
> Elev \<**pick**\> New Elevation: **3** \<return\> New thickness: **3** \<return\>

15.2.2 Drawing a new three-dimensional extruded entity

Prior to drawing a new three-dimensional extruded entity the elevation and thickness for the entity must be set. This is done by using the ELEV command (for Release 10, also see Sec. 17.1). The elevation is to be set to 0 (the current default value) and the thickness to 6 units. A new "hole" is then drawn in the object as follows (for Ver. 2.5, the ELEV command is in a submenu called by the 3-D command):

> AUTOCAD \<**pick**\> SETTINGS (or 3D or MODES) \<**pick**\> ELEV \<**pick**\> New current
> elevation \<0.00\>: \<**return**\> New current thickness \<0.00\>: **6** \<**return**\> AUTO-
> CAD \<**pick**\> DRAW \<**pick**\> Circle \<**pick**\> CEN,RAD \<**pick**\> Center point: **10,5**
> \<**return**\> Radius: **1.5** \<**return**\>

If other entities are to be drawn with the same current elevation and thickness, they are drawn without resetting ELEV. If a different elevation or thickness is desired for an entity, the ELEV command must be used to modify the current elevation and thickness prior to drawing the entity (unless the CHANGE command is used later to modify the elevation and/or thickness of an entity).

15.3 Viewing the z Plane of Three-Dimensional Objects

The VPOINT (ViewPOINT) command is used to view the z axis of the screen. However, you cannot view one object on the screen in three dimensions and leave other objects on the same screen in two dimensions. In order to plot a x,y,z view of an object within a border and title block in the x,y axis, you will have to plot the border and title block separately from the three-dimensional view, on the same sheet. Multiview drawings may be made using Release 10 by defining user coordinate system (UCS) views which are WBlocked and inserted into the drawing (see Chap. 17).

Prior to discussing the VPOINT command options, the command will be used to view the z axis of the object (for Ver. 2.5, the VPOINT command is in a submenu called by the 3-D command):

> AUTOCAD \<**pick**\> DISPLAY (or 3D) \<**pick**\> VPOINT \<**pick**\> Rotate/\<View point\>:
> **−1,−1,1** \<**return**\>

You should now have on your monitor a wire-frame model 3-D view of the object similar to that illustrated in Fig. 15.1.

When the VPOINT command is executed, the current view point is displayed in angle brackets. If you enter a new *x,y,z* view point (as in the preceding commands), AutoCAD regenerates the drawing and displays the new view. If you enter a null response or select the AXIS command, a compass and tripod will be displayed, as illustrated in Fig. 15.2:

```
VPOINT <pick> Axis <pick>
```

The upper right corner of the monitor should now display a two-dimensional representation of globe. AutoCAD refers to the center point of the globe as the north pole (0,0,1), the inner ring as the equator (n,n,0), and the outer ring as the south pole (0,0,−1). A small cross hair indicates the view point looking toward the coordinate origin (0,0,0).

An axis tripod in the center of the monitor illustrates the view position. As the cursor is moved, the cross hair moves in the globe, and the axis tripod rotates indicating the view obtained if that position is selected by pressing the Enter key. In either case you are only specifying the view direction. It is not possible to specify a view distance. The following table illustrates the VPOINTs to enter to obtain standard views:

VPOINT	View
x,y,z	
0,0,1	Plan view (or select PLAN from menu)
0,0,-1	Plan view from south pole
1,0,0	Right side view
0,-1,0	Front view
0,1,0	View from back

Try a number of view points using both the compass and the tripod.

15.4   Suppressing Hidden Lines

The VPOINT command draws a wire-frame display of the object. In a wire-frame display all of the lines are present, including those that would be hidden by other parts of the object. The hidden lines may be eliminated by using the HIDE command:

```
HIDE <pick> Yes <pick>
```

The screen will go blank for a period of time (depending on the drawing's complexity) as AutoCAD proceeds to regenerate the drawing with the hidden lines suppressed (see Fig. 15.3). The wire-frame view

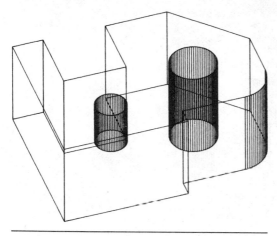

Figure 15.1 Three-dimensional view of project 4.

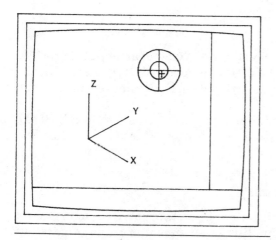

Figure 15.2 Z-plane view selection screen.

will be restored the next time the drawing is regenerated with, for instance, ZOOM, REGEN, PAN, etc.

As illustrated in Fig. 15.2, the HIDE command does not necessarily generate the desired hidden line removal. In the drawing the sides of the circle have been removed only where they are covered by the sides of the object. AutoCAD sees the object as a room with the roof removed. It does not recognize the existence of horizontal planes blocking lines in the z direction.

To plot a three-dimensional view of the object with hidden lines removed, a view does not have to be generated on the monitor with

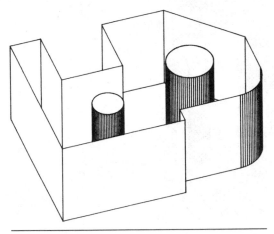

Figure 15.3 Three-dimensional view with hidden lines suppressed.

hidden lines removed. When plotting a 3-D view of an object, AutoCAD will ask if you wish to have hidden lines removed. If Y is entered, the program will process the vectors with hidden lines removed and plot the drawing.

Generate a three-dimensional view of the object and then call **PLOT** and plot the view with hidden lines removed—a scale of $1 = 3$ should fit a 11- by 8.5-in sheet.

15.5 Topographic Map Drawing

A topographic map shows, by countour lines, the spatial configuration of the earth's surface. A contour line is an imaginary line of constant elevation on the ground surface. An example of a contour line is the shore line of a still lake.

In this project a topographic map of a 40- by 40-m lot is drawn. The ground elevations have been determined by a field survey and are illustrated at grid points in Fig. 15.4. The grid spacings are 10 m c/c vertically and horizontally.

To draw the topographical map, points of equal elevation on the drawing will be located. A line joining those points is called a "contour line." Successive contour lines will be drawn at a fixed contour interval of 1 m. The drawing will then illustrate the spatial "flow of the land." Where contour lines are closely spaced, the change in elevation is steep. Where contour lines are spaced far apart, the change in elevation is gradual. The final topographical map is illustrated in Fig. 15.5.

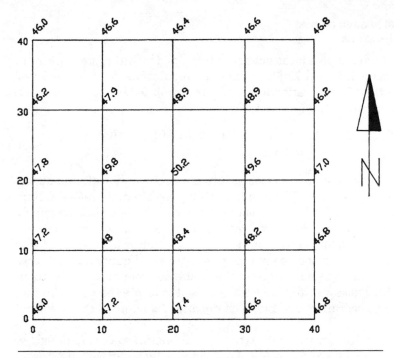

Figure 15.4 Topographic map grid elevations.

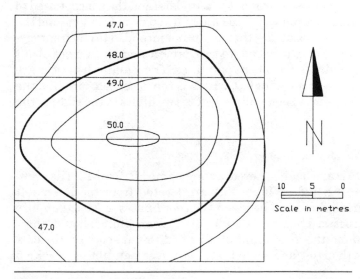

Figure 15.5 Topographic map contours.

15.5.1 Calculation of even-contour elevations

Even-contour elevation locations are determined by interpolating elevations between the grid lines. A sample calculation is illustrated below,where the 47-m elevation location is interpolated between the 0 and 10-m grid point on the horizontal (x axis):

$$\text{Distance} = (47.0 - 46.0)/(47.2 - 46.0) * 10 \text{ m}$$
$$= 8.33 \text{ m}$$

Note that the only 46-m elevation points are at the lower left and upper right corners of the plan. The even elevations required, therefore, fall in the range of 47 to 50 m. The locations where each of those elevations cross the vertical and horizontal grid lines must then be calculated.

To simplify drawing of the contour lines, the lower left corner of the grid is assumed to be located at coordinate 0,0 on the monitor. As each contour location is calculated, its total distance from point 0,0 is then determined. Those coordinates are then used to locate the points on the drawing. The coordinates of the 47-m elevation calculated then become 8.33,0.

The contour line locations illustrated in Table 15.1 were calculated by using the BASIC program in App. C. If you are familiar with programming in BASIC, you may wish to enter the program and generate the data. If you are not familiar with BASIC, manually check a few of the values from Table 15.1 to ensure that you understand the concept used to calculate the values. Do not worry too much if you do not understand the process of calculating the data—this text is not intended to teach surveying. You will still be able to complete this project and learn more about AutoCAD's 3-D abilities and about polylines. The x and y distances are coordinate distances from point 0,0, which is the lower left corner of the plan. The distances have been rounded off to two digits to the right of the decimal.

15.5.2 Draw the contour lines

Boot up AutoCAD and begin a new drawing named **B:Proj-15**. The even-contour distances listed in Table 15.1 are located from the lower left corner of the grid, which will be given the coordinates of 0,0 to simplify the drawing process. The grid is 40 by 40. Screen limits should allow some space around the grid (5 units) plus additional space on the east side for the north arrow and some text. Set the screen limits as **−5,−5** and **65,45**.

TABLE 15.1 Contour Locations

Elevation	x dist.	y dist.	Elevation	x dist.	y dist.
46	0	0	48	36.15	20
47	8.33	0	49	32.31	20
47	25	0	47	0	25
47	0	8.33	48	10	29.47
48	20	6.00	49	10	24.21
47	30	2.50	49	20	29.33
48	30	8.75	50	20	21.54
48	10	10	49	30	28.57
47	38.57	10	47	4.71	30
48	31.43	10	48	11.00	30
49	10	15.56	47	37.04	30
49	20	13.33	48	33.33	30
50	20	18.89	47	10	36.92
49	30	15.71	47	20	37.60
48	1.00	20	48	20	33.60
49	6.00	20	47	30	38.26
50	15	20	48	30	33.91
50	23.33	20	46	0	40
47	40	20			

Set the units as decimal (meters), with two digits to the right of the decimal. Create the following layers (continuous line type for all):

Use	Name	Color
Contour lines	Contour	White
Text	Text	White
Grid lines	Grid	Red
Grid-point elevations	Gridel	Yellow
Elevations	Coord	White

Set **Grid** as the current layer.

15.5.2.1 Set the elevation. Since the three-dimensional function of AutoCAD's ADE-3 package is to be used, an elevation for each entity will have to be defined. Usually, all text, dimensions, grid lines, etc., are placed on elevation 0 (z coordinate = 0); however, the lowest grid elevation is 47 m (there is no contour for elevation 46), so all text and the grid lines will be placed on elevation 47 (z coordinate = 47). This way, if the text or dimension layers are on when the drawing is viewed in three dimensions, the text and dimensions will appear on the same elevation as the lowest contour in the view. Since each contour line represents a single elevation, the contour lines will have elevation but will have a thickness of 0 units.

```
AUTOCAD <pick> SETTINGS (or 3D) <pick> ELEV: <pick> New current elevation
<0.00>: 47 <return> New current thickness <0.00>: <return>
```

Note: With Release 10, also read Chap. 17.

15.5.2.2 Draw the grid. To draw the grid, one grid line will be drawn and the ARRAY command will be used to replicate it:

```
DRAW <pick> LINE <pick> From point: 0,0<return> To point: @40<90 <return>
EDIT <pick> ARRAY: <pick> Select objects: Last <pick> <return> Rectangu-
lar or Polar array (R/P): Rectangular <pick> Number of rows (---) <1>:
<return> Number of columns (|||) <1>: 5 <return> Distance between columns
(|||): 10 <return>
```

Use the same procedure to draw the horizontal grid lines.

15.5.2.3 Add grid elevations and coordinates. The text scale will be based on the drawing being plotted on a 280- by 215-mm (11- by 8.5-in) sheet using a scale of 1:300. The text height on the plotted drawing is to be 3 mm. The drawing text height is then calculated as follows:

$$1/300 * H = 3 \text{ mm}$$
$$H = 900 \text{ mm}$$
$$H = 0.9 \text{ m} \quad \text{(drawing units)}$$

Add the horizontal and vertical coordinates (0, 10, 20, etc.) to the drawing.

Place the north arrow and the text below it on the drawing. The grid elevations are not to be displayed on the final drawing. They are added to the drawing so that a plot of the grid displaying the grid elevations may be generated, following which, the layer on which they reside is turned off. They are therefore placed on a separate layer named Gridel.

Set **Gridel** as the current layer. Rather than entering each of the grid point elevations individually, the lower left corner elevation will be entered, and the ARRAY command will be used to replicate that value across the grid. The CHANGE command will be used to change each of the grid elevations to its proper value. This method is easier than specifying each individual text location, and it also gives a more uniform drawing.

```
DRAW <pick> TEXT <pick> Start point or Align/Center/Fit/Middle/Right/
Style: Digitize the start point for the grid elevation near 0,0. <pick> Height: 0.9
<return> Rotation angle <0>: 45 <return> Text: 46.0 <return>

EDIT <pick> ARRAY: <pick> Select objects: Last <pick> Select objects:
<return> Rectangular or Polar (R/P): Rectangular <pick> Number of rows
```

(---): **5** <**return**> Number of columns (|||): **5** <**return**> Unit cell or distance
between rows (---): **10** <**return**> Distance between columns (|||): **10** <**return**>

AutoCAD will copy the 46.0 elevation text to each of the grid points.
The grid elevation values at points other than 0,0 are now to be changed
to their proper value. When the CHANGE command is called, each grid
elevation to be changed is digitized, indicating the items to be changed.
When AutoCAD requests "Properties/<Change point>:," press Enter.
This informs the program that you wish to change the text value and not
its location. For all of the remaining input, the default values are selected, except for the text itself, which is to be changed.

EDIT <**pick**> CHANGE Select objects: Digitize each of the grid elevations—except for
the text at 0,0. <**return**>

Assuming the first two texts digitized were at grid coordinates 10,0 and
20,0, the entries would be as follows (watch the monitor and you will
notice a line connecting the cursor and each text item, as its turn to be
changed comes up):

Properties/<Change point>: <**return**> Text style: STANDARD New style or RE-
TURN for no change: <**return**> New height <0.9>: <**return**> New rotation angle
<45>: <**return**> New text <46.0>: **47.2** <**return**>

Properties/<Change point>: <**return**> Text style: STANDARD New style or RE-
TURN for no change: <**return**> New height <0.9>: <**return**> New rotation angle
<45>: <**return**> New text <46.0>: **47.4** <**return**>

AutoCAD continues with each text, in the same order as they were
digitized.

Plot the grid elevations and grid using a scale of 1:300 on a 280- by 215-
mm sheet. The scale entered would be 1 = 0.3.

15.5.3   Using polylines

Set **Contour** as the current layer and turn layer **Gridel** off. The contour
lines will be drawn using the PLINE (polyline) command rather than
the LINE command. Polylines have specific properties that lines do not
have (refer to the discussion on polylines in your AutoCAD manual). The
property to be used in this project is the ability to edit a polyline and
create a smooth curve that fits the vertices of the original straight line
segments. This creates a better contour line since real contour lines are
seldom made up of straight line segments unless the ground elevations
have been modified by machinery.

Since the contour drawing will be viewed later in three dimensions,
the elevation of each contour line will have to be set; however, the first
contour to be drawn is at elevation 47, which was previously set.

The PLINE coordinates will be read from Table 15.1. The first coordinate selected for the 47-m elevation is 8.33,0. The procedure used to locate coordinates will be discussed below.

```
DRAW <pick> PLINE <pick> From point: 8.33,0 <return>
```

The coordinate 8.33,0 was selected as the first in the list for elevation 47 in Table 15.1 (the second row of the table). Tick this item off in the table so you remember it was used. The next point to be used is 0,8.33 (the fourth row of the table). The reason for this selection will be discussed later. A line is then to be drawn from point 8.33,0 to 0,8.33.

The PLINE command causes AutoCAD to respond with these options rather than the familiar "to point" of the LINE command. Refer to the *AutoCAD Reference Manual* for a complete discussion of the options. The entry will be the second coordinate of the line, as follows:

```
Current line-width is 0.00
Arc/Close/Halfwidth/Length/Undo/Width/<Endpoint of line>: 0,8.33 <return>
```

The second coordinate, 0,8.33, was selected by reviewing all of the coordinates for elevation 47 in Table 15.1 and considering the possibilities for the next coordinates. If you look at the previous coordinate entered, 8.33,0, and the grid in Fig. 15.3, you should observe that the next coordinate will be either on the column line where $x = 10$ and y falls

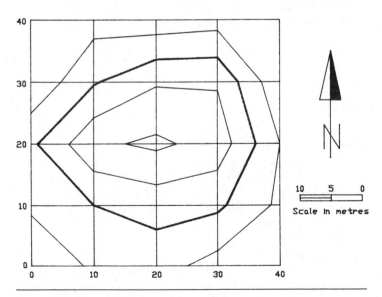

Figure 15.6 Topographic map contour polylines.

between 0 and 10 or the column where $x = 0$ and y falls between 0 and 10 or the row line where x falls between 0 and 10 and $y = 10$. Remember x is horizontal (row) and y is vertical (column). As you use an elevation in Table 15.1, tick it off so you need not consider that one again.

AutoCAD responds with the list of options again. The next point must fall either on column $x = 10$ with y from 0 to 10 or row $x = 0$ to 10 and $y = 10$. None exist in the list; therefore, this contour is discontinuous (see Fig. 15.6).

Recall the PLINE command by pressing **Enter**. The points entered and the reasoning are listed in the following table:

Coordinate	Reasoning
25,0	Next 47 elev. in list
30,2.50	$x = 30-40$; $y = 0-10$
38.57,10	$x = 30-40$; $y = 0-10$
40,20	$x = 30-40$; $y = 10-20$
37.04,30	$x = 30-40$; $y = 20-30$
30,38.26	$x = 30-40$; $y = 30-40$
20,37.6	$x = 20-30$; $y = 30-40$
10,36.92	$x = 10-20$; $y = 30-40$
4.71,30	$x = 0-10$; $y = 30-40$
0,25	$x = 0-10$; $y = 20-30$

Since there are no more 47 elevations and the contour line is not in the proximity to close on the first point at 25,0, the contour is discontinuous. *Press Enter or Ctrl-C to exit the PLINE command.*

The 48-m elevation contour lines are now to be drawn. Prior to drawing any lines, however, the ADE-3 elevation, ELEV, must be set to 48:

```
AUTOCAD <pick> SETTINGS (or 3D) <pick> ELEV <pick> New current elevation
<47.0>: 48 <return> New current thickness <0.00>: <return>
```

When drawing contour lines, it is customary to draw every fifth contour line heavier. For this drawing, the 48-m elevation contour line will be made heavier to demonstrate the procedure to be used with polylines. Assuming that the width of the line on the plotted drawing is to be 0.5 mm and the plot will be done using a scale of 1:300, the width of the polyline in meters (the drawing units) will be:

$$1/300 * W = .5 \text{ mm}$$
$$W = 150 \text{ mm}$$
$$W = 0.15 \text{ m}$$

The polyline will be drawn starting with the first 48 elevation coordinate in the list in Table 15.1. Prior to entering the end point, the Width option for polylines will be selected to enter a PLINE width of 0.15 units:

```
DRAW <pick> PLINE: <pick> From point: 20,6 <return>
Current line width is 0.00

Arc/Close/Halfwidth/length/Undo/Width/<Endpoint of Line>: Width <pick>
Starting width <0.00>: 0.15 <return> Ending width <0.15>: <return>
```

The next "To point:" values entered and the reasoning are as follows:

Coordinate	Reasoning
30,8.75	$x = 20$–$30; y = 0$–10
31.43,10	$x = 30$–$40; y = 0$–10
36.15,20	$x = 30$–$40; y = 10$–20
33.33,30	$x = 30$–$40; y = 20$–30
30,33.91	$x = 30$–$40; y = 30$–40
20,33.60	$x = 20$–$30; y = 30$–40
11,30	$x = 10$–$20; y = 30$–40
10,29.47	$x = 10$–$20; y = 20$–30
1,20	$x = 0$–$10; y = 20$–30
10,10	$x = 0$–$10; y = 10$–20
C	$x = 10$–$20; y = 0$–10

Note that the possible coordinates for the last point are the same as those for the first point; therefore, the C (close) command is entered.

Complete the topographical drawing. Remember, begin by setting the contour elevation (ELEV), then to change the PLINE thickness *back* to 0,00 since only the 48-m elevation is to be heavier. Figure 15.6 illustrates the plan with all of the contours drawn.

15.5.4   Edit polyline for curve fitting

The PEDIT (polyline edit) command allows the user to edit polylines in a number of different ways. Refer to the AutoCAD Reference Manual for a complete discussion. In this project the "Fit curve" function will be used to create a smooth curve that fits all of the vertices of the polyline for each contour.

```
EDIT <pick> PEDIT <pick> Select polyline: Digitize a point on the 47-m elevation
polyline on the east side of the plan. <return>
```

The edit options will now be displayed. The Fit curve option is selected:

```
Close/Join/Width/Edit vertex/Fit curve/Uncurve/eXit <X>: Fit <pick>
```

The 47-m elevation contour will be redrawn by AutoCAD as a smooth curve. Repeat the process for each of the contours. The final contour plan is illustrated as Fig. 15.5.

To complete the drawing, set the current layer to **Text** and the ELEV to **47**. Next, add the contour elevation values and save the file. Plot the drawing using a scale of **1:300** on an A-size sheet (280 by 215 mm or 11 by 8.5 in). The scale specified when plotting is 1 = .3 since the drawing is in meter units and the plot sheet size is in millimeters.

15.6 Three-Dimensional View of Topographical Drawing

If your monitor does not have good resolution, you may want to turn the Grid layer off prior to using the VPOINT (view point) command since some views will look quite cluttered. Try the VPOINT command with layer Grid on and also with layer Grid off to see the difference.

Try a number of view points. When you get a good view point, plot it. If you wish to save a view, see the discussion in Sec. 15.7 on naming views prior to creating another VPOINT.

The HIDE command does not change the views since none of the entities were given thickness; therefore, no lines are hidden behind any other entity.

15.7 Naming (Saving) Views

Often the drafter wishes to return to a view many times. This is especially true in large drawings where the drafter works with specific zones in a drawing and wishes to move quickly from zone (view) to zone (view). In three-dimensional drawings you may also want to save specific view points for later use or reference. The VIEW command is used to name views.

When a view is named, it may be quickly recalled using the VIEW command. Prior to using the VIEW command, use the VPOINT com-

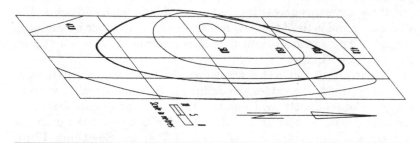

Figure 15.7 Three-dimensional view of contours.

mand to get a three-dimensional view of the topographical drawing you wish to refer to at a later time. The commands to name the view are:

AUTOCAD <**pick**> DISPLAY <**pick**> VIEW <**pick**>

AutoCAD now displays the VIEW options in the command line. The Save option will be selected to save the view as Fig-1:

?/Delete/Restore/Save/Window: Save <**pick**> View name: **Fig-1** <**return**>

Use the VPOINT and PLAN commands from the menu to return to the plan view of the drawing.

To quickly return to our saved three-dimensional view, enter:

DISPLAY <**pick**> VIEW <**pick**>
?/Delete/Restore/Save/Window: Restore <**pick**> View name: **Fig-1** <**return**>

You will recall that, when plotting, one of the first questions AutoCAD asks after the drawing to plot has been specified is:

What to plot—Display, Extents, Limits, View, or Window <D>:

For all previous drawings, the default D (display) has been specified. This plots the last monitor view saved if plotting is being done from the main menu or the view currently on the monitor if plotting from the Drawing Editor menu. If instead the V (view) option is selected, Auto-CAD will request the name of the view, i.e., Fig-1, to be plotted. The named view then would be plotted rather than the current monitor view. Plot the view named **Fig-1**.

15.8   3DLINE and 3DFACE Commands

The 3DLINE and 3DFACE commands were added to Ver. 2.62 of Auto-CAD. The 3DLINE command is used to draw a line with any orientation in space. It requires three coordinates ($x, y,$ and z) for each end point. The 3DFACE command is used to draw a face, or plate, in space by defining three or four corners in any orientation. Each corner of the face, or plate, requires x,y,z coordinates.

With Release 10, AutoCAD is transformed into a true three-dimensional CAD system. All entities are defined in 3-D space with $x, y,$ and z coordinates. Consequently, while most of the 3-D commands from earlier versions are still operational, the 3DLINE command is no longer relevant since all lines may be defined in 3-D space. See Chap. 17 for more information on Release 10.

15.9 Three-Dimensional Storage Bin

The storage bin illustrated in Fig. 15.8 is to be drawn in three-dimensional space to illustrate the use of the 3DFACE command. Begin a new drawing named **BIN**. Set the drawing units to architectural with the denomination of the smallest unit to display as 4 (for 1/4 in). Set the drawing limits to −4′,−4′ and 16′,12′ and use the ZOOM and All commands to zoom the screen to the limits. Use the LAYER and Make commands to make a new layer named **SS** (structural steel) and set it as the current working layer.

The top lip plates of the bin may be drawn using the 3DFACE command or as extruded lines. It is easiest to draw them as extruded lines. If you are using Ver. 2.5 or 2.6 of AutoCAD, you will have to be careful when selecting where to set the current elevation since AutoCAD does not "see" the extruded lines and extruded intersection points. If the intersection of the top and side plates is used as the current elevation ($z = 0$), you will be able to connect onto the intersecting corners with the

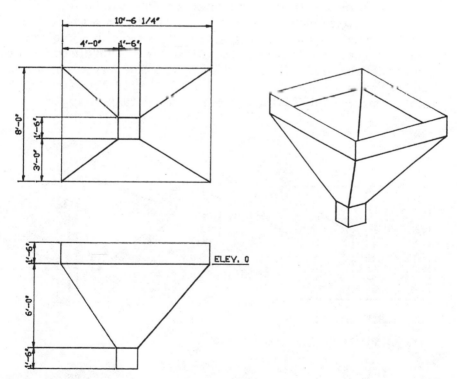

Figure 15.8 Storage bin.

INTersect object snap when drawing the side plates. The top plates are drawn as extruded lines with a thickness (height) of 1'−6":

```
Settings (or 3D) <pick> ELEV: <pick> New current elevation <0'−0">: <re-
turn> New current thickness <0'−0">: 1'6 <return>
```

As the top section is drawn, the lines will have a thickness of 1 ft 6 in:

```
DRAW <pick> LINE <pick> From point: 0',0' <return> To point: @10'6−1/4<0
<return> To point: @8'<90 <return> To point: @10'6−1/4<180 <return> To
point: C <return>
```

If you wish to verify that the plates have been drawn correctly, use the VPOINT command to view the plate in three-dimensional space.

15.9.1   Plates (faces) in space

Prior to drawing the sloping sides of the bin, which are plates (or faces) in space, set the current thickness to 0 (leave the current elevation as 0').

A 3-D face in space is defined by three or four corner points in space using the 3DFACE command. Each corner has an x, y, and z coordinate. The corners are picked in a perimeter sequence (unlike the SOLID command). A continuous series of sides may be drawn with the fourth and third points of the previous plate becoming the first and second points of the next face. In order to draw the sides of the bin in a series, the points will be entered as illustrated in Fig. 15.9. The first, second, third, and fourth points selected are marked as 1, 2, 3, and 4. When the fourth point is entered, AutoCAD will close the face by connecting point 4 to

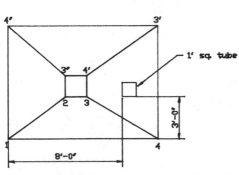
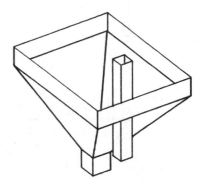

Figure 15.9 Bin 3-D faces and intersecting tube.

point 1. The cursor will remain at point 4 and AutoCAD will request a third point—which is to be the third point on the next face and is indicated as point 3′ in Fig. 15.9. Point 4 of the previous face is point 1 of the new face, and point 3 of the prior face is point 2 of the new face. When coordinates for point 3′ are entered, AutoCAD will request the fourth point for this face, which is indicated as point 4′. When point 4′ is entered, AutoCAD will connect that point with point 3 on the previous face, thereby closing the second face. Point 3 of the next face is then requested and is marked as 3″ in Fig. 15.9, etc.

The sequence of entries is listed below. If you make a mistake, the UNDO command cannot be used to delete an entry, so be careful. The x, y, and z coordinates of point 1 may be digitized on the monitor since the z coordinate falls on the current elevation 0′:

DRAW (or 3D) <**pick**> 3DFACE <**pick**> First point: * * * * <**pick**> INTersec <**pick**> of Place the intersect target on point 1. <**return**> Second point: @4′,3′,−6′ <**return**> Third point: @1′6<0 <**return**> Fourth point: * * * * <**pick**> INTersec of Digitize point 4. <**pick**> Third point:

Notice the different methods of data entry used. For the second point, relative coordinates are used to pick a point in space relative to the last point. For the third point, which lies on the same x,y plane as the second point, relative distance-angle is used. The fourth point is selected by snapping onto the corner of the existing plate at elevation 0′ by using an INTersec object snap. AutoCAD closes the first face by connecting the fourth point to the first point selected. It also assumes you wish to enter a sequence of plates with points 1 and 2 of the next plate, being points 3 and 4, respectively, of the last plate. To discontinue the sequence you would press Ctrl-C or Enter. Do *not* do so since you are to continue the sequence.

Third point: * * * * <**pick**> INTersec <**pick**> of Digitize point 3′. <**pick**> Fourth point: @5′0−1/4,−3′6,−6′ <**return**> Third point

AutoCAD connects point 4′ to point 3, finishing the second face. Continue the sequence by entering points 3″ and 4″ to finish the third face. The fourth face is completed by selecting points 1 and 2. Then press Ctrl-C or Enter to exit the command.

Use the VPOINT command to view the bin in three-dimensional space. If your side plates are not correct, you can erase one or more and redraw them. This can be done while in three-dimensional space and using object snap to snap onto the desired points.

Draw the bottom chute of the bin as sequential 3DFACEs.

15.9.2   Suppressing hidden lines

The three-dimensional view displayed on your monitor is a wire-frame model. Lines that are behind faces may be suppressed by the HIDE command. View the bin in three dimensions and then enter:

    HIDE <pick> Yes <pick>

The screen will go blank while AutoCAD proceeds to do the necessary calculations and regenerate the drawing with the hidden lines removed.

15.9.3   Intersecting planes

When the HIDE command is invoked, AutoCAD only verifies the relationship of surfaces when their edges meet. As a result, it does not draw intersections. To illustrate this, return to the plan view of the bin as follows:

    VPOINT <pick> Rotate/<View point> <current>: Plan <pick> AUTOCAD <pick>
    DISPLAY <pick> ZOOM <pick> All <pick>

Now set the current elevation to 2' and the thickness to −8' and use the line command to draw the rectangular tube projecting through the right side of the bin (see Fig. 15.9). If you then view the bin in 3-D space and enter the HIDE command, you will observe that AutoCAD does not determine the intersection between the rectangular tube and sloping plate on the side of the bin.

15.10   Cone Construction

A 3-D cone is easily drawn in the x,y plan view by initially drawing a triangular face with its base at elevation 0 and its vertex at the desired height of the cone. The circular array command is then used to rotate the face around its vertex, thus creating the other faces of the cone. This creates a cone with a polygon base rather than a circular base. If the vertex angle of the face is reasonably small, however, the base will appear circular. An angle of 15 degrees is usually sufficient.

Begin a new drawing and set the drawing units to decimal with two digits to the right of the decimal.

To facilitate drawing the initial face of the cone, a segment of a circle is drawn on a construction layer as illustrated in Fig. 15.10. Use the LAYER and MAKE commands to create a new layer named **Constr** and set it as the current layer. If you have a color monitor, set the color of Constr as yellow to provide contrast with the final cone.

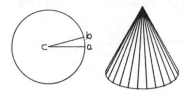

Figure 15.10 Cone and construction lines.

The cone will be drawn in a 1- by 1-cube space and saved as a block for later insertion into drawings. The construction lines are drawn as follows:

DRAW <pick> CIRCLE <pick> CEN, RAD <pick> Circle 3P/2P/TTR <center point>: **6,4** <return> Diameter/<Radius>: **1** <return> _LAST_ <pick> LINE <pick> From point: *** * * *** <pick> CENter <pick> of Digitize the target on the circle circumference. To point: **@.5<0** <return> To point: <return> <return> Line From point: *** * * *** <pick> CENter <pick> of Digitize the target on the circle circumference. <pick> To point: **@.5<15** <return> <return>

The initial 3-D face is drawn by connecting points *a, b,* and *c* in Fig. 15.10. The *z* coordinate (height) of points *a* and *b* are 0 and the *z* coordinate of point *c* is to be 1 (the height of the cone).

Prior to drawing the face, MAKE a new current layer named **Cone.** If you have a color monitor, set the color as red. The initial cone face segment is drawn as follows:

DRAW (or 3D) <pick> 3DFACE <pick> First point: *** * * *** INTersec <pick> of Digitize point *a* in Fig. 15.10. Second point: *** * * *** <pick> INTersec <pick> of Digitize point *b*. Third point: **.xy** The .xy entry may be typed or selected from the menu to request entry of the *x* and *y* coordinates. <return> of *** * * *** <pick> INTersec <pick> of Digitize point *c*. (need Z): **1** <return> Fourth point: <return>

Notice that by entering .xy you were able to digitize the *x,y* coordinates for a three-dimensional point on the monitor and enter the *z* coordinate for the point from the keyboard. This process is called "filtering."

The remaining faces of the cone are completed by rotating the 3-D wedge about its vertex. Prior to doing so, since the construction lines are no longer required, turn the Constr layer off. The face is rotated using the ARRAY command as follows:

EDIT <pick> ARRAY <pick> Select objects: Last <pick> Select objects: <return> Rectangular or Polar array (R/P): Polar <pick> Center point of array: *** * * *** <pick> INTersect <pick> of Place the object snap target over point *c*. <pick> Number of items: <return> Angle to fill (+=ccw, −=cw)<360>: <return> Angle between items: **15** <return> Rotate objects as they are copied? <Y>: <return>

The cone is now completed. Use the VPOINT and AXIS commands to view the cone in three dimensions. If you are satisfied, set the view point to PLAN and use ZOOM and All to reset the monitor to the drawing limits.

15.11   Saving Three-Dimensional Objects as a Block

Save the Cone as a block using a window around the entire cone to define the entities to be saved. When asked for the insertion point, you should not use the intersection object snap to pick the vertex of the cone since the elevation of the vertex is 1 (not 0, the elevation of the base). This is another location where x,y,z filters can be used to advantage, for instance:

BLOCKS **\<pick>** BLOCK: **\<pick>** Block name: **Cone \<return>** Insertion base point: **.xy \<return>** of * * * * **\<pick>** INTersec **\<pick>** of Select the cone vertex. **\<pick>** (Need Z): **0 \<return>** Select objects: Window **\<pick>** Place a window around the cone.

15.11.1   Inserting three-dimensional blocks

Three-dimensional blocks may be scaled about the z axis as well as the x and y axes. In order to scale the z axis, you must select the X,Y,Z option when asked for the scale factor, as follows:

BLOCKS **\<pick>** INSERT: **\<pick>** Block name (or ?): **Cone \<return>** Insertion point: **4,6,0 \<return>** X Scale factor \<1>: /Corner/X,Y,Z: **x,y,z \<return>** X Scale factor \<1>: **3 \<return>** Y Scale factor \<default=X>: **\<return>** Z Scale factor \<default=X>: **5 \<return>** Rotation angle \<0>: **\<return>**

View the cone in three-dimensional space and erase it without exiting the three-dimensional view. Now, use the INSERT command again to insert the cone into the three-dimensional view.

Slide Show

OBJECTIVE *Use AutoCAD's "slide show" facility to display the sequence of operation for a construction or production operation; create a script file to automatically invoke commands; demonstrate further applications of view command.*

DRAWING *A series of "slides" (drawings) which outline the erection sequence for a precast concrete bridge are to be produced. A "script" file will then be used to display the slides in sequence, demonstrating the bridge erection procedure.*

Boot AutoCAD and begin a new drawing named **Proj-16**. Set the limits at 0,0 and 110,70, and invoke the ZOOM <return> A (all) commands.

The drawing is to be done in foot (decimal) units. Set the units to decimal with one digit to the right of the decimal. Angle units may be set at decimal degrees with zero fractional places for the display of the angle.

For drawings of this type a color monitor is very advantageous. The purpose of the slide show is to illustrate the location of various components during the erection of a bridge girder. A color monitor allows the drafter to separate components in the drawing by color, thereby helping the user interpret the views. If you have a color monitor, you must use a new layer for each color. The layers to use are specified below. If you do not have a color monitor, you can draw all the items on one layer unless you intend to plot the views and use a different pen for each component. Create the following layers:

Item	Name	Color	Line type
Misc. data	Const	White (7)	Continuous
Bridge piers	Pier	White (7)	Continuous
Overhead gantry	Gantry	Blue (5)	Continuous
Bridge girders	Girder	Red (1)	Continuous
Gantry supports	Sups	Yellow (2)	Continuous

16.1 Bridge Component Blocks

16.1.1 Gantry

The overhead gantry (see Fig. 16.1) is a box truss arrangement that is used to support the moving hoists for the bridge. The gantry itself is a movable system that "creeps" along the bridge as the bridge girders are erected between piers.

The total length of the gantry is to be 60 ft. Initially, a 15-ft-long section will be drawn and stored as a block. The ARRAY command will then be used to replicate the block four times, creating the 60-ft gantry.

Set **Gantry** as the current layer. Zoom on an area about 20 by 10 units, and draw the outside rectangular of the gantry 15 by 2.6 units, as illustrated in Fig. 16.1. Do *not* dimension the gantry.

Since the web members divide the gantry length into 12 sections, the horizontal distance for each diagonal is 1.25 (15/12) units. The depth of the gantry truss is 2.6 units. The commands to draw the web members are:

DRAW <**pick**> LINE <**pick**> From point : **int** (INTersect) <**return**> of Place the target over the lower left corner of the gantry. <**pick**> To point : @**1.25,2.6** <**return**> To point : @**1.25,−2.6** <**return**> etc.

Save the gantry as a Block named **Gantry**. Designate the lower left corner as the insertion point, using the INT (intersection) object snap to digitize the point.

16.1.2 Girder

Girders are the bridge members that span from pier to pier and support the roadway. The slide show to be created will illustrate the procedure for erecting a precast concrete bridge girder.

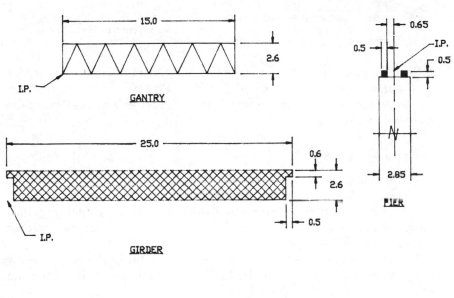

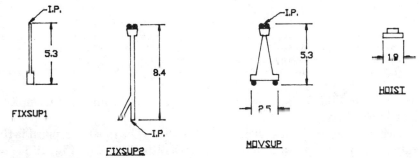

Figure 16.1 Bridge components.

Set the current layer as **Girder**. Zoom on an area that is approximately 30 by 50 units. Draw the outline of the girder, as illustrated in Fig. 16.1. Do *not* dimension the girder.

Rather than selecting an AutoCAD pattern for hatching, a new pattern will be defined. The pattern will be at an angle of 45 degrees, spaced 0.5 units, and double hatched. The commands are:

```
DRAW <pick> HATCH <pick> Pattern (? or name/U,style):
```

The U option allows you to define a pattern "on the fly":

u <**return**> Angle for crosshatch lines <O>: **45** <**return**> Spacing between lines <1>: **0.5** <**return**> Double hatch area?<N>: **y** <**return**> Select objects: **w** <**return**> Place a window around the girder. <**pick**> <**return**>

Save the girder as a block named **Girder**. Select the lower left corner as the insertion point (indicated as I.P. in Fig. 16.1). Be sure that the cursor is exactly on the imaginary lower left corner when selecting the insertion point.

16.1.3   Pier

The piers support the girders of the bridge, as illustrated in Fig. 16.2, and transfer the load to the ground.

Set the current layer as **Pier**. Draw the pier, as illustrated in Fig. 16.1. Rather than use another layer with a center line type, draw the center line using solid line segments.

The bearing pads are the solid squares on the top of the pier. To draw the pads, first draw one using the LINE command. To solidly fill the pad after it is drawn, enter the following:
To fill the bearing pads use:

DRAW <**pick**> SOLID <**pick**> FILL ON <**pick**> First point: Digitize the upper left corner of the pad. <**pick**> Second point: Digitize the upper right corner of the pad. <**pick**> Third point: Digitize the lower left corner of the pad. <**pick**> Fourth point: Digitize the lower right corner of the pad. <**pick**> Fifth point: <**return**>

Draw the second support pad by using the COPY command to make a copy of the first.

Save the pier as a block with the name **Pier**. The insertion point is the middle point of the top line of the pier, as illustrated in Fig. 16.1.

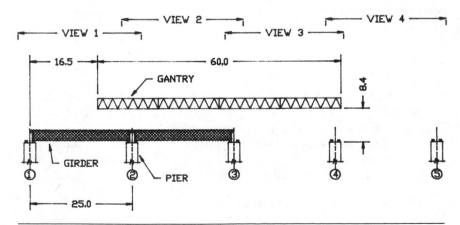

Figure 16.2 Initial position of gantry and view locations.

16.1.4 Gantry supports

The gantry has three supports: Fixsup1, the far left support; Fixsup2, the far right support; and Movsup, the middle support. They are illustrated in Figs. 16.1 and Fig. 16.3.

Set the current layer as **Sups**. Prior to drawing the gantry supports, a roller will be created and stored as a block. The roller can then be inserted onto the supports as required.

Ver. 2.1

```
ROOT MENU <pick> DRAW <pick> PLINE <pick> From point: Digitize a point in a clear
space on the monitor. <pick>

Current line-width 0.00

Arc/Close/Halfwidth/Line/Undo/Width/<Endpoint of line>:
```

To set the width to the radius of the circle select the W (width) option:

```
w <return> Starting width <0.0>: 0.2 <return> Ending width <0.2>: <return>
```

The options will be displayed again. Select the A (arc) option to draw a semicircle:

```
Arc/Close/Halfwidth/Line/Undo/Width/<endpoint of line>: a <return>
```

Select the CE (center) option from the arc options:

```
Angle/CEnter/CLose/Direction/Halfwidth/line/Radius/Second pt/Undo/
Width/<Endpoint of arc>: ce <return> Center point: @0.1<0 (The current cursor
position is at the middle of the 0.2 unit width line, i.e., 0.1 units from the left side. The center
of the 0.4 unit diameter circle is 0.2 which is 0.1 units from the current cursor position.)
<pick>
```

Select A (angle) from the next set of options to specify the number of degrees required to rotate the line and draw the semicircle:

```
Angle/Length/<End point>: a <return> Included angle: 180 <return>
```

Finally, select the CL (close) command to close the arc polyline, forming a circle:

```
Angle/CEnter/CLose/Direction/Halfwidth/Line/Radius/Second pt/Undo/
Width/<Endpoint of arc> : cl <return>
```

Ver. 2.5 to Release 10. Although the previous method can also be used to draw a solid circle, the DOUGHNUT (or DONUT) command is much easier to use:

INITIAL POSITION OF GANTRY ON BRIDGE.

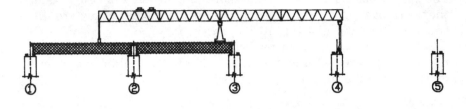

MOVE NEW GIRDER INTO BAYS 2 & 3 (ZOOMED VIEW).

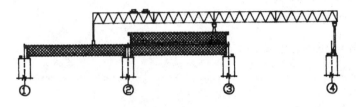

RAISE LEFT FIXED SUPPORT &
MOVE GANTRY 15 FEET TO THE RIGHT.

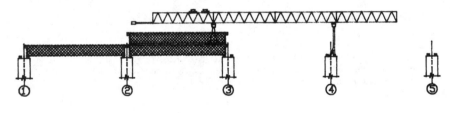

USING HOISTS, MOVE GIRDER INTO POSITION BETWEEN BAYS 3-4.

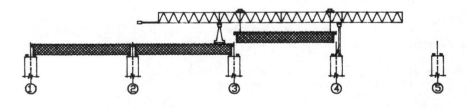

Figure 16.3 Slide show views.

LOWER GIRDER INTO PLACE.

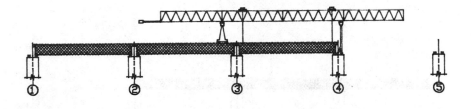

RELEASE HOIST CABLES &
MOVE GANTRY 10 FEET TO THE RIGHT.

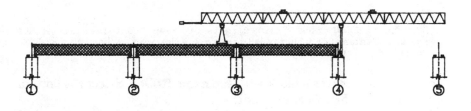

ZOOMED VIEW OF BAYS 2-5.
LOWER LEFT FIXED SUPPORT &
MOVE MIDDLE SUPPORT TO THE RIGHT.

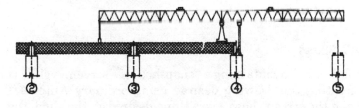

MOVE RIGHT SIDE SUPPORT FROM PIER 4 TO PIER 5.
ZOOMED VIEW

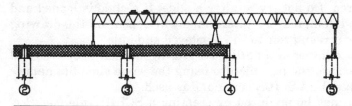

Figure 16.3 *(Continued)*

FINAL POSITION OF SEQUENCE.
START POSITION OF NEXT SEQUENCE.

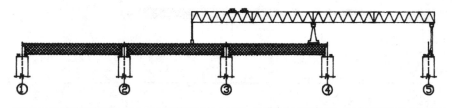

Figure 16.3 *(Continued)*

DRAW **<pick>** DONUT **<pick>** Inside diameter: **0** **<return>** Outside diameter: **0.4**
<return> Center of doughnut: Digitize a point in a clear space on the monitor. **<pick>**
Center of doughnut: **<return>**

Save the solid circle as a block with the name **Roller**. Select the bottom
of the circle as the insertion point.

Draw each of the gantry supports and save each as a block. The critical
dimension is the overall height of each, which is illustrated in Fig. 16.1.
The other dimensions can be estimated.

Draw the hoist block illustrated in Fig. 16.1. The hoist should be
drawn on the **Const** layer.

16.2 AutoCAD Slides

An AutoCAD slide is a file containing a "snapshot" of a screen. A slide is
produced by creating the drawing desired using ordinary AutoCAD
commands. When the screen shows everything desired on the slide, the
MSLIDE command is used to create the snapshot slide file. Slide files
have the extension .sld after the name specified for the file. The file name
is any legitimate AutoCAD file name.

Slide files contain only information describing the snapshot saved and
cannot be altered. Do not try to alter a slide. If a slide is loaded and
alterations are attempted, the alterations will appear on the drawing
that was on the screen prior to the displayed slide file.

The only way to change a slide file is to redraw the picture desired and
use MSLIDE to save the new picture using the same slide file name.

To view a slide the VSLIDE command is used.

A slide show may be produced by creating a SCRIPT file (see Sec.
16.10) which contains a sequence of VSLIDE commands that load sequential files. AutoCAD's script facility allows a sequence of commands
to be read from a text file. The procedure is discussed later in this project.

16.3   Slide Dwg-1

Dwg-1 shows the initial position of the gantry on the bridge, as illustrated in Fig. 16.3*a*. The relative dimensions for the items in the initial position are illustrated in Fig. 16.2.

Set the current drawing layer as **Const**. Use the ZOOM <return> A (all) commands to zoom to the initial limits set for the screen (0,0 and 110,70). Press **Ctrl-D** to display the cursor coordinates.

The coordinates 6,20 will be used for the insertion point of the first pier. Since there are five piers to be inserted at a spacing of 25 units center to center, the MINSERT (multiple insert) command is used to insert an array as follows (with Ver. 2.18 you will have to insert one pier and use the ARRAY command to replicate it:

```
AutoCAD <pick> BLOCKS <pick> MINSERT: <pick> Block name: pier <return>
Insert point: 6,20 <return> X scale factor <1>/Corner/X/Y/Z: <return> Y
scale factor (default = X): <return> Rotation and angle <0>: <return> Num-
ber of rows (--) <1>: <return> Number of columns (||||) <1>: 5 <return> Dis-
tance between columns (||): 25 <return>
```

Insert the two girders using the MINSERT command. The insertion point is the same as for pier 1 (6,20), and the spacing of the girders is 25 units.

The 60-m gantry may also be inserted using the MINSERT command. The insertion point is 22.5,27.9 (where $x = 6 + 16.5$ and $y = 20 + (8.4 - 0.5)$). Refer to Figs. 16.1 and 16.2 to understand the calculations used to determine the coordinates. A single gantry section is 15 units long, so there will be four columns in the MINSERT array.

16.3.1   Designate views

As the drawing is continued, you will often have to zoom on a section of the bridge to locate points more accurately. To speed up the drawing process, each of the bays will be enlarged with the ZOOM command, and the view will be named using the VIEW command. After a view is named, it may be quickly recalled using the VIEW <**pick**> RESTORE commands.

```
AutoCAD <pick> DISPLAY <pick> VIEW <pick> ?/Delete/Restore/Save/Window:
```

The valid replies are listed below:

?   Produces a list of the view names currently saved for the drawing

Delete   Used to remove a view from the list of saved views

Restore   Used to display a saved view

Save   Allows the user to save the current screen view

Window   Allows the user to save a view by placing a window around the
            desired view area

The W (window) command will be used to specify the view. The view is to
be named 1 (reducing the typing required):

w <**return**> View Name: **1** <**return**> First point: Place a window around the bridge
area enclosing piers 1 and 2. See View 1, marked in Fig. 16.2. <**pick**>

Press **Enter** to recall the VIEW command, and then save views 2, 3,
and 4, as illustrated in Fig. 16.2.

To display view 1, the R (restore) command is used. Recall the VIEW
command:

<**return**> ?/Delete/Restore/Save/Window: **r** <**return**> View name: **1** <**return**>

Insert Fixsup1 at the lower left corner of the gantry. Use the INT
(intersect) object snap to digitize the point of insertion.

Restore view 2 and insert Movsup 30 units to the right of the left end of
the gantry. Since the last point was the left end of the gantry, the
insertion point is entered relative to that point as @30<0.

Insert the first hoist on top of the gantry at coordinates 32.5,30.4, and
insert the second hoist at coordinates 35.5,30.4.

Restore view 3, and insert Fixsup2 using an insertion point at the left
side of the right support pad on pier 4 (see Fig. 16.3a).

16.3.2   Use attributes to draw pier
column numbers

The pier mark numbers will be enclosed in a 2.5-unit-diameter circle,
which will allow room for a 1.5-unit-high number inside the circle:

DRAW <**pick**> CIRCLE <**pick**> 3P/2P/TTR <Center point>: Digitize a point on the
screen outside of the current drawing. <**pick**> Diameter/<Radius>: **d** <**return**> Diameter: **2.5** <**return**>

Attributes are used to allow insertion of each pier column-number
block with a different number:

AutoCAD <**pick**> BLOCKS <**pick**> ATTDEF <**pick**>
Attribute modes—Invisible:N Constant:N Verify:N Preset:N
Enter (ICVP) to change, RETURN when done:

Since none of the definitions are to be changed, the Enter key is pressed:

<**return**> Attribute tag: **2** (A number is used to see how it fits inside the circle.)
<**return**> Attribute prompt: **#** <**return**> Default Attribute value: <**return**>

Text. Startpoint or Align/Center/Fit/Middle/Right/Style: Digitize a point inside the 2.5-unit circle indicating the lower left corner of the attribute number. **<pick>** Height: **1.5** **<return>** Rotation angle <0.0>: **<return>**

The attribute tag 2 will now be displayed inside the 2.5-unit circle. Use the MOVE command to locate it properly in the circle (unless it is already centered).

Save the block. The insertion point should be the top of the circle.

Regenerate view 1 and insert the pier column number at the bottom center line of the pier, as illustrated in Fig. 16.2. Add the pier column numbers to each of the other piers.

16.3.3   Adding text

Use the ZOOM <return> A (all) commands to obtain a view of the entire bridge. The start location for the text will be coordinates 6,50. The text height will be selected as 1.5 units to adequately allow reading of the text when the views are displayed.

DRAW **<pick>** next **<pick>** TEXT **<pick>** Start Point or Align/Center/Fit/Middle/Right/Style: **6,50** **<return>** Height: **1.5** **<return>** Rotation angle <0.0>: **<return>** Text: **INITIAL POSITION OF GANTRY ON BRIDGE.** **<return>**

16.3.4   Saving the slide

Be sure that the drawing includes all of the items illustrated in Fig. 16.3*a*. This drawing will be the first slide, which is to be named dwg-1.

AutoCAD **<pick>** UTILITY **<pick>** SLIDES **<pick>** MSLIDE **<pick>** Slide file: **b:dwg-1** **<return>**

It is important to enter the drive letter B: at the beginning of the file name so that the slide view is saved on the disk in drive B. If you are saving your files on a fixed disk, you should replace the drive designation, B:, with the path to the file that the slide is to be stored in.

This screen is now saved on the disk in drive B, with the name dwg-1.sld. The file size will be small since only information locating the vectors on the screen is saved.

Although it is not necessary, you may now wish to save a *drawing* file copy of this screen. Remember that slides cannot be altered—if you later wish to change the slide and you have saved the screen in a drawing file, you can change the drawing file and then resave the slide. The only real problem in saving the drawing file is that it will contain all the information about the drawing and hence use up disk space. If you do wish to save the screen, use the SAVE command and use an original name such as B:Fig__16-1. This can be done for each slide (using consecutive names

B:Fig__ 16-2, B:Fig__ 16-3, etc.). When the project is complete and the slides are considered final, the drawing files can be erased to conserve disk space by typing the DOS command, del B:fig__ 16.2–?.*.

16.4   Slide Dwg-2

Dwg-2 illustrates the positioning of a new girder in preparation for lifting into bays 3 and 4 (see Fig. 16.3*b*). This girder is located 25 units to the right and 3 units (girder depth plus 0.4 units for rollers) above the insertion point of the first pier. The cursor's *last* position will be set on the insertion point of the first pier, and you can then insert the new girder @25,3 units relative to that position. The cursor's *last* position is set as follows:

```
DRAW <pick> POINT <pick> Point: Points example <pick>
```

The point modes will be displayed. Notice that point 1 is a null point. That is set as follows:

```
Pdmode <pick> New value for PDMODE <0>: 1 <return> Remove example <pick>
POINT <pick> Point: * * * * INSert <pick> of Place the target over the insertion point
of the first pier. <pick>
```

Set the PDMODE back to **0** and then insert the new girder @**25,3** units relative to the cursor's last point.

Use the ZOOM command to enlarge a view of the bridge from piers 1 to 4.

At coordinates 31,50, add the text "MOVE NEW GIRDER INTO BAYS 2 & 3."

Use the MSLIDE command to save this screen, using the file name B:Dwg-2.

16.5   Slide Dwg-3

In Dwg-3 Fixup1 is raised and the gantry is moved 15 units to the right.

Use the VIEW command to regenerate view 2 (bays 2 and 3).

To raise Fixsup1, first erase the current Fixsup1. Then insert a new Fixsup1 onto the end of the gantry with an insertion angle of −90 degrees.

Move the gantry, hoists, and Fixsup1 15 units to the right, as illustrated in Fig. 16.3*c*:

```
EDIT <pick> MOVE <pick> Select objects: w <return> First point: Place a
window enclosing the gantry, hoists, and Fixsup1. <pick> <return> Base point or
displacement: @15<0 <return>
```

Use the ZOOM <return> A (all) commands to view the entire bridge. Add the following text to the drawing:

DTEXT <**pick**> Start point or Align/Center/Fit/Middle/Right/Style: **6.50** <**return**> Height <1.5>: <**return**> Rotation angle <0.0>: <**return**> Text: **RAISE LEFT FIXED SUPPORT &** <**return**> Text: **MOVE GANTRY 15 FEET TO THE RIGHT.** <**return**> <**return**>

Save the slide using the name **B:Dwg-3**.

16.6 Slides Dwg-4, Dwg-5, and Dwg-6

In Dwg-4 the girder is picked up by the hoists and moved into position over and between piers 3 and 4. The MOVE command is used to move the girder 25 units to the right. To select the object to be moved, digitize a point on the girder. The "Base point or displacement" is entered as **@25<0**.

The left hoist is then moved 10 units to the right (@10<0), and the right hoist is moved 29 units to the right.

Use the VIEW command to view bays 3 and 4 (view 3), and then use the LINE command to add cables connecting the hoists to the girder, as illustrated in Fig. 16.3*d*.

Enter ZOOM <return> A (all) and then add the text "USING HOISTS, MOVE GIRDER INTO POSITION BETWEEN BAYS 3–4." Save the slide as **B:Dwg-4**.

In Dwg-5 the girder is lowered (moved) into position (@3<270). Add the text to the screen as illustrated in Fig. 16.3*e*, and save the slide as **B:Dwg-5**.

In Dwg-6 the hoist cables are erased and the gantry, including the hoists and the left gantry support, are moved 10 units to the right. Add the text illustrated in Fig. 16.3*f* and save the slide as **B:Dwg-6**.

16.7 Slides Dwg-7, Dwg-8, and Dwg-9

Both Dwg-7 and Dwg-8 are zoomed views of the bridge from bays 2 to 5.

Remember to use views 1 to 4 to provide enlarged views of the bridge bays when drawing.

In Dwg-7, the Fixsup1 is erased and inserted in a lowered position, as illustrated in Fig. 16.3*g*. The Movsup is then moved 25 units (@25<0) to the right.

Add the text to the drawing at coordinates 31,50 and save the slide using the name **B:Dwg-7**.

In Dwg-8, the Fixsup2 is moved from pier 4 to pier 5 by 25 units (@25<0). The hoists are then moved back to the left end of the gantry in preparation for the next girder to be installed. They are moved back by the amount they were moved forward in Dwg-4, i.e., the left hoist is moved @−10<0 and the right hoist is moved @−29<0.

Add the text illustrated in Fig. 16.3*h* and save the slide as **B:Dwg-8**.

Dwg-9 is a ZOOM <return> A (all) view of Dwg-8 with the text illustrated in Fig. 16.3*i* added.

16.8   Writing the Script

A script file is a text file with the extension .scr, which contains a list of AutoCAD commands incorporating a sequence of drawing operations that can be read by AutoCAD. The script file may be invoked while booting AutoCAD or from the drawing editor mode.

In this project, a script file that will automatically load and display the bridge slides, thereby creating a slide show, will be written. The script file will be set up to be invoked from the drawing editor by using the SCRIPT command. The alternate procedure of invoking the script file when booting AutoCAD will also be discussed.

The script file will be written using the EDLIN program (see Sec. 11.6). The syntax for writing script files is different in many ways from that used in menu files. In both, a space invokes the Enter key; however, the semicolon (;) does not invoke the Enter key in script files. Other menu file commands such as / and + also do not apply to script files.

The script file for the slide show is listed below. A discussion of the file will follow the listing. Read the discussion before writing the file with EDLIN. The number and the colon at the front of each line represent the EDLIN prompt and are not part of the file.

Boot up DOS and then load EDLIN. A script file must have the extension .scr. The script file is to be named Bridge-s.scr.

```
C:\>EDLIN B:bridge-s.scr

 1:   layer new const set const
 2:
 3:   limits 0,0 110,70 zoom all
 4:   line 10,10 100,10 100,60 10,60 c
 5:   text c 55,40 2 0
 6:   PRECAST CONCRETE BRIDGE CONSTRUCTION
 7:      BY
 8:      EASY CONSTRUCTION INC.
 9:   vslide *b:dwg−1
10:   delay 2000
11:   vslide
12:   vslide *b:dwg−2
13:   delay 4000
14:   vslide
15:   vslide *b:dwg−3
16:   delay 4000
17:   vslide
18:   vslide *b:dwg−4
19:   delay 4000
```

```
20:   vslide
21:   vslide *b:dwg-5
22:   delay 4000
23:   vslide
24:   vslide *b:dwg-6
25:   delay 4000
26:   vslide
27:   vslide *b:dwg-7
28:   delay 4000
29:   vslide
30:   vslide *b:dwg-8
31:   delay 4000
32:   vslide
33:   vslide *b:dwg-9
34:   delay 4000
35:   vslide
36:   delay 6000
37:   quit
38:   'C (Ctrl-C to exit)
```

Be sure that the file you have written is exactly the same as the one illustrated. Then press e to exit EDLIN. A discussion of the script file follows:

Line 1   Calls the LAYER command, creates a new layer called Const, and sets the current layer as Const. The other layers used in the script drawings do not have to be created since this will be done automatically when the entities on them are inserted into the drawing. Making the current layer Const eliminates the possible problems resulting if layer 0, which was not used in the slide drawings, was turned off when creating the slides. The space between commands invokes the Enter key and is required to call a command. The Enter key is also invoked when the Enter key is pressed at the end of each line when using EDLIN.

Line 2   This is a blank line to invoke the Enter key required to exit the LAYER command. When writing script files, you must keep the *AutoCAD User Reference* manual handy to ensure that the syntax for each command is correct, i.e., in this case the LAYER command is not exited unless the Enter key is called.

Line 3   Sets the drawing limits and zooms.

Line 4   Draws a rectangle on the screen with a 10-unit border.

Line 5   Calls the TEXT command with the C (center) option. The center point is then specified as coordinates 55,40, the text height is 2 units, and the rotation angle is 0 degrees.

Line 6   This is the text to be printed on the screen. The end of that line of text is indicated by the Enter key, which is pressed when ending the line with EDLIN.

Lines 7 and 8 These lines begin with two blank spaces (one space for Ver. 2.18) which invoke the Enter key to recall the previous TEXT command. Remember that when TEXT is recalled, it uses the same height and angle as used for the initial command and places the next text directly below the previous line—in this case, centered since the initial command was for centered text. The text is then printed out.

Line 9 The VSLIDE command is used to call a slide. In this case, the slide file name is preceded with an asterisk (*) indicating that the slide file is to be loaded but not shown yet. It will be shown when VSLIDE is next encountered. If the file name is not preceded with an asterisk, the file is loaded and shown immediately. This preloads the slide, thereby eliminating the delay caused by AutoCAD having to read the file from the disk when it is to be shown.

Line 10 The DELAY command is used to delay the slide show, allowing the viewer to see the current screen before viewing the next screen. The current screen contains the rectangle which encloses the text of lines 6, 7, and 8. A DELAY of 1000 takes about 1 second, so a delay of about 2 seconds is invoked.

Line 11 This VSLIDE command causes AutoCAD to display the slide B:Dwg-1 that was preloaded in line 9.

Line 12 Preloads B:Dwg-2.

Line 13 Delays AutoCAD operations for about 4 seconds to allow the viewer to see the current slide B:Dwg-3.

Lines 14 to 34 A continuous sequence of displaying a preloaded file, preloading the next, and delaying the AutoCAD sequence for about 4 seconds.

Line 36 Delays the AutoCAD operation for about 6 seconds to allow the viewer to see the last slide in the slide show.

Line 37 Invokes the AutoCAD QUIT command. The Y (yes) response cannot follow the QUIT command here. Refer to the discussion in Sec. 16.8.2 for the reason.

16.8.1 Invoking the script

This script is designed to be invoked from the AutoCAD drawing editor by the SCRIPT command. Boot up AutoCAD and begin a new drawing named **B:Bridge**. When the drawing editor is loaded, use the SCRIPT command to load the file Bridge-s.scr. Notice that the .scr extension should not be specified when naming the file to be called. The drive containing the file must be specified:

```
AutoCAD <pick> UTILITY <pick> SCRIPT <pick> Script file: b:bridge-s
<return>
```

The file will now be invoked and the slide show will be displayed. If the show is interrupted because of an error in the script file, exit AutoCAD and correct the error in the script file using EDLIN. If you wish to see the remainder of the file prior to making the corrections, enter the RESUME command.

You may interrupt a slide show at any time by pressing Ctrl-C or the Backspace key. To continue the show enter RESUME.

If you wish to invoke the script file when booting AutoCAD, you will have to add the following line to the beginning of the script file:

```
1: 1 b:bridge
```

The 1 calls the "Begin a NEW drawing" command from the AutoCAD main menu. The name of the drawing is entered as B:Bridge. The modified script file would then be called when booting AutoCAD from DOS as follows:

```
C:\>ACAD b:bridge b:bridge-s
```

Bridge is the drawing name and Bridge-s is the name of the script file. The B: indicates that both reside on drive B.

16.8.2 Continuous scripts

The script file illustrated in Sec. 16.8 is designed to be invoked from the drawing editor. The file ends with the QUIT command. When the program reaches the QUIT command, you will be asked, "Really want to discard all changes to drawing?" If your response is Y, AutoCAD will exit the drawing editor without saving the current drawing file and will display the main menu. If you respond with N, AutoCAD will remain in the drawing editor and wait for you to enter a command. You may rerun the slide show by using the SCRIPT command.

The script may be made continuous by adding the following command to the end of the script file listed in Sec. 16.8:

```
37: RSCRIPT
```

The RSCRIPT command restarts scripts that were *invoked from the drawing editor* using the SCRIPT command from the beginning of the file. This command does not cause AutoCAD to exit the drawing editor and consequently cannot be used in script files invoked from the main menu, as discussed in Sec. 16.8.1. Such files begin with main menu responses that are not valid in the drawing editor.

To create a continuous script for a file invoked from the main menu, add one of the following commands to the end of the file:

37: **QUIT Y**
or
37: **END**

Both commands cause AutoCAD to exit the drawing editor and restart a script file at the beginning.

The script file in Sec. 16.8 is invoked in the drawing editor and begins with drawing editor commands. If line 37 in that file used either of the above commands, AutoCAD would exit the drawing editor and attempt to restart the script file at the beginning but from the main menu. The main menu would not accept the command in line 1 as a valid response.

When the script is rerun, it rewrites the text, in lines 1 to 8, over the previous text. This problem can be rectified by making a drawing of the text screen which is viewed as a slide in place of the text.

Alter the file in Sec. 16.1 to make it continuous, and run it. Then alter the file so that it can be invoked from the main menu and is also continuous.

17

User-Coordinate System

OBJECTIVE *Complete a multiview drawing of an industrial building using Release 10's three-dimensional capabilities, user-coordinate systems, viewports, and view commands. To complete this project you must have Release 10 (or later) of AutoCAD and a mouse or a digitizing tablet.*

DRAWING *Begin a new drawing named* **B:Proj-17**. *Set the units to decimal (mm) with zero digits to the right of the decimal. The drawing is to be plotted on an A4 (297 by 420 mm) sheet using a scale of 1:200. The screen limits are based on the floor plan dimensions of 18,000 by 22,000 mm. In order to allow room for dimensions, set the screen limits as 0,0 and 28000,32000. The completed drawing is illustrated in Fig. 17.1.*

17.1 Release 10 Coordinate Systems

Release 10 uses a fixed "world coordinate system" (WCS) and an arbitrary "user coordinate system" (UCS). The WCS is a fixed cartesian coordinate system illustrated in Fig. 17.2. You are already familiar with the WCS since all drawings completed in earlier chapters of EASY AUTOCAD are done on the WCS.

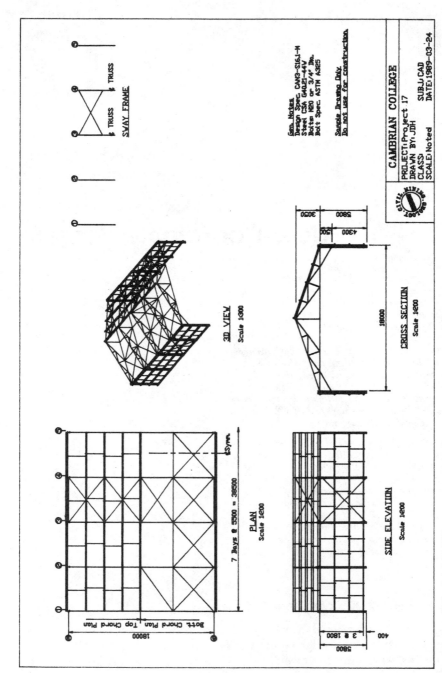

Figure 17.1 Industrial building.

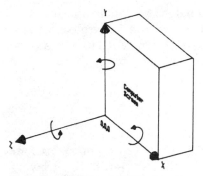

Figure 17.2 WCS and UCS cartesian coordinate system.

Positive rotational angles about an axis are based on the right-hand rule. For example, positive rotation about the z axis is determined by pointing the thumb of your right hand in the positive direction of the axis (out of the screen) and curling your fingers. The direction in which the tips of your fingers point is the direction of positive rotation about the z axis.

The UCS is a cartesian coordinate system which may be defined in any plane of the drawing and is done to facilitate drawing entities on that plane, for instance, on the sloping roof of a house. Any number of UCSs may be defined. The UCS origin is at a location specified by the drafter when the plane is defined.

17.1.1 Coordinate system icon

AutoCAD displays a "coordinate system icon" to show the positive direction of the x and y axis along with other relevant information about the UCS. If the current UCS is the WCS, a W appears in the Y arm of the icon as illustrated in Fig. 17.3a. If the icon is located at the UCS origin, a + is displayed in the base of the icon as shown in Fig. 17.3a and b. If the UCS is viewed from above, a box is formed at the base of the icon (Fig.

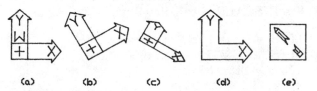

Figure 17.3 UCS icons.

17.3a, b, and c); whereas, if viewed from below, the box is missing (Fig. 17.3d). If either the x or y axis of the UCS is within 1 degree of perpendicular to the screen, the icon displayed is a broken pencil to indicate the UCS is being viewed on edge; therefore, pointing to locations on the screen may be meaningless (see Fig. 17.3e).

17.1.2 Viewports

The computer drawing screen may be divided into as many as four viewports. Each viewport may contain a different view of the drawing and may be zoomed or panned independently. If you modify the drawing or add entities to one viewport, the changes are reflected in each of the other viewports. Since a viewport has a smaller screen area than the full screen, drawing with viewports is only advantageous when the extra view(s) of the entity assist in visualizing and drawing the entity. For instance, since points for an entity may be selected in any viewport, it is easy to envision how the additional views may simplify the drawing of some three-dimensional objects.

Although you can display up to four viewports, only one viewport is the current one. When the cursor is moved into the current viewport, the familiar cross hairs are displayed. If the cursor is moved out of the current viewport into an adjacent one, the cross hairs change to a small arrow pointing in a northwest direction. Changing the current viewport is done by pointing to the desired viewport and pressing the <pick> button on the mouse. The keyboard cursor control keys move the cursor only within the current viewport and cannot be used to select a new viewport.

17.2 Industrial Building

A three-dimensional view of the industrial building to be drawn will fit within a box 18,000 mm wide, 22,200 mm long, and 5800 mm high (at the eave). Prior to drawing the structure, the outline of this box is drawn on a construction layer. Make a new layer named **Constr**. If you have a color monitor, set the color of Constr as **yellow** so the construction lines stand out from the object lines. If you have a monochrome monitor, set the line type as **Dot**. The LTSCALE is calculated using Eq. 6.2 as

$$\text{PLot scale * LTSCALE} = 1 \text{ in * conversion * } 3/4$$
$$1/200 \text{ * LTSCALE} = 1 \text{ * } (25.4/1000) \text{ * } 3/4$$
$$\text{LTSCALE} = 3810$$

The front side of the box is drawn as follows:

> LINE <**pick**> From point: **5000,5000** <**return**> To point: **@22000<0** <**return**> To
> point: **@0,0,5800** <**return**> To point: **@22000<180** <**return**> **C** <**return**>

Notice that the third point entered is 5800 mm along the z axis (perpendicular to the screen). The COPY command is used to draw the back side:

> EDIT <**pick**> COPY <**pick**> Select objects: Window <**pick**> Place a window around
> the front wall. <**return**> Base point or displacement: **0,18000** <**return**> Second
> point of displacement: <**return**>

The end walls are easier to draw on a three-dimensional view of the structure. The VPOINT command is used to view the structure from a point −30 degrees in front of the plan (the negative indicates a clockwise rotation on the x,y plane) and 30 degrees above the plan (positive is counterclockwise from the x,y plane) as follows:

> DISPLAY <**pick**> VPOINT <**pick**> Rotate/<View point> <0,0,1>: Rotate <**pick**>
> Enter angle in X-Y plane from X axis <270>: **−30** <**return**> Enter angle from X-Y
> plane <90>: **30** <**return**>

Complete the box by adding the top and bottom lines on each end wall using the LINE command and the INTersec object snap.

The VIEW command is then used to save the three-dimensional view with the name 3D, as follows:

> DISPLAY <**pick**> VIEW <**pick**> ?/Delete/Restore/Save/Window: Save <**pick**> View
> Name to save: **3D** <**return**>

17.2.1 Coordinate system icon location

The default location of the UCS icon (see Fig. 17.3) is in the lower left corner of the monitor or viewport. When defining a UCS, it is easier to visualize what is being done if the icon is located at the origin of the UCS. The UCSICON command is used to locate the icon at the UCS origin as follows:

> AUTOCAD <**pick**> SETTINGS <**pick**> next <**pick**> UCSICON: <**pick**> ON/OFF/All/
> Noorigin/ORigin <current ON/OFF state>: ORigin <**pick**>

The ORigin option tells AutoCAD to display the icon at the origin of the UCS, provided the origin is on the screen. If the origin is off the screen or too close to the edge of the screen, the icon is displayed in the lower left corner of the screen.

The ON/OFF option visually turns the icon on or off. If the current state is off, select ON to turn the icon on, and then recall the UCSICON command.

The All option is used when you have already created viewports and the UCSICON setting being made is to apply to all viewports. If All is not selected prior to entering an option, the option applies only to the current viewport.

The Noorigin option tells AutoCAD to display the icon in the lower left corner of the viewport.

Since the display currently fills the viewport, the UCS origin is close to the screen edge and, although the ORigin option was selected, the icon is displayed in the lower left corner of the viewport. It will be displayed at the UCS origin if the size of the display is reduced as follows:

```
AutoCAD <pick> DISPLAY <pick> ZOOM <pick> All/Center/Dynamic/Extents/
Left/Previous/Window/<Scale(1)>: .9 <return>
```

The current UCS is the WCS, so the icon is displayed at point 0,0,0 based on the screen limits set.

17.2.2   Defining user-coordinate systems

User-coordinate systems are to be defined on the top (of the box), front side, right side, and sloping roof planes of the building. The origin of the UCS on the top of the box is to have its origin at the left corner on the top of the box and is created as follows:

```
AutoCAD <pick> UCS: <pick>
Origin/ZAxis/3Point/View/X/Y/Z/Prev/Restore/Save/?/<World>:  next
<pick> Origin <pick> Origin point <0,0,0>: * * * * <pick> INTersec <pick>
of Place the object snap box on the far left corner of the top of the box. <return>
```

The UCS icon will move to the top of the box in the lower left corner. Save the coordinate system using the name Roofplan as follows:

```
UCS: <pick>
Origin/ZAxis/3Point/View/X/Y/Z/Prev/Restore/Save/?/<World>:  Save
<pick> Name of UCS: Roofplan <return>
```

A UCS is defined on the front view with its origin at the lower left corner of the view as follows:

```
UCS: <pick>
Origin/ZAxis/3Point/View/X/Y/Z/Prev/Restore/Save/?/<World>:  next
<pick> Origin <pick> Origin point <0,0,0>: * * * * <pick> INTersec <pick>
of Place the object snap target on the lower left corner of the front view directly below its
current position.
```

To put the UCS in the plane of the front view, recall the UCS command by pressing Enter and rotate the UCS 90 degrees in a positive direction about the x axis (based on the right-hand rule) as follows:

```
Origin/ZAxis/3Point/View/X/Y/Z/Prev/Restore/Save/?/<World): X <pick>
Rotation angle about X axis <0.0>: 90 <return>
```

Use the UCS and SAVE commands to save the UCS with the name **Front**. The screen should appear as illustrated in Fig. 17.4.

Define a UCS on the right-side end of the box by moving the UCS origin to the bottom right corner of the front view of the box. Then rotate the UCS 90 degrees about the *y* axis. The view should appear as illustrated in Fig. 17.5. Save the UCS with the name **Rightside**.

The UCS in the plane of the sloping roof is created after the roof trusses have been drawn.

17.3   Columns and Roof Trusses

Building columns are vertical primary structural members that support the building and rest on the footings. Roof trusses are horizontal primary structural members that, in this building, span between columns and support the roof loads. A roof truss is composed of a number of individual members connected in a geometric pattern to form a single member.

The structural framework is to be drawn on a layer named **SS** (structural steel). Use the LAYER command to make the new layer and set it as the current layer.

17.3.1   Columns

The columns are added to the structure by creating a block and inserting it into the drawing using the MINSERT (mutliple insert) command. The

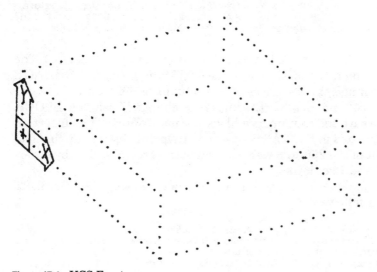

Figure 17.4 UCS Front.

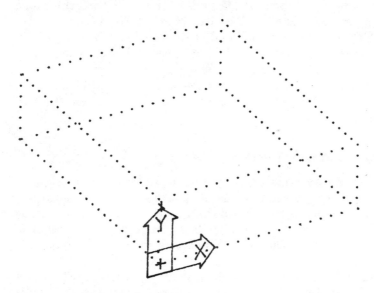

Figure 17.5 UCS Rightside.

column block is to be drawn on elevation 0 in the plan view of the building, which is on the WCS. The WCS is recalled as follows:

```
UCS: <pick>
Origin/ZAxis/3Point/View/X/Y/Z/Prev/Restore/Save/?/<World>: <return>
AutoCAD <pick> DISPLAY <pick> PLAN: <pick> <Current UCS>/Ucs/World:
World <pick> Zoom <pick> Window <pick> Zoom on a window of about 500 by 500 units.
```

Draw the column illustrated in Fig. 17.6*a* (excluding dimensions). The total height (thickness) of the column is 6025 mm. Using the CHANGE command, change the thickness of the column to 6025 units.

After the column height (thickness) is changed, use the BLOCK command to save the column as a block named **Column**. The insertion point is illustrated in Fig. 17.6*a*—use the MIDpoint object snap to select the midpoint of the 250-mm web. Return to the previous view by entering **ZOOM** and **Previous**.

The Column block is inserted into the structure using the MINSERT command as follows:

```
AutoCAD <pick> BLOCKS <pick> MINSERT <pick> Block name (or ?): Column
<return> Insertion point: * * * * <pick> INTersec <pick> of Place the object snap
target over the lower left corner of the structure. <pick> X scale factor <1>/Corner/
XYZ: <return> Y scale factor (default=X): <return> Rotation angle <0>:
<return> Number of rows (---)<1>: 2 <return> Number of columns (|||)<1>: 5
```

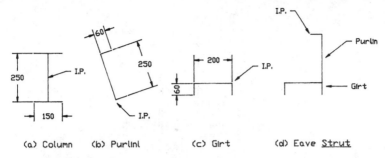

Figure 17.6 Structural components.

<return> Unit cell or distance between rows (---): **18000** <return> Distance between columns (||||): **5500** <return>

In order to see if the columns have been inserted properly, the 3-D view created earlier is recalled:

```
AutoCAD <pick> DISPLAY <pick> VIEW <pick> RESTORE <pick> View name to
restore: 3D <return>
```

The screen view should appear as illustrated in Fig. 17.7.

17.3.2 Roof trusses

The roof trusses are drawn as a block and inserted into the building in each bay using the MINSERT command. Prior to drawing the truss block, the Rightside UCS is restored. In the following command sequence, notice that the view is not displayed when the UCS is restored, and the PLAN command must be invoked to view the *current* UCS:

```
AutoCAD <pick> UCS: <pick>
Origin/ZAxis/3Point/View/X/Y/Z/Prev/Restore/Save/?/<World>:  next
<pick> Restore <pick> Name of UCS to restore: Rightside <return> AutoCAD
<pick> DISPLAY <pick> PLAN: <pick> <Current UCS>/Ucs/World: <return>
```

Use the PAN command to pan the monitor so the building is located in the middle area of the screen.

The Rightside UCS origin (coordinate 0,0) is at the center of the base of the left column. The roof truss' top and bottom chord lines intersect at the center line of left column 5800 mm above its base. The truss width is 18,000 mm, and its peak height is 3050 mm. The truss top and bottom chords are drawn as follows:

```
DRAW <pick> LINE <pick> From point: 0,5800 <return> To point: @18000<0
<return> To point: @-9000,3050 <return> To point: C <return>
```

The truss web members intersect the top chord at its quarter points (see Fig. 17.8). Those points may be located by AutoCAD's DIVIDE command,

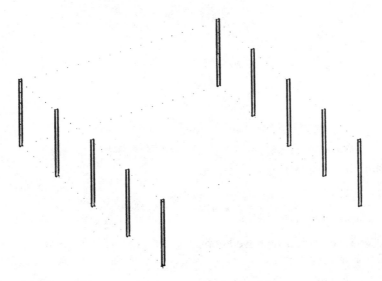

Figure 17.7 3-D view with columns inserted.

which divides a line into equal length segments, placing node points at
the end of each segment (the line is not divided into separate entities).
The nodes can be snapped onto with the NODe object snap. The
PDMODE (see App. F.4) is set to 2 so the segment points are visible. The
commands invoked are as follows:

Draw <**pick**> POINT:<**pick**> Pdmode <**pick**> New value for PDMODE <0>: 2 <**return**> EDIT <**pick**> DIVIDE <**pick**> Select object to divide: Digitize the top chord on the left side of the truss. <**pick**> <Number of segments>/Block: **4** <**return**>

The truss web members illustrated in Fig. 17.8 are to be drawn next.
Since the members are perpendicular to the top chord of the truss, rotate
the snap parallel to the chord:

AutoCAD <**pick**> SETTINGS <**pick**> next <**pick**> SNAP: <**pick**> Snap spacing or ON/OFF/Aspect/Rotate/Style <1>: ROTATE <**pick**> Base point <0,0>: **0,5800** <**return**> Rotation angle <0>: * * * * <**pick**> ENDpoint <**pick**> of Place the target near the top end of the top chord of the truss. <**pick**>

Press **Ctrl-O** to turn the orthogonal mode on.

The truss web members are drawn using the LINE command and
selecting the start point by snapping onto the node points created by the
DIVIDE command. Since snap is set to the angle of the top chord and the
orthogonal mode is on, the lines will be perpendicular to the chord. The
lines are drawn past the bottom chord as illustrated in Fig. 17.8 and will
be trimmed later. The procedure to draw the lines is illustrated below:

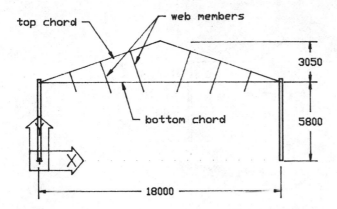

Figure 17.8 Truss mode points.

DRAW <**pick**> LINE <**pick**> From point: * * * * <**pick**> NODe <**pick**> of Place the object snap target at a quarter point on the truss. <**pick**> To point: Extend the line past the bottom chord of the truss. <**pick**> To point: <**return**> <**return**> From point: Repeat the process and draw the remaining three perpendicular chord members.

Points created by the DIVIDE command are placed in the previous selection set, and they are erased by entering the following:

EDIT <**pick**> ERASE <**pick**> Select objects: Previous <**pick**> Select objects: <**return**>

Next, rotate the snap to the angle of the top chord on the right side of the truss, and draw the web members perpendicular to that chord following procedures similar to those used for the left side. After you have completed those members, rotate snap back to the 0,0 origin with an angle of 0.

Press **Ctrl-O** to turn the orthogonal mode off. Draw the remaining web members of the truss illustrated in Fig. 17.9. (Do not draw the knee brace yet.) The web member at the center of the truss extends from the intersection point at the top of the truss to the midpoint of the bottom chord.

The truss is completed by trimming the web members as follows:

EDIT <**pick**> TRIM <**pick**> Select cutting edge(s)... Select objects: Digitize the bottom chord of the truss. <**pick**> Select objects: <**return**> Select objects to trim: Digitize the end of each line that is to be trimmed. <**return**>

Draw the knee brace from the intersection point on the truss to the UCS coordinate 0,4300.

Using the VIEW and Restore commands, restore the view named **3D**. Then use the UCS and Restore commands to restore the UCS named

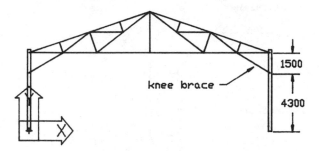

Figure 17.9 Roof truss and knee brace.

Roofplan. You should now have a three-dimensional view of the building displayed with the UCS icon at the far left column, which is the origin (0,0,0) of the Roofplan UCS.

Note: Turn the **Constr** layer off.

Save the roof truss and knee brace as a block named **Truss**. Use a window to select the truss, but select the knee braces individually. Entities selected will be drawn dotted by AutoCAD. If any of the building columns are accidentally selected, use the Remove command to remove them from the selection set. If you make a mistake, use the U (Undo) command to undo the commands and then try again. The block insertion point is at the intersection of the top and bottom chords on the left side of the truss.

The Truss block is to be inserted into the structure using the MINSERT command. Prior to inserting the Truss block, use the ZOOM command and enter a magnification of **0.8**. This is necessary since the Truss block is complex and if part of the truss is off the screen when it is being inserted, your system may be slowed considerably while entering the block.

Use the MINSERT command to insert the block named **Truss**. The insertion point is the origin of the Roofplan UCS, point **0,0**. There are to be 1 row and 5 columns, and the spacing of the columns is 5500 mm. If the trusses are not inserted properly, use the U (undo) command and try again. Your drawing should appear as illustrated in Fig. 17.10.

17.4 Defining the Topchord UCS

A UCS is required on the plane of the top chord of the truss to facilitate drawing entities on that plane. Since there are two sides to the truss, two top chord planes will be defined using the names **Topchordl** (left) and **Topchordr** (right)—as viewed from the right side of the building.

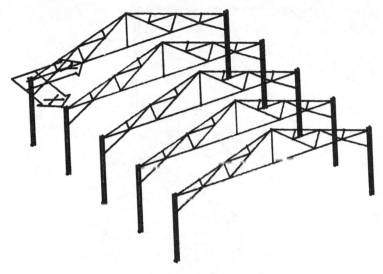

Figure 17.10 Structure with trusses inserted.

The current UCS origin is the top of the building's front left column as illustrated in Fig. 17.10. The Topchordl UCS is defined by rotating the UCS origin so that it lies in the plane of the truss' top chord.

To facilitate the selection of points, use the ZOOM and Window commands to enlarge a view which includes the current UCS icon and the left half of the roof truss located at the left end of the building.

After the view is enlarged, the new UCS is defined using the 3point option as follows:

```
AutoCAD <pick> UCS: <pick>
Origin/ZAxis/3Point/View/X/Y/Z/Prev/Restore/Save/?/<World>:  next
<pick> 3Point <pick> Origin point <0,0,0>: * * * * <pick> ENDpoint <pick>
of Place the target on the left side of the top chord of the end truss. <pick> Point on
positive portion of the X axis <1,5800,0>: The X axis is not being changed so
accept the default. <return> Point of positive-Y portion of the UCS X-Y plane: * *
* * <pick> ENDpoint <pick> of Place the target on the top chord of the truss near the
peak of the truss.
```

The UCS icon should be displayed at the left end of the truss with its x,y axis on the plane of the truss top chord as illustrated in Fig. 17.11. If your UCS icon is located in the lower left corner of the screen, your view may be too close to the edge of the screen (see Sec. 17.1.1). Try panning the view slightly to the right. If you have other problems, enter U (Undo) and retry the commands, being more careful when selecting points.

Save the UCS using the name **Topchordl** (left).

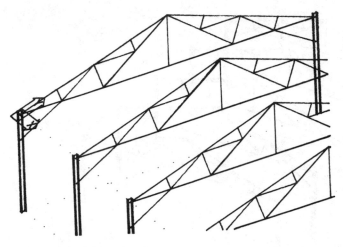

Figure 17.11   UCS Topchordl.

Use similar procedures to define a UCS named **Topchordr** (right). Its origin is the peak of the truss, and the x,y axis is to lie on the plane of the top chord on the right side of the truss, with the y axis pointing to the intersection of the top and bottom chord at the right side of the truss. Save the UCS.

17.5   Roof Purlins

Roof purlins are members on the roof of a structure, spanning between roof trusses, and used to support the roof sheeting. The purlins are to be drawn on the Rightside UCS in the right-end bay of the front of the building. Restore the UCS named **Rightside**, and enter the PLAN command to display the plan view of the UCS.

After the plan view of the Rightside UCS is displayed, use the ZOOM and Window commands to enlarge a view of the left half of the truss. The drawing plane is then rotated parallel to the top chord of the truss as follows:

```
AutoCAD <pick> SETTINGS <pick> next <pick> SNAP: <pick> Snap spacing or
ON/OFF/Aspect/Rotate/Style <1>: Rotate <pick> Base point <0,0>: * * * *
<pick> ENDpoint <pick> of Place the target near the left end of the top or bottom chord
of the truss. <pick> Rotation angle: * * * * <pick> ENDpoint <pick> of Place the
target on the top chord near the peak of the truss. <pick>
```

The truss members are currently drawn as single lines which represent the centroid of the truss members. The roof purlins, however, sit on the top chord of the truss and should be drawn 40 mm above the truss top chord line to account for the actual thickness of the truss member above its centroid.

A line representing the outside edge of the truss top chord is drawn 40 mm above the top chord on a layer named SSLine as follows:

```
AutoCAD <pick> LAYER: <pick> Make <pick> New Current layer <SS>: SSLine
<return> Color <pick> Color <white>: Yellow <pick> Layer name(s) for color
yellow <SSLINE>: <return> <return>

DRAW <pick> LINE <pick> From point: * * * * <pick> ENDpoint <pick> of Place the
target on the truss top chord near the left end. <pick> To point: * * * * <pick>
ENDpoint <pick> of Place the target on the truss top chord near the peak. <pick> To
point: <return>

EDIT <pick> next <pick> OFFSET <pick> Offset distance or Through
<Through>: 40 <return> Select objects to offset: Digitize the line you just drew.
<pick> Side to offset: Digitize a point above the top chord. <pick> <return>
```

You should now have a yellow line offset 40 mm above the top chord of the left side of the truss and a yellow line along the top chord.

Use the ZOOM and Window commands to zoom on a box containing a piece of the truss top chord and sufficient space above the chord in which to draw the purlin illustrated in Fig. 17.6b. Then use the ERASE command to erase the yellow line overlapping the top chord line of the truss. Enter REDRAW to restore the truss top chord line.

Make two new layers named **SSTCL** (SS top chord left) and **SSTCR** (SS top chord right). Set the current layer to **SSTCL**, and press **Ctrl-O** to turn the orthogonal mode on.

In the open space above the truss, draw the purlin illustrated in Fig. 17.6b. After you have drawn the purlin, use the CHANGE and THICK-NESS commands to change the thickness of the purlin to −5500 mm [the c/c spacing of trusses and -'ve since it is into the z axis (screen)]. Save the purlin as a block named **Purlinl** (purlin left). The insertion point is illustrated in Fig. 17.6b.

The roof purlin is to be inserted at the quarter points along the yellow line. Use the DIVIDE command to divide the line into four segments, and insert the **Purlinl** block at the 1/4-, 1/2-, and 3/4-node points along the line, using the NODe object snap (see Fig. 17.12). *Do not insert the purlin at the truss peak.* After the purlins are inserted, erase the node points using the ERASE and Previous commands.

In order to facilitate its connection, the purlin at the truss peak is located 80 mm below the peak along the *yellow* line. The MEASURE command is used to divide a line into equal length segments of a specified length and may be used to locate node points 80 mm apart on the yellow line. Enlarge a view at the peak of the truss using the ZOOM and Window commands. The purlin is inserted as follows:

```
EDIT <pick> next <pick> MEASURE <pick> Select object to measure: Digitize the
yellow line. <pick> <Segment length>/Block: 80 <return>
```

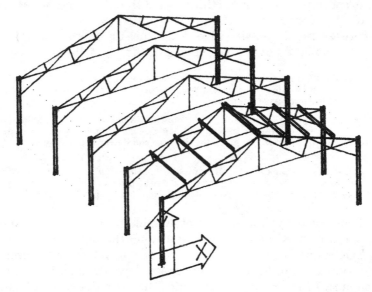

Figure 17.12 Purlins in end bay.

AutoCAD <**pick**> BLOCKS <**pick**> INSERT <**pick**> Block name (or ?): **Purlinl** <**return**> Insertion point: * * * * <**pick**> NODe <**pick**> of Place the target on the first 80-mm node point of the yellow line near the top of the truss. <**pick**> X scale factor <1>/ Corner/XYZ: <**return**> Y scale factor <default=X): <**return**> Rotation angle <0>: <**return**>

The node points defined by the MEASURE command are placed in the *previous* selection set by AutoCAD. Erase them.

Set the current layer as **SSTCR** (SS top chord right), and draw the purlins on the right side of the truss. When you have completed the right side of the truss, use the VIEW and Restore commands to restore the view named **3D**. The completed structure should appear as illustrated in Fig. 17.12. Set the current layer as **SS** and turn the **SSLine** layer off. Set PDMODE to 0 (see App. F.4) so that the points on the drawing revert back to dots.

17.6   Wall Girts and Eave Strut

Girts are members on the exterior walls of a structure, spanning between columns, and used to support the wall sheeting. The girts are initially to be drawn on the Rightside UCS. Restore the **Rightside** UCS and then display the plan view using the PLAN command.

Enlarge a view of the left column using the ZOOM and Window commands.

In an open space, draw the **Girt** block illustrated in Fig. 17.6c. The thickness is **−5500 mm**, and the insertion point is noted.

The Rightside UCS origin is at the center of the base of the left column. The first girt is to be inserted 400 mm above the column base on the outside face of the 250-mm-wide column, so the insertion point is −125,400. The other two girts are spaced 1800 mm and 3600 mm, respectively, above the first girt. Insert the three girts on the left column using the MINSERT command.

The eave strut is a member at the eave of the structure, spanning between columns, and is used to support the roof sheeting and the wall siding.

Enlarge a view as illustrated in Fig. 17.13 and draw line *a* parallel to the top chord by first rotating the snap parallel to the top chord and turning the orthogonal mode on. Use an object snap to snap onto the roof purlin.

Draw the eave Strut block illustrated in Fig. 17.6*d*. It has a thickness of −5500 mm and an insertion point as noted. Insert the strut at the eave of the building as illustrated in Fig. 17.13, and erase line *a*.

Do *not* draw the girts and eave strut on the back wall of the building yet.

17.7   Sagrods

Girts and purlins are constructed from members that are deep and narrow (see Fig. 17 6). As a result they tend to sag about their weak axis and must be supported by sagrods as illustrated in Fig. 17.14.

17.7.1   Viewports

The wall sagrods are easiest to draw if points can be concurrently selected from both the front and right side views. Those two views are displayed in viewports as follows:

```
AutoCAD <pick> SETTINGS <pick> next <pick> VPORTS: <pick> Save/restore/
Delete/Join/SIngle/2/<3>/4: 2 <pick> Horizontal/<Vertical>: Vertical
<pick>
```

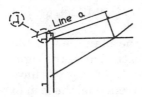

Figure 17.13 Eave strut.

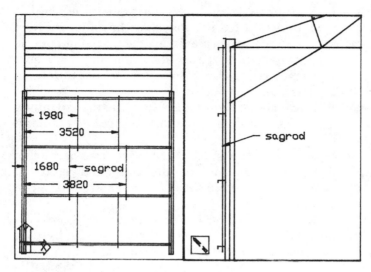

Figure 17.14 Wall sagrod viewports.

AutoCAD divides the screen into two equal size viewports with the current screen displayed in each. The viewport enclosed by the heavier border is the *current* viewport. Move the cursor in that viewport and the familiar horizontal and vertical cursor lines are displayed. Move the cursor into the other viewport and the cursor is changed to a small arrow pointing in the northwest direction. To make that viewport the current one press the <pick> button on the mouse.

Make the viewport on the right side of the screen the current one by moving the cursor into it and pressing <pick>. Enter the following commands to display the Rightside UCS in that viewport:

```
AutoCAD <pick> UCS: <pick> Restore <pick> Name of UCS to restore: Rightside
<return> AutoCAD <pick> DISPLAY <pick> PLAN: <pick> <Current UCS>/Ucs/
World: <return>
```

AutoCAD draws the Rightside UCS plan in the right viewport. Note that the view is zoomed to its extents. Use the ZOOM and Window commands to enlarge a view of the column similar to that illustrated in the right viewpoint in Fig. 17.14.

Make the left viewport current. Then display the plan view of the **Front** UCS in that viewport. Next, enlarge a view of the bay at the right end of the building similar to that illustrated in Fig. 17.14 (sagrods have not been drawn yet). When the Front UCS is the current one, the icon in the right viewport becomes a broken pencil, indicating the UCS is being viewed on edge and pointing to locations on that viewport *may* be meaningless.

The origin of the front UCS is shown in Fig. 17.10. It will be easier to select points in the left viewport if the UCS origin (point 0,0,0) is moved to the bottom of the left column in the viewport. That column is three bays to the right of the current UCS origin, and the column spacing is 5500 mm, so the origin is to be moved 16500 mm (3 * 5500) along the *x* axis. This is done as follows:

```
UCS: <pick> next <pick> Origin <pick> Origin point <0,0,0>: 16500,0,0
<return>
```

The *x* distances to the sagrods on the front wall are shown in the left viewport in Fig. 17.14. (The locations are 150 mm left or right of the one-third points along the girts, to facilitate the connection of the sagrod to the girt.) The *z* position of the sagrods is at the center of the girts as illustrated in the right viewport in Fig. 17.14. When drawing the sagrods, the *x,y* coordinate is selected in the left viewport, and the *z* coordinate is selected in the right viewport. The top row of sagrods are drawn as follows:

```
Ctrl-O (Ortho on)
DRAW <pick> LINE <pick> From point: .xy <pick> of
```

The .XY filter is used to allow entry of the *x,y* coordinates separately from the *z* coordinate. The *x* coordinate is 1980 mm (from Fig. 17.14), and the *y* coordinate is determined by moving the cursor to a point slightly above the eave strut and reading the *y* coordinate from the monitor (press Ctrl-D if the cursor coordinates are not updated as the cursor is moved). The author read the *y* coordinate as 5850. The entries continue as follows:

```
1980,5850 <return> (need Z): Move the cursor to the right viewport. <pick> Pick a
point at the middle of the girt web. <pick> To point: Move the cursor to the left viewport.
<pick> Digitize a point below the middle girt so that the sagrod appears as illustrated in
Fig. 17.14. <pick> To point: <return>
```

Recall the LINE command by pressing Enter, and draw the next sagrod in the top row. The *x* coordinate is 3520 and the *y* coordinate is 5850. Use an .XY filter. The *z* coordinate is picked in the right viewport. Draw the remaining sagrods illustrated in Fig. 17.14. Do not add the dimensions to your drawing.

17.7.2   Back wall girts and sagrods

The girts, eave strut, and sagrods on the front wall are copied to the back wall of the structure using the MIRROR command. The mirror line is a vertical line through the center of the truss in the right side view and must be in the plane of the x,y axis. Use the UCS command to make the **Rightside** UCS current. Next, make the right viewport current and enter ZOOM and ALL to display a full view of the truss in the right viewport.

If the orthogonal mode is not on, press Ctrl-O to turn it on.

Use the MIRROR command to mirror the girts, sagrods, and eave strut. When selecting the objects, digitize them in the left viewport. Use the right viewport and the MIDpoint object snap to select the mirror line at the center point of the truss bottom chord.

Restore the **3D** view in the right viewport to visually ensure that all the purlins and sagrods and the eave strut were mirrored correctly (zoom as required). If necessary use the U (undo) command to undo sufficient commands to retry the MIRROR command.

17.7.3   Roof sagrods

In order to draw the roof sagrods on the left side of the roof, you are to display the plan view of the **Topchordl** UCS in the left viewport and the plan view of the **Rightside** UCS in the right viewport. Zoom on the views as illustrated in Fig. 17.15. (The left viewport illustrates the front half of the roof in the right-end bay of the building.) The current UCS is the **Rightside**.

Set the current layer as **SSTCL** (SS top chord left). Move the cursor into the right viewport and press <pick> making that viewport current

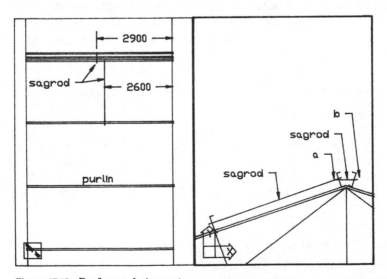

Figure 17.15   Roof sagrod viewports.

(displaying the Topchord UCS). Draw the horizontal sagrod connecting the two purlins at the roof peak as follows:

```
Ctrl-O (Orthogonal on)
DRAW <pick> From point: .xy <pick> of Digitize point a. <pick> (need Z): -2900
<return> To point: .xy <pick> of Digitize point b. <pick> (need Z): -2900
<return> To point: <return>
Ctrl-O <Orthogonal off>
```

The left viewport is not being used to select points. It acts as a visual reference so you can see that the sagrods are being installed correctly.

Prior to drawing the sagrods along the slopping left side of the truss, rotate SNAP parallel to the roof slope. Then turn the orthogonal mode on.

Draw the sagrods by selecting the x,y coordinate from the right viewport and entering the z coordinate from the keyboard. The z coordinate is -2600 or -2900, as illustrated in Fig. 17.15, to stagger the sagrods and allow room for their connections to the purlins. In order to draw the sagrods further down the slope of the roof, you will have to PAN the view in the right viewport to display the purlins that the sagrod spans between. It is expedient to type this command and leave the LINE submenu displayed, as follows:

pan <return> Displacement: Pick a point on the lower girt in the right viewport. <pick> Second point: Pick a point on the next girt up. <pick>

Don't forget to draw the last sagrod connecting the eave strut and the lower purlin.

Set the current layer as **SSTCR** (SS top chord right). Draw the sagrods on the right side of the truss by displacing the plan view of the **Topchordr** in the left viewport and the right side of the truss in the right viewport. Turn the orthogonal mode off and rotate SNAP parallel to the right side of the truss. Then, turn the orthogonal mode on and draw the sagrods following the same procedure used for the other side of the roof.

Restore the **3D** view and ensure that everything drawn is correct before continuing. Leave the 3D view on the screen. Set the current layer as **SS**.

17.8 PGS (Purlins/Girts/Sagrods) Block

The girts, purlins, sagrods, and eave struts in the end bay are to be blocked and inserted into the bays of the building. In order to do so, a number of views of the structure are required. Using the VPORT command, create four viewports and display the following in each viewport:

Upper left viewport. **Roofplan** UCS plan.

Lower left viewport.   **Front** UCS plan. Zoom on the right end bay to enlarge a view containing only the *wall* girts, wall sagrods, and the eave strut.

Upper right viewport.   **3D** view. Zoom magnification 0.9.

Lower right viewport.   **Rightside** UCS plan.

Before continuing, restore the **Front** UCS as the current UCS.

A block composed of the purlins, girts, sagrods, and eave struts in the end bay is to be created. The block insertion point is the lower left corner of the panel, which is a point 16,500 mm along the *x* axis. When asked to select the objects, the Crossing option is used. The Crossing option is similar to the Window option; however, it selects all objects within *or crossing* the window boundary. The commands are:

AutoCAD <**pick**> BLOCKS <**pick**> BLOCK: <**pick**> Block name: **PGS** <**return**> Insertion base point: **16500,0,0** <**return**> Select objects: Crossing <**pick**> Make the lower left viewport current. Then pick the window corners so that the window sides cross the girts and the eave strut and all wall sagrods are enclosed within the window. <**pick**> Select objects: Crossing <**pick**> Make the upper left viewport current. Then pick the window corners so that the sides cross all purlins and the roof sagrods are enclosed within the window. <**pick**> Select objects: <**return**>

If all of the girts, purlins, sag rods, and eave struts do not disappear from the screen, use U (undo) to undo the BLOCK command, and then retry the block entries.

Use the MINSERT (multiple insert) command to insert the **PGS** block into the four bays of the structure. The insertion point is the Frontview UCS origin, point **0,0,0**. The multiple insert is for one row and four columns.

17.9   Bracing

Bracing is used in a structure to prevent the building from collapsing under horizontally applied loads such as wind. It also prevents twisting and racking of the building and must be installed on all planes of the structure.

Create the two viewports illustrated in Fig. 17.16. Turn layers **SSTCL** and **SSTCR** off to provide a clear view of the bottom chord of the truss. Create two new layers named **SSBCL** (SS bottom chord left) and **SSBCR** (SS bottom chord right), and draw the bottom chord bracing illustrated in Fig. 17.16. Bracing on the truss bottom chord along the frontside of the building is to be on layer SSBCL, and bracing along the backside of the building is to be on layer SSBCR. Use the transparent zoom command, 'ZOOM, and/or filters to pick difficult points on the screen. Draw one panel of bracing, save it as a block, and use the

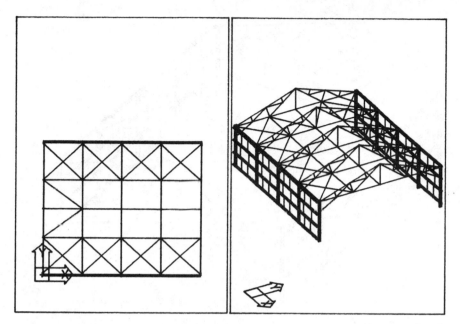

Figure 17.16   Bottom chord bracing.

MINSERT command to insert it into the structure; however, do the front and back bracing separately since they are to reside on different layers.

The **third** bay of the building is to act as a rigid braced frame. Display the view named **3D** in a single viewport as illustrated in Fig. 17.17, and add the side wall and truss top and bottom chord X-bracing to the third bay of the structure, as illustrated in Fig. 17.17. The bracing along the top and bottom chords of the truss extends across the full width of the building. (In Fig. 17.17 the **SSTCL, SSTCR**, and **SSBCR** layers are turned off for clarity. You are to draw bracing on both sides of the bay. Table 17.1 lists the UCS to use when drawing the bracing and the layer on which the bracing is to reside.)

Complete the structure by adding the vertical sway frame to layer **SS**, connecting the third and fourth trusses. In order to draw the sway frame, move the **Front** UCS to point 11000,5800,−9000 creating the UCS shown in Fig. 17.18. The X-brace lines are drawn by entering *x,y,z* coordinates from the keyboard (the UCS origin is always point 0,0,0).

17.10   Multiview Drawing

When a block is created, the UCS in effect at the time of creation becomes the WCS for the block, with its origin as the block's insertion

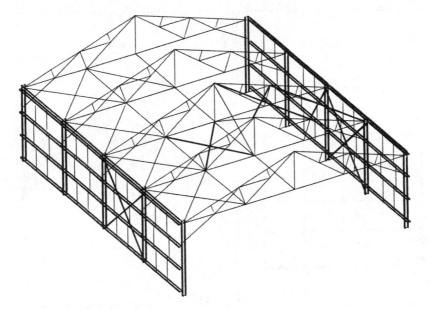

Figure 17.17 Third bay bracing.

TABLE 17.1 Third Bay Bracing

UCS	Layer	Comments
Front	SS	Front wall (use x,y filter, $z = 0$)
Rightside	SS	Back wall (mirror front bracing)
Roofplan	SSBCL	Truss bottom chord, left side
Roofplan	SSBCR	Truss bottom chord, right side
Topchordl	SSTCL	Truss top chord, left side
Topchordr	SSTCR	Truss top chord, right side

base point. When the block is inserted into a drawing, the block's coordinate system is aligned parallel to the UCS in effect in the drawing. As a result, multiview drawings may be easily created by aligning a UCS with the desired view and saving the view as a block for insertion into the multiview drawing. The block may be written to file using the WBLOCK command.

17.10.1 Creating the block files

Turn the following layers on: **SS, SSTCR, and SSBCL**. Turn the following layers off: **SSTCL and SSBCR**. Use the WBLOCK command to

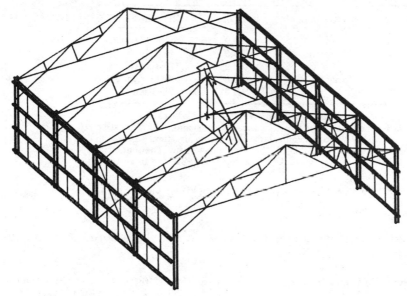

Figure 17.18 UCS sway frame.

create the drawing (block) files listed in the Table 17.2. In each case you
are to display the plan view of the UCS indicated and turn specified
layers on or off. The WBLOCK command is then used to save the plan
view of the structure as follows:

WBLOCK <**pick**> File name: **B:Fig17-rp** <**return**> Block name: <**return**> Insertion
point: **0,0,0** <**return**> Select object: Window <**pick**> Place a window around the
entire structure in the appropriate viewport. <**return**>

After each WBLOCK, restore the screen by entering oops.

17.10.2 Create the multiview drawing

The files listed in Table 17.1 are to be inserted into an A3 (B-size, metric)
sheet. Begin a new drawing named **B:Fig17-p**, and use the Border menu
you created in Sec. 12.7.3 to set the screen limits and draw the border
and title block. [Or, if you do not have the Border menu, set the screen
limits to the size of an A3-sheet, which is 420 by 297 mm (or 430 by 280
mm if you are using B-size paper) and draw a border and title block.]
    Insert each of the files listed in Table 17.1 into the drawing. When

TABLE 17.2 WBlock Files

File name	UCS plan	Ins. point	View in Fig.17.1
FIG17-FV	Front	0,0,0	Side elevation
FIG17-RP	Roofplan	0,0,0	Plan
FIG17-RS	Rightside	0,0,0	Cross section
FIG17-SF	Sway frame	0,0,0	Sway frame*
FIG17-3D	†	0,0,0	3D View

*Only the sway frame and trusses are selected to be Wblocked.
†In order for the block to be stored as three dimensional, a UCS must be created with its x,y plane perpendicular to the viewing direction. Restore the Rightside UCS and the view named 3D in the right viewport. Then enter the following commands to create a UCS in the plane of the 3D view in the right viewport:

```
AutoCAD <pick> UCS: <pick> next <pick> View <pick>
```

using the INSERT command, the scale may be entered *prior* to the insertion point as follows:

```
BLOCKS <pick> INSERT <pick> Block name (or ?): B:Fig17-rp <return> Inser-
tion point: Scale <pick> Scale factor: 0.005 (1/200) <return> Insertion
point: Drag the plan view into location <pick> Rotation angle <0>: <return>
```

The insertion scale for the 3-D view is 1/300.

The final drawing is illustrated in Fig. 17.1. Add the dimensions on a layer name DIM, and plot the drawing using a scale of 1 = 1.

Introduction to AutoLISP

OBJECTIVE *To provide an introduction to the capabilities of AutoLISP through writing, loading, and running an AutoLISP program incorporating the following functions: setq, prompt, user-defined functions, setvar, getdist, list, and command.*

DRAWING *The function draws the plan view of a 3-D house illustrated in Fig. 18.1.*

18.1 Introduction

LISP is an acronym for LISt Processing. It was initially developed for programming artificial intelligence and has numerous dialects. Auto-LISP is one of them. Programs written in AutoLISP allow the drafter to write functions that can interact with the user and automate drawing sequences. All LISP instructions are evaluated as mathematical functions—they take some values, operate on them, and return a value. The function and its values are enclosed in parentheses, ( ). The function name immediately follows the left parenthesis and it is in turn followed by the values to be operated on. A right parenthesis marks the end of the function.

Boot AutoCAD, start a new drawing (use any name), and enter the following LISP functions:

LISP function	Answer
(+ 5 3)	8
(− 8 2)	6
(* 6 5)	30
(/ 18 6)	3
(+ 12 23.0)	35.0 (or 35.000000)
(/ 9 2)	4
(/ 9 2.0)	4.5 (or 4.500000)

You should now understand how to use AutoLISP functions to add, subtract, multiply, and divide. Each expression is enclosed in parentheses, with the first item in the parentheses being the function to be invoked. The +, −, *, and / are AutoLISP's defined functions, which are referred to as "primitives."

Press the **F1** key to display AutoCAD's text screen. Note the difference in answers obtained for the last two expressions. The former expression uses integer data and returns an integer. The latter uses one real number and returns a real number. If the output returned is to be a real number, always ensure that one of the data in the expression also is.

Enter the following: (* 3 (/ 12 4)). AutoLISP returns **9**. Now enter: (/ 24 (* 2 3)—do not add the missing right parenthesis. AutoLISP returns 1>. Enter), and AutoLISP returns the result of the expression, **4**. Notice how you were prompted for the missing right parenthesis.

18.2   User-Defined Functions

In the preceding chapter you used some of AutoLISP's predefined functions. You can define your own functions that may incorporate Auto-

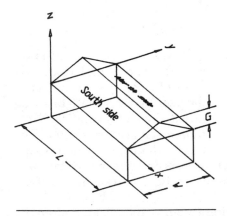

Figure 18.1   3-D house.

LISP's functions and may also incorporate functions you have written. This is the secret of LISP—large functions can be written by incorporating a number of smaller functions.

To improve the readability of the text, AutoCAD's predefined functions are referred to as primitives, and user-defined functions are called "functions."

A program to draw a 3-D house is to be written. It will be made up of a main program that envokes a number of user-defined functions. As such, it can be written and tested in stages. The program incorporates the following:

- Set AutoCAD units to architecture with 1/4-inch precision

- Get input of the building width, length, eave height, and gable end height

- Set the drawing limits (screen width 1.5 * building length, screen height 1.5 * building height)

- Draw the house

18.3 House Function

Begin a new drawing called **HOUSE**. From the drawing editor, enter EDIT to load EDLIN and open a file named **HOUSE.LSP**. (You may precede the file name with a path.) All AutoLISP files must end with the extension .lsp. Enter the following (do not enter the EDLIN line numbers and colon that precede each line):

```
 1:  ; This program draws a 3D house.
 2:  (defun house ()
 3:  ;          ** set system variables **
 4:    (setvar "lunits" 4)   ;Architectural units
 5:    (setvar "luprec" 2)   ;1/4 inch precision
 6:  ;          ** PROGRAM **
 7:    ;(input)              ;Call INPUT function
 8:    ;(drawlim)            ;Call DRAWing LIMits function
 9:    ;(housedrw)           ;Call HOUSE DraW function
10:  )
11:  ; - - - - - - - - - - - - - - - - - - - - - - - - - - - - - - - - - - -
```

The lines preceded with a semicolon, ;, are comment lines and are ignored by the LISP evaluator. They are generally used to improve the readability of the program.

Line 2 of the program uses AutoLISP's DEFUN primitive to define a function named HOUSE (this name does not have to be the same as the LISP file name). The function begins with a left parenthesis on line 2 and ends with a right parenthesis on line 10. All data between those parentheses is part of the function. The right and left parentheses following the function name are necessary. Their function is beyond the scope of this chapter.

Line 4 uses AutoLISP's SETVAR primitive to set an AutoCAD system variable. The variable set is lunits, which defines the linear units in which AutoCAD will be working (1 = scientific, 2 = decimal, 3 = engineering, 4 = architectural).

Line 5 sets luprec, the system variable containing the linear unit's decimal places or denominator. For decimal units the assignment is the number of digits to the right of the decimal. For architectural and engineering units: 0 = no fraction, 1 = 1/2, 2 = 1/4, 3 = 1/8, 4 = 1/16, 5 = 1/32, and 6 = 1/64.

Lines 7, 8, and 9 are currently comment lines since they are preceded by a semicolon. These are actually function calls which will be invoked, by deleting the semicolon, when the program is completed.

Line 10 ends the function with a closing parenthesis. The reader should observe how the entire function is enclosed in parentheses, as are individual expressions within the function.

18.4   Input Function

A user-defined function named INPUT is invoked in line 7 of the HOUSE function. Using EDLIN, add the function to the end of the HOUSE LISP file:

```
12:  ;
13:  (defun input ()
14:     (prompt "\nEnter dimensions in ft & in (ex.6'3–1/4)")
15:     (setq W (getdist "\n\tHouse width: ")
16:           L (getdist "\n\tHouse length: ")
17:           V (getdist "\n\tHouse eave height: ")
18:           G (getdist "\n\tHouse gable height: ")
19:     )
20:  ; - - - - - - - - - - - - - - - - - - - - - - - - - - - - - - - - - - - - -
```

Lines 12 and 20 are comment lines which make things look better in the program listing.

The DEFUN primitive is used in line 13 to define a function named INPUT. The function is enclosed with an opening parenthesis in line 13 and a closing parenthesis in line 19.

The PROMPT primitive in line 14 prints a literal string in AutoCAD's prompt area of the monitor. The literal string is enclosed in quotation marks. The "\n" in the literal string is a control code recognized by the interpreter as a line feed, and it *must* be lowercase text.

Line 15 uses two primitives—SETQ and GETDIST. SETQ binds data to a symbol. For example, (setq a 2) binds the integer 2 to the symbol a, and (setq b 3) binds the integer 3 to the symbol b. The expression (+ a b) returns the value 5.

The GETDIST function pauses for input of a distance. In line 15, (getdist "\n\tHouse width: ") prints the string "House width: " on a new line, controlled by the code "\n", and tabbed to the right one tab distance, controlled by the code "\t". Both control codes \n and \t must be in lowercase text.

The value entered in response to the GETDIST primitive is bound to the symbol W by the SETQ primitive.

Multiple assignments may be made with the SETQ function; for instance, (setq a 2 b 3) binds 2 to a and 3 to b. This is used in lines 15, 16, 17, and 18 to assign the house width to W, length to L, eave height to V, and gable height to G. Each of those values is obtained by a GETDIST function. As required for LISP functions, each GETDIST function is enclosed with a left and right parenthesis, as is the SETQ function which begins with an opening parenthesis in line 15 and a closing parenthesis in line 19. That is how the AutoLISP evaluator keeps track of things.

18.5   Testing the Program

Prior to continuing, the program is to be tested. Exit EDLIN and then load the program from within AutoCAD as follows:

```
Command: (load "house") or (load "b:house")
```

If you saved HOUSE.LSP with the file path \acad\lisp\house.lsp, you must enter:

```
Command: (load"/acad/lisp/house")
```

Note the forward slash used for the file path when working inside of AutoCAD.

The file is loaded when AutoCAD returns INPUT, the name of the last function loaded. If you get 2> instead, you are missing two closing parentheses in your program and must now enter them. If that doesn't work, try entering ")). You will have to fix your program using EDLIN before continuing. Compare it to the one in the text and add the missing parantheses or quotation marks.

To run the HOUSE function enter:

```
Command: (house)
```

AutoCAD will respond with nil. Run the INPUT function by entering:

```
Command: (input)
```

You will be prompted to enter the house dimensions. If that happens, everything is okay. After you have entered all the data requested, enter the following:

```
Command: !w
```

AutoCAD should return the value you entered for the house width—in inches. Data bound to a symbol may be returned while in the AutoCAD editor by preceding the symbol name with !. Get the data bound to L, V, and E. If the data is incorrect or you have other problems, edit the HOUSE.LSP file and compare it to that in the text. Then run it again. Do not continue until you get correct responses.

18.6   Drawing Limits Function

Edit the HOUSE.LSP file and add the following:

```
21:  ;
22:  (defun drawlim ()
23:    (setq min (list (* -1 (/ L 4.0)) (* -1 (/ W 4.0)))
24:          max (list (+ L (/ L 4.0)) (+ W (/ W 4.0)))))
25:    (setvar "limmin" min)
26:    (setvar "limmax" max)
27:    (command "zoom" "all")
28:  )
29:  ; - - - - - - - - - - - - - - - - - - - - - - - - - - - - - - - - - - - - -
```

Line 22 defines a function named DRAWLIM that ends on line 28.

The LIST primitive is used in line 23. An example of LIST is (list 2 3), which returns the list (2 3). LIST is used in line 23 to define a 2-D point specifying the lower left corner of the screen. The lower left corner of the plan view of the house is to be 0,0. The x value of the lower left corner of the screen is calculated as $-1 * (L / 4)$. The y value is $-1 * (W / 4)$. In LISP the expression to calculate the x value is (* -1 (/ L 4.0)). Note that each expression is enclosed in parentheses.

You should note the opening and closing parentheses for the LIST function in line 23 and the SETQ function which starts at line 23 and ends at the end of line 24. The SETQ function assigns a list to the symbol MIN and a list to the symbol MAX.

In lines 25 and 26 the lists bound to MIN and MAX are assigned to the AutoCAD system variables LIMMIN and LIMMAX, which control the screen limits.

After the screen limits are set, the AutoCAD ZOOM and ALL commands are invoked in line 27 using AutoLISP's COMMAND primitive.

Exit EDLIN and then reload the HOUSE.LSP file into AutoCAD using the **LOAD** command (see Sec. 18.4). Since you have not exited the drawing since the last function was run, you do not have to rerun the

HOUSE and INPUT functions because the values calculated by those functions are still resident in the drawing. (If you did exit the previous drawing, you will have to rerun HOUSE and INPUT.)

Run the DRAWLIM function by entering (**drawlim**). Check the screen limits to see that they suit the length and width you entered under INPUT. If not, correct the DRAWLIM function before continuing.

18.7   House Draw Function

Using EDLIN, add the following to your HOUSE.LSP file:

```
30:  ;
31:  (defun housedrw ()
32:    ;                 Draw walls using extruded lines
33:    (setq t (* −1 V))
34:    (command "elev" 0 t)
35:    (setq a (list 0 0) b (list L 0) c (list L W)
36:         d (list 0 W))
37:    (command "line" a b c d "c")
38:    (setvar "thickness" 0)
39:    ;                 Draw roof using 3Dface
40:    ;                    South side
41:    (setq a (list 0 0 0)
42:          b (list 0 (/ W 2.0) G)
43:          c (list L (/ W 2.0) G)
44:          d (list L 0 0))
45:    (command "3dface" a b c d)
46:    (command " " )
47:    ;                    North side
48:    (setq e (list 0 W 0)
49:          f (list L W 0))
50:    (command "3dface" e b c f)
51:    (command " ")
52:    ;                    West gable
53:    (command "3dface" a b e)
54:    (command " ") (command " ")
55:    ;                    East gable
56:    (command "3dface" d c f)
57:    (command " ") (command " ")
58:  )
```

The HOUSEDRW function begins at line 31 and ends at line 58, as indicated by the opening and closing parentheses.

The eave of the house is to be at elevation 0. The side and end walls of the house are drawn as extruded lines, as illustrated in Fig. 18.2. The thickness of the extrusion is calculated in line 33 and bound to the symbol t by the SETQ primitive.

In line 34 AutoLISP's COMMAND function is used to invoke Auto-CAD's ELEV command and to set the current elevation to 0 and the thickness to the value bound to the symbol t.

Two dimension coordinate lists defining the plan corners of the house (see Fig. 18.2) are bound to the symbols a, b, c, and d in line 35. The house

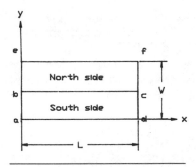

Figure 18.2 Roof plan of house.

walls are drawn by the expression in line 37. Note how the CLOSE command c is enclosed in quotation marks so that the AutoLISP interpreter does not interpret it as a symbol.

In line 38 the SETVAR primitive is used to set the current thickness to 0 since extruded lines are no longer desired.

The remainder of the function uses AutoCAD's 3DFACE command to draw the roof and gable ends. In line 46 the COMMAND primitive is invoked with a null value to exit the 3DFACE command.

In lines 54 and 57 a null value is entered twice in order to exit the 3DFACE command. This is necessary because only three points on the face have been entered in the previous command. Try a three-point 3DFACE AutoCAD using AutoCAD to verify this.

Exit EDLIN and reload the HOUSE.LSP file. Run HOUSEDRAW. If the house plan is not drawn, edit the file and try again.

When you have debugged each of the functions, edit the HOUSE.LSP program and remove the semicolons preceding the function calls in lines 7, 8, and 9. The function calls in those lines will no longer be comment lines and will be invoked when the HOUSE function is run. Erase the house drawing from the screen and reload the HOUSE.LSP file. Run the HOUSE function again. Notice the difference in operation?

For additional information on AutoLISP programming, refer to *Using AutoCAD with AutoLISP* (J. D. Hood, McGraw-Hill, New York, 1990).

18.7.1 Assignment

1. Release 11 of AutoCAD may not have the Elev command. Modify the Housedrw function to run with later releases by removing the Elev command in line 34. Set the thickness by using the system variable Thickness.

2. Modify the House function to draw $1'-0''$ eaves on the roof of the house. Add a function to draw a chimney.

Trouble Shooting Hints

A.1 General Hints

1. Always make backup copies of important drawing files. Remember that disks are a volatile storage device and data may be easily lost. Very important data should have two backups. One backup should be stored in a different location from the others.

2. To run Ver. 2.18 on a floppy disk system you should transfer the following files from the "support files" disk onto your .ovl disk: Txt.shx and Acad.dwg. The file Acad.mnu will have to be placed on each of your data disks.

When AutoCAD is booting, it will indicate that it cannot locate the MENU file and will request the name and location of the file to use. Respond with **b:acad** (assuming your data disk is in drive B).

3. If your menu disappears (you probably typed in the word "menu" as in root menu—which you shouldn't), it can be recalled by entering:

MENU <**return**> Menu file name or . for none <acad>: **acad** (If the Acad.mnu is on the data disk in drive B (see item 2 above), enter **b:acad.**)

4. With using Ver. 2.18 on floppy disks, never remove the .ovl disk from its drive when AutoCAD is loaded.

5. If you enter ZOOM <return> Last and AutoCAD responds with "No previous view saved," that does not indicate a problem. Enter ZOOM

<return> All, and then if you want another view, use ZOOM <return> Window.

6. If you are using a Tandy 1000 microcomputer and the keyboard suddenly appears "dead," press the HOLD key once. Then try the keyboard keys again. If they are still dead, press HOLD again and look elsewhere for the problem.

7. If you press the Enter key to digitize a point and AutoCAD does not accept the point, press the Backspace key a few times and then try the Enter key again. You may have inadvertently pressed another key prior to pressing Enter.

8. If you do not have a plotter connected to your computer, do not call for a plot. Some computers have a nasty habit of hanging up when an unknown peripheral device is called, and they have to be rebooted. If this happens, you will lose your current drawing.

9. Remember that both AutoCAD and EDLIN create backup files with the extension .bak; therefore, if you do not want EDLIN to write a text .bak file over your drawing .bak file, do not use the same name for an EDLIN file and a drawing file.

10. If you plot a drawing and your noncontinuous lines are plotted as continuous lines, you probably have not set LTSCALE properly. This is often forgotten when inserting drawings into the border drawing (see Sec. 12.7).

11. When writing a custom menu, place ^C^C (Ctrl-C) at the beginning of primary commands (i.e., LINE, CIRCLE, INSERT, etc.). This way any residual commands are canceled prior to the primary command being called.

12. When working on a large drawing:

   a. Set LTSCALE to a large value so that all lines appear as continuous. This speeds up drawing regeneration and also simplifies screen picks since AutoCAD does not "see" lines in the gaps. Alternatively, initially set all layer line types as continuous. Then, prior to plotting, set the layers to the desired line type.

   b. Leave all hatching until the end to speed up drawing regenerations.

   c. Use the FREEZE command to freeze any layers not required to be displayed. THAW them prior to plotting.

   d. If the drawing contains a lot of text, use the QTEXT command to speed up drawing regenerations.

   e. Turn FILL off to speed up drawing regeneration. Turn it on prior to plotting.

   f. Use transparent commands extensively to pick points in complex areas. To invoke a transparent command, precede the command with an apostrophe ('). Some useful transparent commands are 'ZOOM, 'PAN, 'VIEW, and 'REDRAW. An example is as follows:

```
LINE <pick> From point: 'zoom <return> >>All/Center/Dynamic/Extents/
left/Previous/Window/<Scale(X)>: Window <pick> >>First corner: (Select)
<pick> >>Other corner: (select) <pick>
Resuming LINE command.
```

From point: Pick the point and use the Dynamic Zoom and Previous commands to return to the original screen.
Another dynamic zoom may be used for the next point also.

13. To make two lines meet perfectly, use the FILLET command with a radius of 0.

14. When working with architectural or engineering units, AutoCAD will give an "invalid entry" response if you attempt to enter dimensions including an inch symbol, i.e., 4'–6". Feet and inches are to be entered with only the foot symbol, i.e., 4'6, with no dash or space between them.

15. When indicating a file path from "inside" of AutoCAD (for instance in a menu file), AutoCAD will accept a forward slash (/) for the file path marker [as opposed to the DOS backslash (\) path marker]. The forward slash must be used for the file path in AutoCAD menu files since, in menu files, the backslash (\) is a keyboard input prompt for AutoCAD.

16. Color can be set *by layer* or *by block* (*entity*). To set color by entity use SETTINGS <pick> COLOR <pick>, etc. All entities drawn will have the entity color regardless of the layer color. It is recommended that you set color by layer only, however.

17. Color by entity can, unfortunately, be set from the COLOR subcommand in the LAYER menu when the LAYER command has been canceled. If you find that entities on a layer have a different color than the layer, you have inadvertently set the color by entity. To fix the problem enter:

```
AUTOCAD <pick> SETTINGS <pick> COLOR <pick> Color <by block>: BY LAYER
<pick>
EDIT <pick> CHANGE <pick> Select objects: Digitize the entities that have the wrong
color. <return>
```

If entities on a block still have the wrong color, you will have to edit the block (see Sec. 10.6).

18. The EXPLODE command is useful to split associative dimensions or blocks into their component parts; however, with some versions of AutoCAD, it also moves them onto layer 0. The CHANGE command can be used to change the entities back onto their original layer and to change the color from BYBLOCK to BYLAYER.

19. Considering item 18, you may wish to turn associative dimensioning off using:

```
DIM <pick> DIM VARS <pick> DIMASO <pick> off <pick>
```

With DIMASO off you can also edit dimension entities individually. But, the commands UPDATE, NEWTEXT, and HOME (see next hint) work only for dimensions drawn with DIMASO set on. DIMASO can be turned on and off throughout the drawing process—but the new setting will only affect dimensions entered after the setting.

20. To change the value of dimension text with Ver. 2.6 to Release 10 use:

DIM <**pick**> next <**pick**> NEWTEXT <**pick**> Enter new dimension text: (do so) <**return**> Select objects:

21. After changing any of the dimension variables, dimensions done earlier may be updated as follows:

DIM <**pick**> next <**pick**> UPDATE <**pick**> Select objects:

The UPDATE command can be used to align text that was printed horizontally by setting DIMTOH and DIMTIH off and then invoking UPDATE.

22. To view all the dimension variables and their settings select the STATUS command in the DIM submenu.

23. Attribute tags, prompts, text locations, etc., can be edited using the CHANGE command.

24. Circles, arcs, and fillets can be smoothed out on the monitor by setting VIEWERS to a larger value (try 500). This will slow down the regeneration of a large drawing, however.

25. If PDMODE is set to 1 (no point), the NODe object snap cannot locate any node along a member placed with the DIVIDE or MEASURE commands.

26. MINSERTed blocks cannot be exploded.

27. Use the UNDO command extensively. The format of the command is as follows:

UNDO <**pick**> Auto/Back/Control/End/Group/Mark/<Number>:

If you respond with a number, that number of preceding operations will be undone. This is a very easy way to get out of trouble. If you undo something that you do not want to, enter REDO.

If you want to experiment with some commands, use the MARK option to place a marker at the beginning of the command string. Later use the UNDO command to undo back to the marker by selecting the Back option.

28. To undo the last command enter U. This is the same as responding to the undo command with the number 1. This is quite useful to restore an entity that was broken with the BREAK command.

29. During dimensioning, the UNDO command erases the most recent sequence. You can repeat UNDO and remove all of the dimensions done during the current dimensioning session, but no further. If you exit from the dimensioning session and then select the UNDO command, it will undo all of the dimensioning done in the session. The REDO command can be used to restore the dimensions.

30. The SCALE command may be used to rescale an entire drawing. To change a drawing from inches to millimeters, first increase the screen limits to suit the larger metric drawing (multiply them by 25.4), then use the commands:

EDIT <**pick**> next <**pick**> SCALE <**pick**> Select objects: Window <**pick**> Window the entire drawing. <**return**> Base point: Enter the lower left corner of the screen (usually 0,0). <**return**> <Scale factor>/Reference: **25.4** <**return**>

31. The STRETCH command is used to stretch entities or move a selected portion of the drawing. The prompt is as follows:

EDIT <**pick**> next <**pick**> STRETCH <**pick**> Select objects: Window <**pick**> Place a window around the entities to be moved and crossing any other entities that are to be stretched when the entities enclosed in the window are moved. <**return**> Base point: Pick the point from which movement is to start. <**pick**> New point: Pick the point to which the entity is to be moved.

32. Use the TRIM and EXTEND commands extensively when drawing. It is often quicker to draw entities longer or shorter than required and to edit them later. Both have a similar format. TRIM is invoked as follows:

EDIT <**pick**> next <**pick**> TRIM <**pick**>
Select cutting edge(s) . . .
Select object: Select the cutting edge. More than one may be picked. <**return**> Select objects to trim: Pick the side of the entity that is to be trimmed off.

33. The digitizing tablet overlay supplied with AutoCAD is very useful if you have a digitizer. The instructions for configuring the tablet are discussed in Appendix A.2.3 of the *AutoCAD Reference Manual* and are quite simple to follow.

34. The SETUP command is used to pick a drawing sheet size and set the scale, units, limits, and snap. It invokes a series of AutoLISP functions. Don't select it unless you intend to use it. Remember that it does not draw a border. The lines represent the sheet size.

35. The size of a drawing file can be reduced considerably by creating a WBLOCK using the drawing name for the WBLOCK file name. When asked for the block name, press Enter. Use an insertion point of 0,0, and window the entire drawing when selecting objects.

Do *not* WBLOCK a Release 10 drawing. If you do, the current UCS becomes the WCS and all UCSs, named views, and viewport configurations are deleted from the WBLOCK file (see Sec. 17.10).

36. When working with two-dimensional drawings with Release 10 the coordinate system icon can be distracting. It may be turned on or off by entering:

SETTINGS <**pick**> next <**pick**> UCSICON <**pick**> (Select ON or OFF)

A.2 AutoCAD Crashes

1. Always read the message displayed after AutoCAD crashes. It will tell you in general terms what the problem is.

2. If your system does not have 512K memory, you may have a number of crashes caused by AutoCAD running out of RAM (memory) space. If that happens, some versions of AutoCAD will display the following message:

Fatal error. If you answer Y to the following, all new entities added to the drawing since the last SAVE will be discarded. Discard entities <N>:

If you wish to save all of the new work you have done on the drawing, answer N (no) or just press Enter to select the default N.

Other systems display a different message:

FATAL ERROR. AutoCAD cannot continue, but all changes to your drawing made up to the start of the last command can be saved. Do you want to save your drawing changes?<Y>:

This message requires a Y (yes) response to save the drawing. Note, however, that in both cases the default answer is the proper answer to save the drawing—so for either message press Enter.

3. If you receive an "Error in copying file." message when configuring AutoCAD, exit to DOS and do the following:

A>**delete acad.bak** <**return**>

Now retry configuring AutoCAD.

4. If AutoCAD crashes and displays the message "Disk full," one of the following may be the problem:

    a. You are using Ver. 2.18 on a floppy system and did not specify in the file name, b:, indicating that the file is to be saved on the disk in drive B.

    b. Your data disk is full. Save the drawing. Exit to DOS and format a new data disk. Then transfer any files related to the current drawing from the previous disk to the new data disk using the COPY command (see Sec. 1.2.8).

c. Your data disk is full *but* you do not have sufficient files to have used all of the disk space. When a system crashes, it does not close out any open files. Often the space used by those files is closed off to other programs; however, the files cannot be accessed by programs since they are incomplete. The abandoned data is referred to as "lost clusters." To delete the lost clusters, releasing the lost space from the disk in drive B, enter the following from DOS:

```
C:\>chkdsk b:/f
```

DOS will report any lost clusters and ask if you wish them deleted. Answer **Y**.

5. Not all "crashes" are crashes. AutoCAD may appear to "hang up" when the ZOOM command is used with drawings where layers containing a lot of entities are turned off. When nothing appears to be happening, AutoCAD is actually going through the process of drawing the layer that is turned off and hence not displayed. Press Ctrl-C and use the LAYER and Freeze commands to freeze the layers that are off, then rezoom. Frozen layers are ignored by AutoCAD when regenerating the drawing.

6. If you are saving your drawing on a floppy disk, do *not* remove the disk from the drive while the drawing editor is loaded. If you do so and continue to use AutoCAD, you *will* have a crash.

A.3 Debugging Drawings

1. To see the data stored for an entity use:

```
AutoCAD <pick> INQUIRY <pick> LIST <pick> Select objects: Select objects to list
data for. <return>
```

2. To see the data stored for an entire drawing use:

```
AutoCAD <pick> INQUIRY <pick> DBLIST <pick>
```

This command may take a long time. To abort the command use Ctrl-C. To momentarily stop the list use Ctrl-S. Pressing any key continues the list. To send the listing to the printer use Ctrl-Q.

3. If you wish AutoCAD to echo all prompts, status listings, and keyboard inputs to the printer, press Ctrl-Q. This key is an on/off toggle.

4. To see the current drawing setup use:

```
AutoCAD <pick> INQUIRY <pick> STATUS <pick>
```

5. If you insert a block or drawing into another drawing and Auto-CAD appears to have taken the time to do something but the entity is not

displayed, enter ZOOM and Extents. The entity may have been inserted off the current screen. If the entity is on the drawing, it should now be apparent.

6. If dots appear when you insert a block into a drawing try setting PDMODE to 1 (see App. F.4).

A.4   AutoCAD's Setup Command

The Setup command in AutoCAD's root menu allows the drafter to select the drawing units and scale and plot sheet size from the menu. Auto-CAD uses the input to set the screen limits so that entities are drawn full size on the screen, and it also draws a box around the extents of the screen limits to outline the *edges* of the plot sheet selected.

If you wish to use the Setup command, it will not be necessary to set the screen limits or the system of units for the projects in *Easy Auto-CAD*. The Setup command does *not* set the units' precision or determine the text height, dimension scale (dimscale), line-type scale, or hatch scale. The CAD drafter must still know how to make those settings. The Setup commands are invoked as follows:

```
Setup <pick> Loading setup...
Select the Units from the Screen menu:
```

The units available are: scientific, decimal, enginrng (engineering), archtect (architectural), and metric.

After you select the desired units, you are asked to "Select the scale from the screen menu:." Depending on the units selected, one of the following scale menus is displayed:

Scientific or Decimal	Metric	Archtct	Enginrng Scale
4 TIMES	1:5000	1/40"=1'	1"=10'
2 TIMES	1:2000	1/20"=1'	1"=20'
FULL	1:500	1/16"=1'	1"=30'
HALF	1:200	1/8"=1'	1"=40'
QUARTER	1:100	1/4"=1'	1"=50'
OTHER	1:75	1/2"=1'	1"=60'
	1:50	3/4"=1'	1"=80'
	1:20	1"=1'	1"=100'
	1:10	3"=1'	OTHER
	1:5	6"=1'	
	FULL	FULL	
	OTHER...	OTHER...	

If your desired scale is not displayed, select OTHER and you will be prompted to enter the scale.

Next, you are prompted to "Select the Paper size from the screen menu:." One of the following menus is displayed, depending on whether you selected an Imperial or metric scale:

Imperial	Metric
Horizntl	Horizntl
Sheet	Sheet
size	size
A-8.5×11	1189×841
B- 11×17	1000×707
C- 17×22	841×594
18×24	594×420
D- 22×34	420×297
24×36	297×210
E- 34×44	OTHER...
OTHER...	VERTICAL>
VERTICAL>	

If your sheet size is not displayed, select OTHER. If you want to use the long side vertical, select VERTICAL> and a set of sheet sizes with the long side vertical will be displayed.

Before proceeding with your drawing, set the units' precision by invoking AutoCAD's UNITS command. You will also have to set the desired DIMSCALE, etc.

Chapter 12 of *Easy AutoCAD* introduces a menu that accomplishes what is done by the Setup menu and, *in addition*, draws a border with a title block *within* the drawing sheet boundaries.

Chapter 14 introduces a procedure that allows you to draw multiscale drawings in a drawing with a border and title block.

Plot Drawing Scale Factors

Scale	Scale factor	Scale	Scale factor
	Drawing units = meters (decimal)		
1:1	1000	1:30	33.33334
1:1.5	666.6667	1:40	25
1:2	500	1:50	20
1:2.5	400	1:100	10
1:3	333.3334	1:200	5
1:4	250	1:250	4
1:5	200	1:300	3.333334
1:10	100	1:400	2.5
1:15	66.66667	1:500	2
1:25	40		
	Drawing units = millimeters (decimal)		
1:1	1.0	1:30	3.333334E-02
1:1.5	.6666667	1:40	.025
1:2	.5	1:50	.02
1:2.5	.4	1:100	.01
1:3	.3033334	1:200	.005
1:4	.25	1:250	.004
1:5	.2	1:300	3.333334E-03
1:10	.1	1:400	.0025
1:15	6.666667E-02	1:500	.002
1:25	.04		
	Drawing units = feet (architecture)		
1/16″ = 1′0″	5.208334E-03	1/2″ = 1′0″	4.166667E-02
3/32″ = 1′0″	.0078125	3/4″ = 1′0″	.0625
1/8″ = 1′0″	1.041667E-02	1″ = 1′0″	8.333334E-02
1/4″ = 1′0″	2.083333E-02	1 1/2″ = 1′0″	.125
3/8″ = 1′0″	.03125	3″ = 1′0″	.25
	Drawing units = feet (engineering)		
1″ = 1′0″	8.333334E-02	100″ = 1′0″	8.333333E-04
1.5″ = 1′0″	5.555556E-02	150″ = 1′0″	5.555556E-04
2″ = 1′0″	4.166667E-02	200″ = 1′0″	4.166667E-04
2.5″ = 1′0″	3.333334E-02	250″ = 1′0″	3.333334E-04
3″ = 1′0″	2.777778E-02	300″ = 1′0″	2.777778E-04
4″ = 1′0″	2.083333E-02	400″ = 1′0″	2.083333E-04
5″ = 1′0″	1.666667E-02	500″ = 1′0″	1.666667E-04
10″ = 1′0″	8.333334E-03	1000″ = 1′0″	8.333334E-05
15″ = 1′0″	5.555556E-03	1500″ = 1′0″	5.555556E-05
20″ = 1′0″	4.166667E-03	2000″ = 1′0″	4.166667E-05
25″ = 1′0″	3.333333E-03	2500″ = 1′0″	3.333333E-05
30″ = 1′0″	2.777778E-03	3000″ = 1′0″	2.777778E-05
40″ = 1′0″	2.083334E-03	4000″ = 1′0″	2.083334E-05
50″ = 1′0″	1.666667E-03	5000″ = 1′0″	1.666667E-05

Contour.bas Program

```
10 CLS:KEY OFF
20 PRINT TAB(25);:PRINT "CONTOUR CALCULATION PROGRAM":COLOR 7,0:PRINT
30 PRINT "The output for this program is printed on a lineprinter. Turn the li
neprinter on NOW."
40 PRINT:COLOR 0,7:PRINT "Press any key to continue":COLOR 7,0
50 C$=INKEY$:IF C$="" THEN 50
60 LPRINT TAB(10) "ELEVATION";TAB(25) "X-DIST.";TAB(40) "Y-DIST"
100 CLS:INPUT "Distance between rows of grid ";DROW
110 PRINT:INPUT "Distance between columns of grid ";DCOL
120 PRINT:INPUT "Enter number of rows in grid ";NROW
130 PRINT:INPUT "Enter number of columns in grid ";NCOL
140 PRINT:INPUT "Enter contour interval";UNIT:PRINT
150 DIM EL(NROW,NCOL)
160 FOR I=1 TO NROW
170    FOR J=1 TO NCOL
180    PRINT "Enter elev. of row";I;" column";J;": ";:INPUT EL(I,J)
190    NEXT J
200 NEXT I
210 FOR I=1 TO NROW
220    FOR J=1 TO NCOL-1
230    ELL=EL(I,J):ELR=EL(I,J+1)
240    IF ELL=ELR AND ELL<>INT(ELL) THEN 340
250    IF ELL=ELR THEN XDIST=DCOL*(J-1):YDIST=DROW*(I-1):ELEV=ELL:GOSUB 500:IF
J=NCOL-1 THEN XDIST=DCOL*(J):YDIST=DROW*(I-1):GOSUB 500
260    IF ELL<ELR THEN LO=ELL:HI=ELR ELSE LO=ELR:HI=ELL
270    ELEV=INT(LO+.99)
280        WHILE ELEV<=INT(HI):IF ELEV=HI AND ELR>ELL AND J<NCOL-1 THEN 320
290        XDIST=(ELEV-LO)/(HI-LO)*DCOL:YDIST=DROW*(I-1)
300        IF ELL<ELR THEN XDIST=XDIST+DCOL*(J-1) ELSE XDIST=DCOL*(J)-XDIST
310        GOSUB 500
320        ELEV=ELEV+UNIT
330        WEND
340    NEXT J
350 IF I=NROW THEN 480
360    FOR J=1 TO NCOL-1
370    ELB=EL(I,J):ELT=EL(I+1,J)
380    IF INT(ELB)=INT(ELT) THEN 470
390    IF ELB<ELT THEN LO=ELB:HI=ELT ELSE LO=ELT:HI=ELB
400    ELEV=INT(LO+1)
410        WHILE ELEV<=INT(HI):IF ELEV=HI THEN 450
420        YDIST=(ELEV-LO)/(HI-LO)*DROW:XDIST=DCOL*(J-1)
430        IF ELB<ELT THEN YDIST=YDIST+DROW*(I-1) ELSE YDIST=DROW*(I)-YDIST
440        GOSUB 500
450        ELEV=ELEV+UNIT
460        WEND
470    NEXT J
480 NEXT I
490 END
500 LPRINT TAB(10) ELEV;TAB(25) XDIST;TAB(40)YDIST
510 RETURN
```

Preparing the Hard Disk

1. Get yourself a good file management systems program. The author uses 1dir from Bourbaki Inc.

2. Make a subdirectory named Acad on your fixed disk (drive C). Transfer all of the AutoCAD files from the Acad.ovl and Acad.exe disk into that subdirectory. Refer to your *AutoCAD Drafting Package, Installation Guide,* and the discussion below. In the following commands the backslash (\) indicates a DOS path and is to be typed in as part of the command.

    a. If the current drive is drive A, set the fixed drive, C, as the current drive (if the display is C>_, skip to step *b*):

A>**c:** <**return**>

    b. Use the MD (make directory) command to create a subdirectory named acad on your fixed disk:

C:>**md\acad** <**return**>

    c. Log onto the Acad subdirectory using:

C:>**cd\acad** <**return**>

    d. Place your AutoCAD Executable disk in drive A and transfer all of the files to the acad subdirectory on the fixed disk using:

```
C:>copy a:*.*/v <return>
```

    e. Repeat step *d* for the each of the AutoCAD Overlay disks.

    f. Repeat step *d* for the AutoCAD Support Files disk.

3. Create a branch of the Acad subdirectory for your drawings. You may want to create a separate branch for groups of drawings. For instance, the branch **Sample** may contain the AutoCAD Sample Drawing files, **Easy** may contain the drawings files created using this text, and **Job-1** may be for other files, etc.

Create the Sample and Easy branches of Acad as follows:

```
C:>md\acad\sample <return>
C:>md\acad\easy <return>
```

4. To transfer the AutoCAD Sample Drawing files to the Sample branch of the Acad subdirectory enter:

```
C:>cd\acad\sample <return>
```

Place the AutoCAD Sample Drawings disk in drive A and enter:

```
C:>copy a:*.* <return>
```

You are now set to use AutoCAD. The first time you run a new copy of AutoCAD you will be required to configure the program to suit your system. Refer to your *AutoCAD Installation Guide* and Chap. 7 in *Easy AutoCAD* for a discussion on configuration.

To return to the DOS root directory enter:

```
C:>\ <return>
```

Refer to Sec. 1.3 of *Easy AutoCAD* for instructions on using AutoCAD on a system with a hard disk drive.

In the exercises that use EDLIN (Chaps. 11, 12, 13, 14, 16, and 18), if you are storing your drawing and text files on the fixed disk follow the procedure outlined below:

    a. Give DOS the path to locate EDLIN. If it is in your root directory enter:

```
C:> path \ <return>
```

    b. To store the file created by EDLIN in the Easy subdirectory of Acad, change the directory as follows:

```
C:> cd\acad\easy <return>
```

In all of the EDLIN files in this text, the author has assumed you will be
storing your files on a floppy disk in drive B. If you are using a fixed drive
system and wish to store your files on the fixed drive, and have followed
Sec. 1.3.1.1, do not precede any file names with the drive designation **b:**.

If you are storing your menu files on a floppy disk, you may follow the
procedure in each of the examples.

With most versions of AutoCAD EDLIN can be loaded from the drawing editor. In order to do so, you must copy the EDLIN.COM file into the
Acad subdirectory. Place your MS-DOS disk into drive A and enter the
following:

```
C:>copy a:edlin.com <return>
```

EDLIN may now be loaded from within the drawing editor by entering
the EDIT command. To load EDLIN and write to a file named house on
drive B, enter the following:

```
command: edit <return>
file name: b:house.mnu <return>
```

When EDLIN is exited, you will be returned to the drawing editor.

Pull-Down Menu

If the graphics card in your system supports the Advanced User Interface (AUI) and you have a mouse or digitizing tablet, you can use the pull-down menu and dialogue boxes to execute AutoCAD commands.

To use the pull-down menu move the cursor to the top of the screen using the mouse or digitizer tablet puck. When the cursor reaches the top of the screen, the "menu bar" illustrated on the top line of Fig. E.1 is displayed. Move the cursor along the Menu Bar until the desired pull-down menu *heading* is highlighted. Press the <**pick**> button to display the pull-down menu.

The pull-down menu under each heading is displayed in Fig. E.1. Only one pull-down menu is displayed at a time. Items are selected from the pulled-down menu using the <**pick**> button. Selections that display a submenu, iconmenu, or a dialogue box are illustrated in Fig. E.1.

A pulled-down menu is removed from the screen when you:

- Select an item from it
- Pull down another menu
- Digitize an unused area in the menu bar
- Digitize a point on the graphics screen
- Type a character from the keyboard
- Move the cursor into the screen menu
- Pick an item from a tablet or button menu

(Menu Bar and Pull-Down Menus)

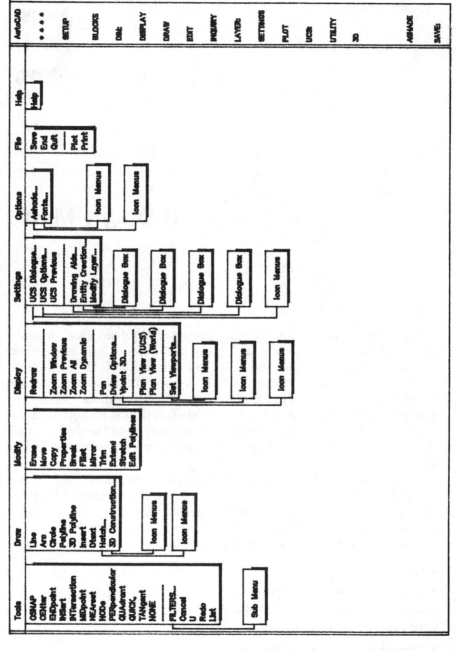

Figure E.1 Menu bar and pull-down menus.

Dialogue Box. The selections **Settings** <**pick**> **Drawing Aids. . .** <**pick**> display the Drawing Aids Dialogue Box illustrated in Fig. E.2. In Fig. E.2 the Snap, Grid, and Isoplane Left mode switches are on as indicated by the check mark in their "check button" (box). If the check button is blank, the mode switch is off. To set a mode switch, the cursor is moved to the desired button and the <**pick**> key is pressed.

The Snap X Spacing is entered by moving the cursor to the X Spacing "input button" (shown shaded in Fig. E.2). When the cursor moves into the input button, the button is shaded by AutoCAD. The desired value may then be entered from the keyboard. The settings are completed by digitizing the OK button, and the drawing editor is returned. To cancel selections and return to the drawing editor, the Cancel button is digitized. Other dialogue boxes are utilized in a similar manner.

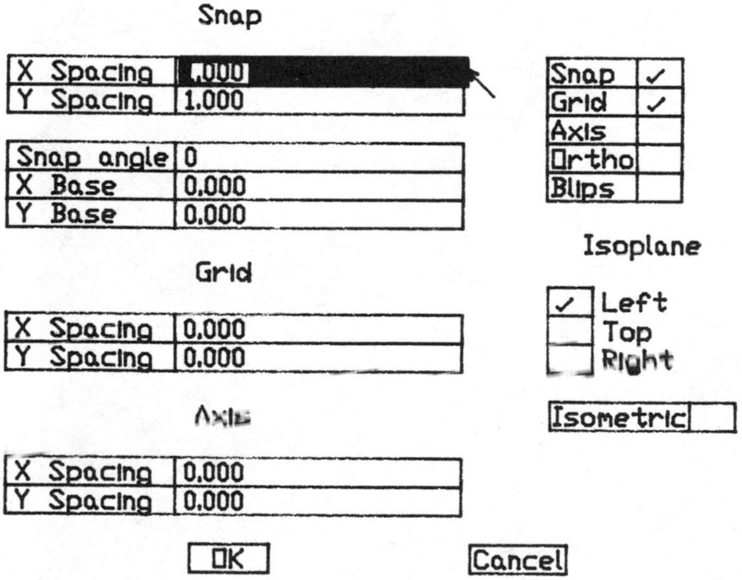

Snap

| X Spacing | .000 |
| Y Spacing | 1.000 |

Snap angle	0
X Base	0.000
Y Base	0.000

Snap	✓
Grid	✓
Axis	
Ortho	
Blips	

Grid

| X Spacing | 0.000 |
| Y Spacing | 0.000 |

Isoplane

✓	Left
	Top
	Right

Axis

| X Spacing | 0.000 |
| Y Spacing | 0.000 |

Isometric

OK   Cancel

Figure E.2 Drawing Aids Dialogue Box.

Other Commands

F.1 Three-Dimensional Draw Commands

The 3DFACE command and defining three-dimensional extrusions of two-dimensional entities are explored in Chap. 17. There are other three-dimensional drawing commands that are beyond the scope of this text. The following is a brief introduction to some of those commands. For a more thorough review the reader is referred to the *Tutorial* notes provided with Release 10 of AutoCAD.

The 3DPOLY command is used to draw three-dimensional polylines.

The 3DMESH command is used to create a three-dimensional polygon mesh with m columns and n rows.

The RULESURF command is used to draw a ruled surface between two previously drawn curves. Both curves must be either open or closed.

The TABSURF command is used to extrude a tabulated surface in a specified direction from a predrawn curved path.

The REVSURF command is used to create a surface by revolving a predrawn profile around a selected axis.

The EDGESURF command creates a surface between four predrawn adjoining edges.

The 3DOBJECTS command loads an AutoLISP file named 3D.LSP that provides commands to construct a number of three-dimensional objects, for example a cone, dome, sphere, and torus. To view and use the available objects, select the 3D Construction... command in the DRAW pull-down menu (see App. E), which will display an icon menu from which you can select objects. These commands are discussed in App. A of the *AutoLISP Programmer's Reference* manual for Release 10.

F.2   Dynamic Viewpoint Commands

In Chap. 17 the VIEW command is used to rotate entities in three-dimensional space. The **DVIEW** (Dynamic VIEWpoint) command allows you to view a three-dimensional model in space by pointing a "camera" at a target. The camera can then be moved in or out along its viewing plane, and the focal length of the camera lens can be adjusted to provide a view similar to that obtained from a wide-angle or zoom lens.

The model can be viewed in parallel or perspective projection. Cutaway sections can be created by positioning front and back "clipping planes."

The DVIEW settings may be input from the keyboard or by using a "slider bar" displayed along the edge of the screen. Entities may also be selected to visually reflect the changes made while you are entering data.

For more information on the DVIEW command refer to Sec. 6.6.2 in your *AutoCAD Tutorial* manual.

F.3   Dimension Variables

Useful dimension variables added to Release 10, not covered in the text, are:

DIMTOFL on forces a dimension line between the extension lines even when the text is placed outside the extension lines.

DIMTIX on forces the dimension text within the extension lines.

DIMSOXD on prevents AutoCAD from drawing dimension lines outside the extension lines. If the dimension line would normally be placed outside the extension lines, no dimension line is drawn.

F.4   SETVAR Command

AutoCAD saves the settings for the various modes, limit values, and unit values in a collection of "system variables." The system variables can be set by the various AutoCAD commands or can be set directly using the SETVAR command. The system variables that can be set are listed in App. A.7 of the *AutoCAD Reference Manual*.

An illustration of a system variable used by AutoCAD is the PDMODE under the POINT command, which is invoked as follows:

```
POINT <pick> Point: Points example <pick> The point modes are displayed. Pdmode
<pick> New value for PDMODE <0>:
```

AutoCAD has invoked the SETVAR command to allow you to set the PDMODE system variable. When a point is drawn, AutoCAD places a specific point based on the value stored in PDMODE. Some of the options are:

PDMODE	Point drawn
0	.
1	(nothing)
2	+
3	×
4		

If you add 32 to one of the above numbers, the specified point is placed within a circle; adding 64 places it within a square box; and adding 96 places the point within a box and a circle combined. Entering 34 will cause all points to be drawn as a cross enclosed by a circle.

System variables may be set directly by the SETVAR command, i.e.:

```
AutoCAD <pick> SETTINGS <pick> next <pick> SETVAR <pick> Variable name or
? : pdmode <return> New value for PDMODE <0>: 66 <return>
```

If you enter ?, AutoCAD will display all the system variables and their current values.

G

AutoCAD Scale and Text Heights

TABLE G-1 AutoCAD Scale and Text Heights—Imperial Units

A. - Drawing units: FEET (AutoCAD Decimal Units)

Drawing Scale	HATCH	LTSCALE	3/32" TEXT TXT	DIMSCALE	1/8" TEXT TXT	DIMSCALE	3/16" TEXT TXT	DIMSCALE
1/8"=1'0"	8.00	6.00	0.75	4.17	1.00	5.56	1.50	8.33
3/16"=1'0"	5.33	4.00	0.50	2.78	0.67	3.70	1.00	5.56
1/4"=1'0"	4.00	3.00	0.38	2.08	0.50	2.78	0.75	4.17
5/16"=1'0"	3.20	2.40	0.30	1.67	0.40	2.22	0.60	3.33
3/8"=1'0"	2.67	2.00	0.25	1.39	0.33	1.85	0.50	2.78
1/2"=1'0"	2.00	1.50	0.19	1.04	0.25	1.39	0.38	2.08
5/8"=1'0"	1.60	1.20	0.15	0.83	0.20	1.11	0.30	1.67
3/4"=1'0"	1.33	1.00	0.13	0.69	0.17	0.93	0.25	1.39
7/8"=1'0"	1.14	0.86	0.11	0.60	0.14	0.79	0.21	1.19
1"=1'0"	1.00	0.75	0.09	0.52	0.13	0.69	0.19	1.04
1.5"=1'0"	0.67	0.50	0.06	0.35	0.08	0.46	0.13	0.69
2"=1'0"	0.50	0.38	0.05	0.26	0.06	0.35	0.09	0.52
1/4 size	0.33	0.25	0.03	0.17	0.04	0.23	0.06	0.35
1/2 size	0.17	0.13	0.02	0.09	0.02	0.12	0.03	0.17
Full size	0.08	0.06	0.01	0.04	0.01	0.06	0.02	0.09

TABLE G-1 *(Continued)*

B. - Drawing units: AutoCAD Architectural or Engineering Units

Drawing Scale	HATCH	LTSCALE	3/32" TEXT TXT	DIMSCALE	1/8" TEXT TXT	DIMSCALE	3/16" TEXT TXT	DIMSCALE
1/8"=1'0"	96.00	72.00	9.00	50.00	12.00	66.67	18.00	100.00
3/16"=1'0"	64.00	48.00	6.00	33.33	8.00	44.44	12.00	66.67
1/4"=1'0"	48.00	36.00	4.50	25.00	6.00	33.33	9.00	50.00
5/16"=1'0"	38.40	28.80	3.60	20.00	4.80	26.67	7.20	40.00
3/8"=1'0"	32.00	24.00	3.00	16.67	4.00	22.22	6.00	33.33
1/2"=1'0"	24.00	18.00	2.25	12.50	3.00	16.67	4.50	25.00
5/8"=1'0"	19.20	14.40	1.80	10.00	2.40	13.33	3.60	20.00
3/4"=1'0"	16.00	12.00	1.50	8.33	2.00	11.11	3.00	16.67
7/8"=1'0"	13.71	10.29	1.29	7.14	1.71	9.52	2.57	14.29
1"=1'0"	12.00	9.00	1.13	6.25	1.50	8.33	2.25	12.50
1.5"=1'0"	8.00	6.00	0.75	4.17	1.00	5.56	1.50	8.33
2"=1'0"	6.00	4.50	0.56	3.13	0.75	4.17	1.13	6.25
1/4 size	4.00	3.00	0.38	2.08	0.50	2.78	0.75	4.17
1/2 size	2.00	1.50	0.19	1.04	0.25	1.39	0.38	2.08
Full size	1.00	0.75	0.09	0.52	0.13	0.69	0.19	1.04

C. - Drawing units: Engineering (Feet) (AutoCAD Decimal Units)

Drawing Scale	HATCH	LTSCALE	3/32" TEXT TXT	DIMSCALE	1/8" TEXT TXT	DIMSCALE	3/16" TEXT TXT	DIMSCALE
1:3000	250.00	187.50	23.44	130.21	31.25	173.61	46.88	260.42
1:2500	208.33	156.25	19.53	108.51	26.04	144.68	39.06	217.01
1:2000	166.67	125.00	15.63	86.81	20.83	115.74	31.25	173.61
1:1500	125.00	93.75	11.72	65.10	15.63	86.81	23.44	130.21
1:1250	104.17	78.13	9.77	54.25	13.02	72.34	19.53	108.51
1:1000	83.33	62.50	7.81	43.40	10.42	57.87	15.63	86.81
1:750	62.50	46.88	5.86	32.55	7.81	43.40	11.72	65.10
1:600	50.00	37.50	4.69	26.04	6.25	34.72	9.38	52.08
1:500	41.67	31.25	3.91	21.70	5.21	28.94	7.81	43.40
1:400	33.33	25.00	3.13	17.36	4.17	23.15	6.25	34.72
1:300	25.00	18.75	2.34	13.02	3.13	17.36	4.69	26.04
1:200	16.67	12.50	1.56	8.68	2.08	11.57	3.13	17.36
1:100	8.33	6.25	0.78	4.34	1.04	5.79	1.56	8.68
1:50	4.17	3.13	0.39	2.17	0.52	2.89	0.78	4.34
1:25	2.08	1.56	0.20	1.09	0.26	1.45	0.39	2.17
1:20	1.67	1.25	0.16	0.87	0.21	1.16	0.31	1.74

TABLE G-2   AutoCAD Scale and Text Heights—SI Units

A. - Drawing units: METRES

Drawing Scale	HATCH	LTSCALE	2.5 mm TEXT TXT	DIMSCALE	3 mm TEXT TXT	DIMSCALE
1:10	0.25	0.19	0.03	0.14	0.03	0.17
1:20	0.51	0.38	0.05	0.28	0.06	0.33
1:30	0.76	0.57	0.08	0.42	0.09	0.50
1:40	1.02	0.76	0.10	0.56	0.12	0.67
1:50	1.27	0.95	0.13	0.69	0.15	0.83
1:100	2.54	1.91	0.25	1.39	0.30	1.67
1:200	5.08	3.81	0.50	2.78	0.60	3.33
1:250	6.35	4.76	0.63	3.47	0.75	4.17
1:300	7.62	5.72	0.75	4.17	0.90	5.00
1:400	10.16	7.62	1.00	5.56	1.20	6.67
1:500	12.70	9.53	1.25	6.94	1.50	8.33
1:750	19.05	14.29	1.88	10.42	2.25	12.50
1:1000	25.40	19.05	2.50	13.89	3.00	16.67
1:2000	50.80	38.10	5.00	27.78	6.00	33.33
1:5000	127.00	95.25	12.50	69.44	15.00	83.33

B. - Drawing units: MILLIMETRES

Drawing Scale	HATCH	LTSCALE	2.5 mm TEXT TXT	DIMSCALE	3 mm TEXT TXT	DIMSCALE
1:1	25	19	2.5	14	3.0	17
1:2	51	38	5.0	28	6.0	33
1:3	76	57	7.5	42	9.0	50
1:4	102	76	10.0	56	12.0	67
1:5	127	95	12.5	69	15.0	83
1:10	254	191	25.0	139	30.0	167
1:20	508	381	50.0	278	60.0	333
1:50	1270	953	125.0	694	150.0	833
1:100	2540	1905	250.0	1389	300.0	1667
1:200	5080	3810	500.0	2778	600.0	3333
1:250	6350	4763	625.0	3472	750.0	4167
1:300	7620	5715	750.0	4167	900.0	5000
1:400	10160	7620	1000.0	5556	1200.0	6667
1:500	12700	9525	1250.0	6944	1500.0	8333
1:750	19050	14288	1875.0	10417	2250.0	12500

Index

ABOUT THE AUTHOR

John D. Hood is department head of civil, mining, and geology engineering technology at Cambrian College in Sudbury, Ontario, Canada. He has taught AutoCAD® for over 6 years and has conducted AutoCAD® seminars both in Canada and the United States. He is the author of *Using AutoCAD® with AutoLISP®* published by McGraw-Hill.